The Weidenfeld and Nicolson Natural History

THE ORIGIN OF LIFE

The Weidenfeld and Nicolson Natural History

Editor : Richard Carrington

Associate Editors :

Dr L. Harrison Matthews FRS

Professor J. Z. Young FRS

The Origin of Life

J. D. BERNAL

Professor of Crystallography
University of London

WEIDENFELD AND NICOLSON
5 WINSLEY STREET LONDON WI

Made and printed in Great Britain by
William Clowes and Sons, Limited, London and Beccles

Contents

Plates

26 An autoradiograph showing the DNA in the single loop chromosome of the bacterium *Escherichia coli*.
27 Reef of *Conophyton* in the Pharusian, Pre-Cambrian of the Hoggar.
28 Photomicrographs of actual fossils preserved in the Gunflint formation, Lake Superior, Canada.
29 Photograph of Mars taken by *Mariner IV* from a distance of 7,800 miles.

Acknowledgements

The preparation of this book has largely been the collection and collation of material from a large number of recent works, in the form of extracts, diagrams or photographs. This work, done under my direction, has involved the task of examining material from many sources covering disparate sciences from Physics through Biochemistry to Geology and even Astronomy.

In view of my illness which, for the last three years, has virtually immobilized me, this heavy task has been carried out largely by my scientific literary assistant, Mr Francis Aprahamian, and I cannot sufficiently praise the efficiency and devotion with which he carried it out. My thanks are due to him and to my secretary, Miss Anita Rimel, who has been generally responsible for the considerable correspondence inseparable from the preparation of such a book, which certainly could not have appeared without her aid.

My thanks are also due to Mrs Ann Synge for the translation of Academician A. I. Oparin's 1924 paper on the origin of life, which appears in Appendix 1; Professor G. Mueller for preparing Appendix 2 on the carbonaceous meteorites; to Miss Margaret Denny for typing the manuscript; to Mrs Jenny Brown for preparing the Glossary; to Mr Brian Rosen and Mrs Nina Middle for help in preparing the Bibliography and Index respectively.

I should like, also, to thank the Rationalist Press Association for permission to reproduce Professor J. B. S. Haldane's essay on the origin of life, and the following for permission to reproduce the illustrations used in this volume:
Dr A. H. Weir and Mr G. Brown, plate 1; Dr M. N. Bramlette, plate 2; Dr R. S. Edgar and *Scientific American*, plate 3; Dr A. Keller, plate 4; Dr H. G. Davies, plate 5; Professor H. Fernandez–Moran, plates 6, 17, 19; Dr A. V. Grimstone and Dr A. Klug, plate 7, from *J. Cell Sci.* (1966) 1, 351–362; Dr J. Lowry and Professor Jean Hanson, plates 8, 13; Professor K. R. Porter, plate 9; Dr W. Bernhard, plate 10; Sir John Randall, plate 11; Dr H. E. Huxley, plates 12, 14, 24; Dr E. F. J. van Bruggen, plate 15 (below); Professor M. Bessis, plate 15 (left); Dr R. B. Park, plate 16; Dr J. B. Finean, plate 18; Professor S. P. Mason, plate 20; Professor H. J. Morowitz, plate 21; Dr C. Chapman–Andresen, plate 22; Professor F. C. Steward, plate 23; Drs A. Klug and J. Finch, plate 25; Dr J. Cairns, plate 26; Dr M. Gravelle, plate 27; Professor E. S. Bargehoorn, plate 28 and the cover picture; Jet Propulsion Laboratory, CIT, Pasadena, Calif., plate 29; Professor H. C. Urey, table 1; Professors L. V. Berkner and L. C. Marshall, figures 2, 5; Dr R. Dearnley, fig. 4; Professor A. G. Fischer, fig. 6; Dr S. W. Hurry, fig. 7.

Preface

THIS BOOK is an expression of the interest, extending over thirty years, of a physical scientist in the phenomena of life. The original differentiation between the physical and the biological sciences was one which I had never accepted, even in my schooldays; and while at Cambridge I had the good fortune to frequent the laboratory which was, after the Cavendish, the centre of scientific advance in that university, the Dunn Biochemical Laboratory under the direction of Sir Frederick Gowland Hopkins. Naturally, I was struck both by the affinities and the differences between the physical and biological sciences. I was impressed by the precise way in which all biological phenomena, when carefully investigated, turned out to be in accordance with physical laws, including those of chemistry, and not to involve any special vital principles.

The rise of biochemistry, which Hopkins had fathered, provided yet another link between these two aspects of human thought, and yet there were enormous differences. I remember being struck, as was my friend C. H. Waddington in his geological studies, with the extreme persistence of complex patterns in fossils, or, like my friend Joseph Needham, with the sequential evolution in chemical processes: with the different ways that organisms, as they evolved, got rid of their nitrogen products successively as ammonia, urea and uric acid, for biological reasons that were quite clear in themselves but depended, essentially, on teleological considerations on how far the processes helped the organism in its way of life on sea or land.

Underlying both these examples was the concept of biological chemical action, occurring on a different basis from that of the chemical laboratory, namely, as a reaction brought about by enzymes, at that time mysterious but tangible substances which effected chemical changes at ordinary temperatures in the absence of strong reagents. This was then the field of interest of another of my friends, the late J. B. S. Haldane. It was from Haldane, in particular, that I acquired the interest in the *origin* of life. I knew he had written on it, but I had not then read his short essay in the *Rationalist Annual* of 1929 [50]. I had also heard of, and had actually met, on my visits to the Soviet Union in the 'thirties, the Soviet scientist A. I. Oparin, who had written a book in 1924 on the origin of life, based on the idea of chemical evolution [75]. I thought it was a subject I would like to study myself, rather as speculation than experimentally. But the atmosphere at Cambridge at that time was, and possibly still is, opposed to any idea of speculation – it was not sound science. Rutherford's dictum was: 'Don't let me catch anyone talking about the Universe in my laboratory'. For that matter, he also thoroughly disapproved of any discussion of the use of nuclear energy, which was probably due only to his native caution and the British empirical tradition.

My own contribution to the problem of the origin of life, on the side of observational science, was in my chosen field of crystallography, through the analysis of the detailed structures of complicated molecules like the sterols and amino acids – not very complicated, looking back on it, compared with what has been done since. In this way, I thought I could approach one or two steps nearer the junction between the biological and the physical sciences, through the structure of proteins and, later on, of viruses. It was to be the beginning of the new field of molecular biology, the foundations of which were being laid at that time by William Astbury and Linus Pauling. All agreed then that the key molecules for living things were the protein molecules, but, on the way, there were simpler things to be examined, the sterols, which I had the good fortune to be able to study in the 'thirties, both in the form of sex hormones, provided by Professor Solly Zuckerman, and of Vitamin D, brought to me by Haldane, which was the centre of medical interest at that time.

I had then not quite broken off my interest in the mineral side of crystallography and was able to do something to interpret the structure of the various layers of the Earth. Comprehensive study of minerals and their formation arose from the work of the not generally recognized genius, Victor Moritz Goldschmidt, the man who kept the 'account books' of the Universe, in his *Geochemische Verteilungsgesetze der Elemente* [48].

It was then that I felt the necessity actually to get something down, and I delivered a lecture with the famous title, 'The Physical Basis of Life' [12], used by Huxley in a lecture delivered in Edinburgh in 1868 [58]. My lecture was delivered in 1947, in the first stages of the post-war era, when the time seemed ripe for such a development and, indeed, this period has now been recognized as one of the great eras in the whole history of science. The interest in the origin of life suddenly burst out from many sides. Though interest was notably lacking on the biological side, it was strongly represented on the chemical side through H. C. Urey and his pupil S. L. Miller, who carried out the first experiments on the synthesis of pre-organismal chemicals by means of ultra-violet light acting on the composition of the presumed earliest Earth's atmosphere of methane and ammonia.

It was apparent to me that the subject of biology was not of the same logical character as that of physics, let us say. This is because of the predominantly contingent character of biological science depending on particular organisms whose chemical mechanisms are common to all living things on Earth, but only on Earth. This contrasts with the universality of physics and chemistry, as will be shown on other planets. Biochemistry had already shown that all terrestrial life was one at chemical level: however much variation there might be in individual species, the basic mechanism of enzymes and coenzymes appeared everywhere, and many special molecules played an absolutely key part, for instance, the porphyrins like haemoglobin and chlorophyll and the nucleotide, ATP, adenosine triphosphate. These are all particular, and not general, molecules.

All this shows that the field of biology is a particular field of the behaviour of certain common chemical systems occurring on this Earth which have differentiated into a number of different kinds of organisms and yet have an underlying unity. I had a very interesting discussion on this point with Einstein in Princeton in 1946, from which it appeared to me that the essential clue was that life involved another element, logically different from those occurring in physics at that time, by no means a mystical one, but an element of *history*. The phenomena of biology must be, as we say, contingent on events. In consequence, the unity of life is part of the history of life and, consequently, is involved in its origin.

My particular contribution in my 1947 lecture on this fundamental physical basis of life was specifically to the second stage of that evolution, from chemicals suspended in a primitive ocean, the so-called primary soup, to the concentrations leading to the formation of definite organisms, the 'eobionts' of Pirie. I suggested that the mechanism of this was essentially that of adsorption of the active chemicals on fine clay particles derived from earlier rocks and deposited in estuarine waters.

Apart from this, my own work was frankly based on Oparin and earned me the disapproval of many of my old biological and biochemical friends, notably, N.W.Pirie [92], who criticized it as 'vital blarney', pointing out, quite correctly, that we knew so little about the subject that it was entirely premature to commit it to paper. He implied that what was true was not new and what was new was not true. This led to a controversy which, being largely due to a difference in temperament, was not very productive.

What I have written so far is in the nature of explaining my interest in the problem of the origin of life. It does not by itself explain why such a book should be written at this particular time. In fact, the rapid growth of interest in the subject might be a deterrent to such publication. More than in any other field of science is it difficult to find the right time to issue such a comprehensive statement: at present hardly a week passes without the appearance of a paper or study which bears on the question of the origin of life, including the origin of pre-life, such as is shown in the solar system in the meteorites. There is also a deeper understanding of the molecular biology of hereditary processes, the origin of the code for translating biological orders for a sequence of nucleotides to that of amino acids in proteins.

The Watson-Crick hypothesis of 1953 has now become the great turning-point of biology and, in fact, of general science. Its implications for the origin of life are obvious, but they have not yet been fully appreciated, even by its originators. There is a justified feeling that science is having the greatest difficulty in keeping up with itself. Those who know enough to understand it should know enough to change it. The problem of the origin of life is apparently very easily stated: at one time there existed nothing more complex than an ordinary inorganic chemical, subject to a possible heating to several thousand degrees Centigrade; at the end there is the whole panorama of the multiplicity of living organisms covering the world and possibly spreading to other planets. If we are no longer prepared to accept miracles, the first state turned into the second by no other external agents than were contained in itself. However, to find a real solution to the problem is quite another matter. It is now apparent that such a solution could not have been found at an earlier stage of the consideration of the problem, even by such great minds of the last century as Huxley and Tyndall. The knowledge necessary to understand the essence of the first stages simply did not exist then and to a certain extent does not exist now.

The success of biology as a descriptive science and its practical capacity to direct and explain medical and agricultural science could well be achieved despite the incomplete nature. These explanations essentially describe what actually happens to organisms in natural conditions or in contrived conditions approximating to natural ones. They are essentially dependent on particular structures, either visible structures, as seen in the microscope or in electron-microscope cytology, or chemical structures of a peculiar kind, as studied in biochemistry. The ultimate questions in fact do not get asked. We are asked to describe what a thing is, what a thing does, but we are not asked to describe how it got that way, except in a very relative sense, as a modification of some other mechanism known to exist in some other organism. We are still very far from asking – let alone answering – the basic questions concerning the origin of life, questions framed essentially in chemical language. Our essential failure is not so much in being unable to answer as in not seeing that there is anything *to* answer, in saying that everything is natural. In fact, it is the very *naturalness* of life that is the first obstacle to understanding it.

The new developments in molecular biology make us examine and question again many of the subjects we had completely taken for granted. We take it as natural that an organism should produce its like: it is simply covered by a 'know nothing' word like reproduction. It has taken the Watson-Crick-Nirenberg demonstration of the complexity of protein genesis to show that the thing we are concerned with here is the precise reproduction mechanism, not so much of organisms as of the very molecules of which they are composed. This implies absolute or quasi-absolute identity. We did not necessarily see this, but it was already implied in much simpler things which have been known for hundreds of years, namely, the existence of regular crystals in living organisms. Crystals, by definition, are evidence of precise equality in molecular reproduction, which in turn calls out for a mechanism to produce it. This is a further example of the explanation of actually microscopically visible structures, or electron microscopically visible structures, various kinds of crystals first noted in the tobacco mosaic virus particles. All the structures found in cells seem to be of this character, whether of sheets, tubules or fibres or, occasionally, three-dimensional crystals. The beauty of life is, therefore, a geometrical beauty of a type that Plato would have much appreciated: sets of identical particles which hold themselves together by the principles of self-assembly in the most elaborate structures. This also goes far to explain, though not completely, the mobile aspect of biology, the movement of bodies produced by muscular contraction, ciliary vibration and the electrical changes exhibited by nerve tissue.

The new intra-cellular histology – the examination of the independent particles forming the cell, the organelles – gives a completely new aspect to the study of structures. This process is as important in biology – and probably more important – as the advent of the optical microscope and its development in the seventeenth and nineteenth centuries. This time we have the structures right down the atomic scale and, therefore, there cannot be a range of magnitude missing. They have become intelligible for the first time. The inner structures explain the outer properties. Yet this has become visible only in general, in principle, not in detail. In detail, there are certainly many surprises still for us.

Every individual organism, in its development and decay, consists of a set of patterns of biochemical responses to the external environment, set off in sequence along internally prescribed directions. The patterns are coded in the germ cells and some of the patterns can subsequently be mixed within the limits of a species of which it is effectively the definition. The tree, in the mathematical sense, of all these generic mixings constitutes the life history of the species, as determined and coded as is the life history of the individuals which compose it. From time to time, with the origin of new species, the tree divides into branches. When any one of these branches fails to reproduce, for internal or external reasons, it marks the extinction of the species. The same can happen to larger branches, corresponding to genera and classes. These species can be bodily simple or multiple. The multiple can share the same body as in the obligatory parasites or commensals, or they may form part of a multi-corporal ecological unit, a food chain, for instance. The parts of a multiple organism, in serially-built metazoa, for instance, may have been originally separate, but may have remained as one composite organism. The same may be true on a cellular level in the case of organelles, but here the separateness must be far further back. The hereditary unity of terrestrial life as a whole is still in question, but it must transcend the separations I have already mentioned.

All forms of life are subject to two kinds of effectively external restraints, one biochemical and the other morphological and geometrical. The first of these is already implicit in the common biochemical channels of living matter. In general, simple and fundamentally the same conservative patterns persist throughout the whole of life, but they permit individual variations of enzyme patterns producing new substances, for example, colours and biochemically active substances like growth factors or poisons.

The morphological restrictions depend on the questions of size of the part or the whole of the organism. It involves, first of all, the preservation or necessary change of shape of part or whole (see D'Arcy Thompson's *On Growth and Form* [110]), which also involves a time factor. This, for large organisms, determines the necessity to preserve shape at different stages of embryonic development. Secondly, it involves transport, the moving of nutritious material and its incorporation into solid or liquid bodies. After transport comes communication, either through chemical diffusion, which is itself a form of transport, or through electrical impulses which constitute the nervous system. All these involve, for instance, stimulus and reaction, together with memory to link the two, and create a new structural and functional unity in the organism and a mental quality different from that which went before. But all are strictly necessary and any form of evolution is likely to involve them in one form or another, more or less effective and economical in formation and use. Once life has started, its further evolution follows lines which are prescribed, but not in detail. They are of the same kind, but not identical.

There is an essential difference between the sciences that we qualify as dealing with life, biology in general and those of the so-called exact sciences. In a sense the older scientists were right when they talked about life as something with its own character and kind, radically different from anything that was not life. Why they went wrong, and could not help being wrong, was because they could not follow the reason for this: this was a strictly *material* reason and not a spiritual one. My provisional definition of life: *Life is a partial, continuous, progressive, multiform and conditionally interactive, self-realization of the potentialities of atomic electron states*, should be sufficient to show that all life has some material structures in common, in the form of enzymes, nucleic acids and essentially reproducing organs or molecules. Particular, or terrestrial, biology is the science of these substances and of their necessary inter-reactions. Generalized, or cosmic, biology is the science of all such systems of chemical atoms and arrangements unified by some basic minimal requirements of a formal character, that is, having the property of producing identical complex molecules indefinitely at the expense of inorganic atoms, simple molecules and physical sources of free energy such as light, directly or indirectly, through already organised or living substances.

Now that the problem of the origin of life has become one of general interest to biologists, for a non-biologist to publish a book on this subject will appear especially arbitrary at this time. Even a few months of waiting will certainly result in many more important contributions to the work. However, if this principle of waiting were universally followed, no book would get written at all because a better one could always be on the way. But there is some advantage – at any rate for the normal, intelligent reader – in publishing now, because at this moment the questions that are raised are as important as those already answered. We have now reached such a stage that it is possible, even without much specialist knowledge, to give intelligent answers or, at least, do work of an intelligent character on the basis of them and to plan intelligent research work. In Bacon's words, this is not so much a lesson to be learnt as a task to be done. It requires at the present moment the most energetic and coordinated follow-up in various directions.

Of these, probably the most important is genetics, especially the new genetics, using various special tools such as radioactive tracers. Important, too, is biochemistry in its new form of molecular biology: more has been got out of this than has so far gone into it. First of all, in this space age, it could be a basis for the development of a new generalized biology, not depending on the peculiar forms existing on Earth. With that, too, will come a deeper understanding and putting together of these complex structures, the new generalized crystallography of which the old three-dimensional order of classical crystallography is a special case (see Appendix 3).

Because, therefore, the study of the origin of life today raises more questions than it answers, it is appropriate that it should be the basis of a new kind of scientific book or, rather, the revival of a very old kind, a book of queries. I have used this formulation in the setting up of this book, beginning, as is customary, with an historical introduction, pointing out that the problem as such did not arise at a time when everything, including life, was considered as a natural evolution of vital processes; then going on to the time when an answer could not be given because the necessary sciences, particularly molecular biology, had not yet developed. From this I pass on to a description of one particular sequence of development which might account for the origin of life on Earth and on other suitable planets. It is divided into three sections: from atoms to molecules, from molecules to bio-molecular complex and from the bio-molecular complex to organisms. I do not wish to assert, however, that the sequence indicated here is the true one: in a further chapter I also consider others. Finally, I discuss the difficulties and problems that still remain and include a list of such problems in the penultimate chapter. In the concluding chapter I have discussed the effects of our outlook on the world due to the recognition, not only of the existence, but of the precise mechanism of the development of life.

As supporting documents I have added reprints, *in toto*, of the original works of Oparin and Haldane that initiated the modern phase of the study. I can see now what a great step that was in the understanding of life in the Universe and particularly of the central question of reproduction of identical molecules by the nucleic acid-protein mechanism. As I followed this step by step, I became acquainted with most of the persons concerned with the advancement of knowledge of the origins of life. I have necessarily drawn most of my ideas from those of others, but by combining them with some of my own find the results much more interesting and possible.

I have discussed only old parts of the first chapter of the total history of life. There are more chapters to be written of that history and still more chapters to be added for its future. For *life does not die* or, more accurately, *life on Earth has not died*. If life itself came about by the working out of logical processes independent of any conscious will, this is no longer so. In the future it will become more and more a function of human understandings and human virtues. If life is not to die, we have to see to it that we stop now the forces threatening its very existence.

xvi

Chapter 1

Introduction

Creation and Evolution

SINCE two hundred years ago, any book on natural history would begin with the description of those parts of nature that are most familiar and, therefore, supposed to be most understood by us – with the beasts, the birds, the fishes, passing on perhaps to the less well-known parts of life, the reptiles, the insects and the other animalculae; it might go on to include plants and stones. The general guiding idea was that of degrees of perfection, the great ladder of life, beginning with man as nearest to the angels and going on to less and less perfect realizations of the divine archetype.

The triumph of Darwin changed all that; now it was felt more appropriate to begin at the beginning with simple protozoa and then to go on to the higher and more evolved species following the ever more branching evolutionary tree. But the question would still remain – where to begin. This is a question which was evaded at the beginning of evolutionary theory because it was quite enough to have to fight for the animal ancestry of man, not to have to go on to explain the inorganic origin of life. So, such questions were, for the best part of a hundred years, neglected in serious scientific works in biology. Nevertheless, interest in the origin of life is now growing to such an extent that it would be very limited and one-sided to leave it out, just as it would have been limited, after Darwin, to leave out an account of the origin of species and the doctrine of evolution from any comprehensive natural history. Indeed, the words 'natural history' have written into them the question of the origin of life because 'nature' stands for the birth of things and 'history' must imply development in time as well as the description in space of the enormous variety of living things.

However, a volume on the origin of life must necessarily be of a different character from the other volumes in this series which are concerned with describing and, to a certain extent, explaining the actions of various groups of living creatures, plants and animals (including those animals and plants whose appearance and mode of life it is possible to reconstruct with ever increasing accuracy from the fossil record). But with the origin of life we are going into unknown territory without any concrete facts to guide us and certainly with nothing that can be illustrated.

The question of the origin of life is essentially speculative. We have to construct, by straightforward thinking on the basis of very few factual observations, a plausible and self-consistent picture of a process which must have occurred before any of the forms which are known to us in the fossil record could have existed. The process of the logical reconstruction of the earlier forms of life has, in fact, only been going on for the last forty years and most intensely only for the last ten. Apart from certain genial guesses, it could not have been going on for longer because the sciences through which it could be understood had not yet themselves developed. Further, by definition, the origin of life cannot be the origin of some complex form of life which has developed from some simpler form, but must be the origin of the simplest form that could be found or imagined. This, with our new knowledge of biochemistry and molecular biology, reduces the search for the origin of life to the origin of the simplest molecular mechanisms which can carry out any functions parallel to life. Such structures and functions were simply not known before 1940. Consequently, the scientific history of the origin of life can date only from that time. This does not mean that more could not have been said about the origin of life at an earlier period and logical deductions could have been made from what was already well known, such as the phenomena of heredity, but the fact was that they were not made and the origin of life remains a branch of science which belongs to the great revolution in biology of the mid-twentieth century.

The Nature and Measure of Life

The very title *The Origin of Life* conceals the assumption from which we are now trying hard to get away, that is, that life is something quite specific and definite which originated in some given time or place. Actually, as this book will try to show, the process of the origination of life is one of great complexity, involving many stages, and it is a somewhat metaphysical point to decide which of these is really *the origin of life* or whether life, as such, has a single origin. We might more properly speak of the origins of life or the origin of the processes of life. In any case, the discussion as to which of these stages can be deemed to be the origin of life must be deferred until we know more about the various stages.

Life, as we know it now, has certain characteristic features, such as metabolism and reproduction, and as long as we deem that these can be traced back, we are dealing with the development or evolution of life and not with its origins. However, the processes themselves can hardly have appeared absolutely *de novo*; if we accept any idea of continuity, they were preceded by similar and simpler processes, and it is these we wish to discuss in dealing with the origin of life. It must be admitted here, and it will become apparent throughout the book, that the discussion of these first stages is still in an extremely tentative state. It is speculative science and not by any means observational or experimental science, although observation and experiment are used in its study.

We do not know enough to separate the first stages of the evolution of primitive organisms from that of the origin of life itself but, strictly, that process belongs to the evolution of life and not to its origin. In one sense, the original forms of life must necessarily be less familiar than those that we meet in recent or even in fossil biology; in another sense, because they have to be traced back to a simpler state, they must be composed of elements more familiar to us than those of current life when looked at inorganically and chemically. Life must have been simpler the further back we go. However, that simplicity must have expressed itself in chemical or atomic terms, not at all familiar in our ordinary experience.

We now see that long before there could have been an organic evolution in the Darwinian sense, there must have been a chemical evolution longer and perhaps less rapid in its changes than those which have occurred since the evolution of actual cells towards the multiple forms by which they reveal themselves today. Thoroughly to understand this picture and the arguments through which it is sustained would require a more sophisticated chemical understanding than I possess or than can be expected from a general reader of natural history, but some effort must be made to present it in these terms. Failing that, the very real advances that have been made in the understanding of life and its history in recent years may remain largely an esoteric secret. However, as it is one that concerns everybody and not only the privileged and sophisticated biochemist or quantum chemist, it is important to attempt to present it in some generally intelligible form.

The questions which are dealt with in this provisional and partly finished study are vital questions not only in biology but in general philosophy. The study of the origin of life bears on such matters as the nature of life itself, the distinction between living and non-living matter, the relation of life here on Earth to life in other planets and in other parts of the Universe, and on the meaning and origin of such general characters of life as growth, reproduction, movement, sensation and thought. Essentially, the problems to be dealt with are very old ones: those of the relations between the

3

macrocosm of the outside world, reaching out beyond the stars and galaxies, and the microcosm of the inner parts of the cell right down to the minute molecules and atoms.

The Unity of Terrestrial Life

Now, it is in both these fields that the greatest advances have been made in recent decades; by recognizing the unity of life on Earth, we see in this a simple example – the only one accessible to us at present – of a much larger field of nature's spontaneous self-generation. We have no convincing reasons for considering that we are unique. Life may and, indeed, must have occurred in other parts of the Universe, particularly in parts of stellar planetary systems similar to our own, of which thousands of millions may exist in the visible Universe. Far from being rare and uncommon, the material bases of life are the commonest of all the elements of the Universe: hydrogen, carbon, oxygen and nitrogen. Any discussion of origins must deal not only with material substances but also with the appropriate conditions in stellar systems where we might expect to find life.

Our new knowledge of the history of the parts of the Universe close to us, that of the Earth and the solar system, has in the last decade given us the absolute time scale with which we can measure the stages leading to the origin of life as we know it now on Earth and, presumably, of life as it may occur in other places in the Universe. Life, indeed, now appears as a relative newcomer to our Universe. The three or four thousand million years that we give to its evolution may seem an extremely long time to us, but it is short compared with the age of the Earth, some five or six thousand million years, or with that of the solar system, of ten thousand million years, or with that of the elements of which it is composed, some fifteen thousand million years. All these, however, are essentially local times and eras; if the Universe as a whole is much older than any particular part of it, the same processes may have occurred in other places at quite different epochs, for the varieties of life which have occurred in different parts of the Universe may also have occurred at very different epochs in it.

The discoveries of recent years have also entirely recast our ideas on the scale of complexity of the microcosm. Only thirty years ago it was still possible for N.W.Pirie [91] to write about the meaninglessness of the terms life and living. Nowadays, for life on Earth and presumably also for any kind of life that may occur in any part of the Universe, we can be much more precise from the point of view of the elements and compounds that take part in it. A hundred years ago, Engels hazarded the guess that life

4

was the mode of motion of albuminous substances – what we now call proteins. Now we can afford to make a far more definite statement: that terrestrial life is in the main a function of the mutual reactions of nucleic acids and of proteins.

The nucleic acids are polymers of nucleotides, themselves consisting of nitrogenous bases of the type of adenine, pentose sugars like ribose, and phosphates. The nucleotides are active on their own as *coenzymes*. The proteins are, similarly, polymers of amino acids, whose chief functions seem to be to further specific chemical reactions as organic catalysts, the *enzymes*. Biochemistry has shown us how extraordinarily complicated these reactions are, but at the same time it has shown them as a system that makes sense. Further study may show that these enzymes can be arranged in some reasonable order of derivation, the later ones being derived from the earlier by various chemical mutations. This derivation should also provide a self-consistent and closed system of operation of metabolism in every stage of its development.

Biogenesis

The task of the makers of the new history of life, biogenesis, which will occupy this volume, is essentially that of bringing together the evidences of the macrocosm and those of the microcosm, from astro-physics to biochemistry, continually trying to improve its self-consistency and at the same time checking it by means of actual observations and experiments. The result cannot have the same descriptive completeness in the later as in the earlier chapters. It is necessarily a work of imagination, but of imagination controlled by science. It will long remain a subject for dispute, but a dispute which can take place between scientists who speak the same language and who will admit, at least provisionally, the superiority of some ideas over others.

In such subjects as the origin of life, the provisional aspect of science is most apparent. So much has to be done, so much has to be found out before any firm statement can be made. But there is room both for those who like to have a picture before their minds as to how the thing might have happened and for those who prefer to remain sceptical and hold back their opinions until firmer ground is established for one view or the other.

The methods I shall use in this book will be to begin with the study of what has been thought on this subject in the past, for, indeed, the question of origins goes back to the very beginning of history, to the creation myths which have been found at the basis of all religious ideas in every part of the world at some epoch in their history. By analogy with the history of ideas about the Universe as a whole, we may expect these ideas to arise by refinement of the primitive ones and the gradual assimilation of other emergent scientific ideas from other fields.

Indeed, speaking much more generally, it would appear that much of the history of science has been that of trying to square the beliefs from earlier ages, particularly on such subjects as the creation and the nature of the Universe, with the traditions of religion. This took the form in Western Europe of a break-away in stages from the old geocentric, Earth- and man-centred, view of the Universe in the great Copernican, Galilean, Newtonian syntheses of the sixteenth and seventeenth centuries. Later, with the Darwinian concept of evolution in the nineteenth century, was to come the displacement of man as the centre of the Universe and his assimilation into the rest of animate nature. The controversies on the origin of life have also had religious undertones, particularly at the beginning when spontaneous generation was considered to conflict with special creation and was thought definitely to have been refuted by Pasteur's experiments.

After this general introduction to the subject will follow in much more detail the evidence for new views as to the origin of life: first of all the external evidence of the new cosmogonic ideas and then the internal evidence, derived very largely from biochemistry and even from experimental organic chemistry.

Molecular Replication

This will lead to the central new idea of the transition from the inorganic to the organic, based on the mechanism of precise *reproduction* or replication of molecules which has achieved perfection only in living systems. The great turning-point came with the discoveries culminating in molecular biology. This includes the molecular explanations of the processes of reproduction through the mechanism of nucleic acid replication and the ribosomes, that is, essentially with the Watson-Crick hypothesis of the interactions of nucleic acids and proteins.

This has turned out to be a system of such complexity that it must itself have quite a long history and one which we have to trace in examining the origin of life. It contains at least two processes; one a replication process by which a particular molecule of nucleic acid is repeated exactly an indefinite number of times; another that of transference by which the pattern in the nucleic acids becomes that of amino acids in a protein which again can be reproduced any number of times. The precision of the reproduction replication or transference is not always perfect. Room is left for small, non-lethal mutations which assure the working of evolution and the pairing process of the survival of the fittest. Through the principles of molecular biology a link has now been formed between the disciplines of biochemistry and genetics, and this discipline points directly towards the origin of life itself.

According to modern ideas, molecular reproduction is necessary not only for the reproduction of the actual species of organisms, but also for every aspect of biological structure and action, including metabolism. This modern aspect of reproduction, as responsible for the continuation of the normal carrying out of life, is what distinguishes living from dead matter. Molecular reproduction is, consequently, a means of active transfer of information, assuring at the same time that of the characteristic form and action of the organism or the species. What has happened in the history of our knowledge of nature is that we started to study heredity practically and scientifically before realizing these extensions, which make the heredity of whole organisms a general expression of the far deeper reproduction of molecules.

Apart from these general features, particularly in the replication of nucleic acids on the molecular chemical scale, it will be necessary to look into many of the ideas of the means by which order can be derived from disorder and into the objections that have been raised to them. What we have to explain here is not so much *how* life originated, but why life *had* to originate under the conditions in which it did. Was it some kind of crystallization, in the widest sense, which led to the features which we now find common to all living things on earth ? Further, was this the only way in which this could have occurred ? Or is it possible that it occurred in radically different ways in other places under different conditions ?

Processes of Origins of Life

What follows in this book is not all on the same level of scientific abstraction and argumentation, but is rather an attempt to produce a plausible history of the origins of these chemical-physical processes on the actual Earth surface, which was probably not so very different then from what it is now in its gross physical features. It is here, also, that the central Oparin-Haldane hypothesis appears: the postulated initial absence of oxygen in the atmosphere and its appearance through the development of photosynthetic molecules like chlorophyll. This would have enabled the energy of the Sun to be used most effectively to promote life on the Earth and on any other planet similarly situated.

7

The cradle of life on the Earth is certainly the oceans, and the appearance of land animals and land plants represents portions of the ocean which life was able to lift out and to preserve in their liquid state within the skins of these organisms. Life is, indeed, an *epiphenomenon of the hydrosphere*. The appearance of life on this Earth was not so much a matter of change of substance for, in fact, life made use of all substances already occurring on Earth, particularly the universal medium of water. It was, rather, an enormous increase in the information and the complexity with which these elements were combined both in spacial arrangement, forming the molecules of which life is built, and in dynamics, enabling them to reproduce the patterns through endless and varied generations. *Life is essentially, therefore, a matter of the growth and self-complication of the informational aspects of the potentialities of matter.*

The myth of the provisional history of the origin of life is contained in the latter chapters of this volume. It divides naturally into three major sections. They are, after Ponnamperuma: *from atom to molecule; from molecule to polymer; from polymer to organism.*

From Atom to Molecule

The first stage is the formation – probably from water, methane and ammonia – of the intermediate organic molecules which are characteristic of life, mostly carbon and nitrogen compounds of moderate complexity such as the organic bases like adenine and the amino acids. These are the constituents of the 'primary soup' of the Oparin-Haldane hypothesis. We now have positive evidence that this may have occurred in many other places than on this Earth, particularly in the small bodies where the process can go no further, the asteroids from which the meteorites are developed.

From Monomer to Polymer

Next follow the second-stage processes of polymerization of such molecules leading to the decisive event of the dynamic organization of the process which we now call living, but which does not imply, as it does now, the existence of separate organisms.

From Polymer to Organism

The development of these and their internal organization belong to a third stage, the passage from a mere living area of metabolizing material without specific limitations into a closed *organism* which separates out one part of the continuum from another, the living from the non-living. This is a matter of discussing the entirely hypothetical but essentially intermediate *eobionts*, and from them the more complex portions of living matter which we find inside cells, the *organelles*. These include the mitochondria, responsible for the metabolism of cells; the chloroplasts, responsible for photosynthesis; and the essential feature which gives identity and continuity, the chromosomes, or chromatic material in simpler, 'prokaryotic', organisms, that ensure the reproductive continuity of the particular systems in which they are found. Finally, these must come together in the building up of what we now recognize as common to all higher life, the nucleated, 'eukaryotic', cell. With the nucleated cell, life has definitely arrived and, once there, continues to evolve in its variation and multiplicity. But this is no longer a question of the origin of life, it is a question of organic evolution, a logical follow-up of Darwinism which is to be found in the later volumes of this series.

It should be kept in mind that this account of a *myth* of the origin of life, tentative as it is, is not necessarily a generally accepted one. It represents a single interpretation of the evidence, and there are several. The last three chapters of the book refer effectively to these. Although, in general, I have followed the main Oparin-Haldane line of biogenesis, I have added at various times different readings, namely, the evidence of the meteorites which, in my opinion, does not support the hypothesis of the origin of life on their parent bodies – asteroids or Moon – but it is a valuable clue to the first stages of the origin of life on any planet, in particular life on the Earth. Further, I still believe that adsorption on mineral particles, rather than the formation of coacervates, led to the first concentrations of living material; and I still maintain, though without the same certainty, the priority of biochemical life in extended areas over the formation of individual organisms and the evolution of biochemical life in them.

Alternative Paths of Origin

However, in order to give a fair and unbiased account of the whole problem, I have, in Chapter 8, attempted to set out the alternative paths to life which have been suggested in recent times, notably the theories of Professor S. Fox, of the high-temperature production of proteins.

Although there has been great advance in our understanding of the problems of the origin of life, this has very often served only to show how intractible they are. In Chapter 9 I have attempted to list the outstanding problems that still remain, not so much to suggest solutions as to indicate where these may be looked for. A key problem is that of the evolution of the *order* of organic bases in nucleic acids and of amino acids in proteins, which between them provide the chemical *prescription* for living processes even down to the simplest cell. The difficulties are real enough. Many of them have been ignored in the past because they have not been seen sufficiently clearly and some, in this sense, are quite new. In the past they have been insisted on by those who did not believe in the origin of life by natural causes, as indicating its fundamental impossibility and therefore the need to invoke immaterial or spiritual causes. To many, however, who do believe in the spontaneous origin of life, they have been glossed over by various types of escape clauses which might explain the difficulties, but have the awkward property of being able to explain almost anything and, consequently, of being intellectually useless.

A further set of queries is put in Appendix 4, representing what still has to be done in trying to provide a satisfactory theory. Finally, in Chapter 10, I have said something about the effect the recent studies on the origin of life have had on our general outlook on science and life, on such major questions as that of life itself and the meaning of such age-old problems as life and death.

Chapter 2

Notions of the Origins of Life in the Past

> No species is ever changed, but each remains so much itself that
> every kind of bird displays on its body its own specific markings.
> This is a further proof that their bodies are composed of change-
> less matter. For, if the atoms could yield in any way to change,
> there would be no certainty as to what could arise and what
> could not, . . . nor could successive generations so regularly
> repeat the nature, behaviour, habits and movements of their
> parents.
>
> LUCRETIUS, *De rerum natura*

Man and His Animal Relations

MAN'S ideas on the origins of life have gone through almost as many changes as must have occurred in the origin of life itself. The problem has been thought of and stated in many different ways, successively mythical and scientific, until it has reached its present stage which is clearly not a final one. The idea of origin itself, the creation myth, is the basis of religions in all parts of the world at all stages of history. To understand what the world is and how it came to be has always been taken to be the foundation of all wisdom and philosophy.

In these various enquiries and their dogmatic answers, the origin of the animate from the inanimate parts of nature has been a central question, but it has taken many forms quite different from those that it has today. Mankind grew up closely associated with the animate parts of nature. Hunting and food gathering were the occupations which brought man closest to other orders of beings: in the first place with the animals that he hunted or that hunted him; in the second place with plants, as witness the first paintings and carvings of paleolithic man, from which all human art is derived. And not only the passive and ornamental arts, but also their active equivalents, dance and tragedy (literally the wild goat song), had their origin in the chase and in the fertility rituals with animal masks that emphasized the unity of man and animate creation.

Man's first acquaintance with the outside living world has been through the analogy with the world of man himself. Animal species and human clans are intimately associated together in the whole practice of totemism and its associated taboos. Man's relation with the animate world is necessarily ambivalent. He hunts and eats, he is hunted and eaten. Man kills animals because he must – at least to live – but he must not kill too many if they are to flourish: before and after killing them he must apologize and propitiate. Animals, and particularly the totem animals, are in some form taken to be aberrant tribesmen; they may easily be actual dead members of the tribe. The idea of transmigration of souls is one of the earliest and most fundamental ideas of mankind. Animals are at the same time a danger to man and absolutely necessary to his existence. In the earliest creation myths, man and animal are equivalent.

In this circle of ideas, the question of the origin of life hardly entered: animate and inanimate, man, beast and herb formed one mysterious complex kind of being. When man was in the primitive hunting state, he could by no means easily understand even his own birth and generation. Women had babies – where did they come from? From the trees, the wind, the stones? All animal origins are essentially mysterious and no less equivocal. If men can become animals, animals can also become men. Man can draw his courage from the lion and swiftness from the deer. Some animals are deceptive, but they can also be deceived. Decoys and masks and animal dances are powerful and effective magics. The cries of animals also provided a link between them and man. It was deemed that animals had a language and that it was possible to learn this language, preferably through magic. Animals were also credited with wisdom of their own. Now, some of this was imaginary, but some was true, as modern animal psychologists are beginning to find out; be that as it may, it served to strengthen the feeling of unity between man and the animals.

Domestication, Breeding and Agriculture

One of the greatest achievements of primitive man was the domestication of animals; it must have been the fruit of millennia of trial and error, of patient learning of animal habits and making use of their reactions. The uniqueness of this achievement is shown by the fact that very few species of animals, apart from those originally domesticated in the New Stone Age, have been domesticated since. With domestication came breeding, the deliberate fashioning of animals to suit man's needs, the creation of varieties of breeds, such as hunting dogs or race-horses, of economic, sporting or military value. The knowledge of the techniques of breeding, mixed as it was with much magic, was sufficiently realistic and proved by practice to become ultimately the basis of Darwin's theories.

With the coming of agriculture, plants have to be accounted for and dealt with as well. But they were, in the first place, essentially woman's business: to distinguish between good and bad plants, to sow, plant and propagate them, were practical mysteries to be learnt by experience and handed on. The domestication and, even more, the breeding of plant species were to have a more decisive effect on human development even than animal domestication. It is an unwritten story which, however, in these latter years, archaeologists are beginning to read from the actual remains of pollen and seeds and the importance of which they are beginning to appreciate. The plant products as presented by nature are generally varied but poor. Food gathering, except in very favoured districts, can support at best a very sparse population. However, once food grains can be harvested and some sown year after year in the same region, and once the idea that the best grains can be sacrificed for this is accepted, there comes a slow but steady improvement by selection in their quality and yield. Ultimately, but only after millennia, it led to the improved grains like our modern wheat, rice and maize, which gave rise to civilization and still support it.

The mysteries of the preparation of food and drink, and especially of the drink that makes people wild, were vitally important. These mysteries come from the Earth Mother, who is also the corn Mother – Mother of the Gods, Demeter – reduced later to John Barleycorn. Hence the myths of sacrifice and rebirth and the stories of the wine god, Dionysus, and his wild train.

All these notions of changes of life forms, these metamorphoses, obscured from the start any notions of an origin of life as such, because they linked animate life with the most necessary, the most deeply felt and the most sacred of human occupations. We are still a long way from being able to get rid of them even today. The history of ideas on the origin of life has not yet been disentangled from their past in myths and custom, and they are deeply linked with the basic beliefs of all religions – and not the least the Christian-Hebraic religion which incorporates in its various stories of genesis much myth of earlier ages. However, it is not only in these old mythical notions, and in their subsequent incorporation into the religious creeds which are still current, that the main difficulty of facing a scientific theory of the origin of life arises. The problem itself is always changing. As long as people believed, as everyone did at one time and most people still do, that life forms can change into each other at will, or at least by magic – as in Samson's riddle of the lion and the bees or the mysteries of transubstantiation – the problem of the origin of life cannot be said to exist at all. Life just *arises* because it is natural for it to do so; the *natural*ness or *birth*ness of things is taken for granted – there is really nothing to explain.

Creation Myths – Genesis

The rituals and religious creeds that have grown up to account for the creation of the world, the elaborate patchwork of ideas that have somehow been fitted into a book like the Bible, all began to be rationalized by the Greeks in the sixth century BC. They had not so much to find new solutions as to try and make sense out of the old ones. What we know of the views of Thales and some of the older Milesian philosophers on the origin of the world are reckoned to be the first scientific, as against mythical, accounts. It is true they do not invoke any gods or spiritual influences and they simply assert that things happened in this particular way; but otherwise they are merely transpositions of very old creation myths only partially rationalized. In particular, they echo the Babylonian creation myths of the Earth monster, Tiamat, who was torn in two by the divine hero, Marduk, making the sky out of her back and the Earth out of her belly. It is more familiar to us in the legend of creation in the first chapter of the Book of Genesis, where God separated the waters above the Earth from the waters below the firmament. In both the rationalized and the mythical accounts, the primacy of water is asserted. This primacy may not be astronomically justified, but it is eminently suitable to account for life which is, after all, made out of water.

Originally, creation was, or seemed to be, a simple idea – somebody makes something, always out of something: the creator, God, the demiurge (or worker of the people) is a technician, he is a divine potter or carpenter, occupied in copying and recopying a model. The technomorphic interpretation based on *making* followed the more primitive naturalistic one of things *growing* to be what they are. In making animate things, the creator made first of all the forms or models and then the substance which had to be put into them or from which they are carved into shape. Lastly, in the animate world, including man himself, he had to add a soul, something which gave them a vitality; 'a breath of life' was the other term of matter and spirit, something breathed in, which was later to play such a large part in theories of chemistry. This was the pneuma or psyche which provided the spirit to *animate* the matter and make it come alive.

The Breath of Life

We find this conception in the second account of the creation of man contained in the second chapter of the Book of Genesis. It appears from intrinsic evidence actually to be the earlier form of the legend. There, God makes man out of clay and breathes life into him:

And the Lord God formed man of the dust of the ground, and breathed into his nostrils the breath of life, and man became a living soul.

The account given in the first chapter is more sophisticated and quite clearly inspired by astronomical conceptions, relating creation with the planets and using it to justify the seven days of the week, itself a later development of a moon-based (twenty-seven-day month) calendar [74]. The creation begins with the separation of the waters, then light appears and then, as a kind of afterthought, the sun, moon and stars are created, essentially as calendrical markers, a conception which could only have been set out by astronomers. The herbs, beasts, birds and, finally, man himself, appear in a kind of proto-evolutionary order by a fiat.

The evolution of the classification of organisms came even in the early stages. At first, as can be seen in Australia, the totems, which themselves represent an identity of man and beast or plant, were arranged almost at random. Later, as we see it among the totems of the North-west American Indians, there was an approach to the idea of animal relationships. In the civilized world, as the Book of Genesis shows, the great divisions of beasts, bird and fish among the animals, and herbs and trees among the plants, had already been made. This process of classification acquired a further rationality among the Greeks with Aristotle and Theophrastus, and then passed through Linnaeus to Darwin, emphasizing the unity of all life.

Then, in the Bible story, very much as an afterthought, comes the creation of woman from Adam's rib. There are known to us a very large number of creation myths, some in great detail. In most of these creation is carried out by some kind of creator, god or spirit, acting on inanimate matter or drawing men out of earth or rocks.

The Greek Approach: Physics and Nature: Growth and Decay

The early Ionian Greeks had the idea that they could account for creation just as well as the old religions by leaving the gods out of it and saying that things just happened like that. But the simple ' 'spect I growed' of Topsy was not enough for them. They demanded some kind of mechanism for generation and growth. They were determined to understand them. We see now that they were doomed to failure, for the sciences that could provide this understanding lay far below the historical horizon and have appeared only in our own time. The effort, however, was not wasted. What could not be understood fundamentally could always be rationalized and the rationalization itself could be the basis for further scientific advances. The Greeks considered the Universe as a field of work of definite forces, highly complex forces as they turned out to be ultimately, but at the time they seemed simple enough. There was growth and there was decay – generation and corruption. The notions of Aristotle, himself a backward and somewhat conventional thinker, but one who carried out a wonderful range of biological investigation, came from his observation of nature in its many forms and in its transformations. In contrast to the early Ionic philosophers, who were, as I have just said, essentially technomorphic in their approach, Aristotle's [6] world was biomorphic based on the analogy of how animals and plants grow, change and die. The notion of growth and decay, which has its proper application to the life and interrelations of organisms, was elevated into universal principle:

Furthermore, why should not bodies from time to time come to be from other bodies and be dispersed into bodies, and thus by dissolution the processes of generation and decay always balance one another?

Works, Vol. VI, De Melisso, 975b, 34

Acute as he was, Aristotle could not observe everything. The multiplication of the legends about animal births and behaviour was almost as great as the multiplication of the animals themselves, although the legends were much more exciting and mysterious than the truth. It is not surprising, therefore, that what was good enough for Aristotle was good enough for his successors in classical times. These notions were also taken up and became even more wonderful right through the great transformation from the pagan into the Christian world and through the corresponding transformations that took place in the early days of Mohammedanism and Taoism. Indeed, to doubt the transformation of animals and their monstrous and overabundant appearance, as in showers of frogs or fish or, for that matter, manna or blood, was to doubt the power of God, for examples of that power were shown in the sacred books themselves. The plagues of Egypt are described in the Book of Exodus. They included turning rivers to blood, the appearance of frogs, lice, fleas, hail, fire, locusts – all very unpleasant, but both familiar and likely. The rapid multiplication of animals always appears as the equivalent of a fresh creation.

And Aaron stretched out his hand over the waters of Egypt; and the frogs came up, and covered the land of Egypt.

Exodus, 8, 6

Even more drastic plagues are described in the Book of Revelations:

And the second angel poured out his vial upon the sea; and it became as the blood of a dead man; and every living soul died in the sea.

Revelations, 16, 3

None of the legends were more difficult to explain than were the real plagues of locusts, which came unpredictably, as did the equally unpredictable physical misfortunes of earthquakes, lightning and drought.

Animals as Emblems: Bestiaries

The tendency, which had its roots in antiquity and which flourished mightily in the late Middle Ages, was to treat the animate creation in its emblematic sense, that is, as symbols of human virtues or vices. Deeply buried in our language, we have the courage and nobility of the lion, the slyness of the fox, the stupidities of the ass or the goose, and our first natural history books were the bestiaries of the Middle Ages, which used such descriptions of animals for moral edification.

Figure 1. The Barnacle Goose Tree, 15th century.

To explain away these extravagances was for long a hopeless task, for new ones grew as the old ones disappeared, like the barnacle geese which came from the north or the hundreds of werewolves that turned into men and back again, or the swallows that hid in the mud under the ponds in the winter time. The breaking down of these fantastic stories, as they seem to us now (they were common sense then), was due on the one hand to the new spirit of scepticism that arose with the Renaissance in Europe, and only

C

there in the first place, and on the other to very practical considerations – what made meat go bad and why; when it went bad, did maggots grow in it. Aristotle would have said that they were generated by the corruption of the meat but Redi showed in 1660 that if you kept the flies off you got no maggots. Harvey, in 1651, had stated the basic generalization about the origin of organisms when he said 'Omni animal ex ovo' – every animal comes out of an egg. This is a hard saying: taken with the older problem still, of the chicken and the egg, it would appear to deny any possibility of a natural origin of life as a whole. Once it is granted that without exception there cannot be merely corruption-generated animals in the Aristotelian sense, then every maggot must grow from a particular egg laid by a particular fly and so on back to the beginning of flies.

Renaissance Cataloguing: Special Creation

The great cataloguing of all the species of animals and plants that went on in the seventeenth and eighteenth centuries and the accompanying classification associated with the name of Linnaeus, reinforced this idea of the fixity of species; this, at least as far as the large animals and plants were concerned, also fitted in with the doctrines of the early nineteenth century and, as it were, put the whole idea of the origin of life out of court, for the species were created in the beginning and would endure until the end of the world. But there were two loopholes to this comforting theory, both small and far away. One was provided by the small animals that were first discovered in the microscope by Leeuwenhoek in the seventeenth century and were arousing much interest. These were the infusoria, the kind of creatures that came from infusions of hay or in drops of putrid pond water. They were plainly alive and moving but had a great variety of unfamiliar shapes and seemed to have escaped the general laws of generation. These forms of life, it was thought, must generate themselves or be produced by the chance concourse of chemical substances. This was the concept of spontaneous generation and it battled with that of the fixity of species.

The Geological Record

The other loophole was provided by geology, the record of the rocks as revealed by the operations of coal-mining and railway building. They seemed to show, indubitably, that the animals were not always what they are now: species we did not recognize had existed and presumably died out. These could, of course, be put down to acts of special creation and cataclysmic

destruction, which would satisfy the pious, but they multiplied the incredi-
bilities of Noah's flood many times and they inevitably left behind a residue
of doubt – was all this creation and destruction really necessary for the
divine purpose? This is how Tennyson saw it in *In Memoriam:*

> Oh yet we trust that somehow good
> Will be the final goal of ill,
> To pangs of nature, sins of will,
> Defects of doubt, and taints of blood;
>
> That nothing walks with aimless feet;
> That not one life shall be destroy'd,
> Or cast as rubbish to the void,
> When God hath made the pile complete;
>
> That not a worm is cloven in vain;
> That not a moth with vain desire
> Is shrivell'd in a fruitless fire,
> Or but subserves another's gain . . .
>
> Are God and Nature then at strife,
> That Nature lends such evil dreams?
> So careful of the type she seems,
> So careless of the single life;
>
> That I, considering everywhere
> Her secret meaning in her deeds,
> And finding that of fifty seeds
> She often brings but one to bear . . .
>
> 'So careful of the type?' but no.
> From scarped cliff and quarried stone
> She cries, 'A thousand types are gone:
> I care for nothing, all shall go.
>
> 'Thou makest thine appeal to me:
> I bring to life, I bring to death:
> The spirit does but mean the breath:
> I know no more.' And he, shall he,
>
> Man, her last work, who seem'd so fair,
> Such splendid purpose in his eyes,
> Who roll'd the psalm to wintry skies,
> Who built him fanes of fruitless prayer,

> Who trusted God was love indeed
> And love Creation's final law –
> Tho' Nature, red in tooth and claw
> With ravine, shriek'd against his creed –
>
> Who loved, who suffer'd countless ills,
> Who battled for the True, the Just,
> Be blown about the desert dust,
> Or seal'd within the iron hills ?

The logical consequences of this observed succession of species in different successive strata, which had been glimpsed at often enough by previous biologists not frightened into religious conformity, were that the species themselves gradually changed and evolved from simpler to more complex forms under the influence of natural selection.

Darwin and Evolution

This was as the genius of Darwin saw it. If this were the case, there could no longer be a question of spontaneous generation: all was ordered by inheritance. If one primitive germ could somehow be postulated, then the whole of multifarious creation would follow from it by the action of natural selection. For Darwin did not only state the fact of the evolution of species but provided in natural selection a mechanism for their doing so. The mechanism was very imperfect: it was not really understood for more than fifty years after Darwin. The overlooking of Mendel's experiments and his laws of the unitary inheritance of characters for the last forty years of the nineteenth century prevented this and the implications have only become clear in our own days. In asserting that inheritance of characters was an atomic phenomenon, he had already been foreshadowed by Lucretius (p. 11).

Nevertheless, even without this, Darwinian evolution made the multitudinous animal species intelligible as part of a tree of life – animal and plant. In doing so, however, it raised a barrier larger than there had ever been before between the inanimate and the animate. After Darwin, the question of the origin of life became a precise and definite one. Where did the original animate germ come from ? Well, Darwin [40], with for him unusual caution, in his published work refused seriously to face this problem, but the following two quotations, both from letters, indicate that he had thought of it:

... It will be some time before we see 'slime, protoplasm, &c.' generating a new animal. But I have long regretted that I truckled to public opinion, and used the

Pentateuchal term of creation, by which I really meant 'appeared' by some wholly unknown process. It is mere rubbish, thinking at present of the origin of life; one might as well think of the origin of matter.　　To J. D. Hooker, 29 March 1863

(It is interesting to note that the origin of the elements is now possible in nuclear machines, where elements are actually being made every day.)

It is often said that all the conditions for the first production of a living organism are now present, which could ever have been present. But if (and oh! what a big if!) we could conceive in some warm little pond, with all sorts of ammonia and phosphoric salts, light, heat, electricity, &c., present, that a proteine compound was chemically formed ready to undergo still more complex changes, at the present day such matter would be instantly devoured or absorbed, which would not have been the case before living creatures were formed.　　1871

The Rise and Fall of Spontaneous Generation

Meanwhile, approaches from other parts of science had put the question in an even sharper form. Those who wished, following the materialist tendencies of the seventeenth and eighteenth centuries, embodied, for instance, in the works of Descartes, to believe that animals were merely machines, naturally thought that spontaneous generation offered them a way of demonstrating the truth of their theories. The chemistry of organisms was only a branch of general chemistry: Wöhler had already shown by his experiments in 1828 that urea could be produced from inorganic materials. The more idealistic and religious, like Pasteur, who wished to see the division between the animate and the inanimate, the organic and the inorganic, made as definite as possible, had dealt telling experimental blows at the ideas of spontaneous generation and had shown that fermentation and putrefaction were not due to any kind of non-living chemical agents but demonstrably due to germs provided from the ambient air. Heating and sealing up in hermetic vessels and the use of disinfectants could protect all organic material from decay, a telling philosophical point, which was at the same time the basis of the industry of canned and frozen food, so essential for maintaining the industrial population at the end of the nineteenth century, besides becoming the basis of aseptic medicine and surgery.

The Impasse of the Physical Basis of Life

By putting the ideas of Pasteur and Darwin together, the question of the origin of life on Earth had been sharply posed and seemed to preclude any possibility of an answer. Both for the believer – and Pasteur was one – and for the unbeliever – and Darwin was one – life had been demonstrated to be something of a unique and inimitable character and, consequently, its origin to be totally incomprehensible and, by implication, better not enquired into. These negative conclusions were to put all discussion on the origin of life into a limbo of insoluble problems, but it was not to remain there indefinitely. Already, even in the nineteenth century, a few daring spirits had suggested, without going into too much detail, that life had, in fact, originated from inorganic matter in some primitive ocean. Huxley, himself, in 1868, had talked about the physical basis of life [58], and Tyndall, making his Presidential Address to the British Association in Belfast in 1874 [112], defied the religious by treating the origin and development of life as a natural process not involving any supernatural creative element:

Trace the line of life backwards, and see it approaching more and more to what we call the purely physical condition. We come at length to those organisms which I have compared to drops of oil suspended in a mixture of alcohol and water. . . . Believing, as I do, in the continuity of Nature, I cannot stop abruptly where our microscopes cease to be of use. Here the vision of the mind authoritatively supplements the vision of the eye. By an intellectual necessity I cross the boundary of the experimental evidence, and discern in that Matter which we, in our ignorance of its latent powers, and not withstanding our professed reverence for its Creator, have hitherto covered with opprobrium, the promise and potency of all terrestrial life.

A few other eminent biologists joined their ranks, notably Schäfer, Haeckel and Pflüger. What they did, essentially, was only to assert the possibility of life originating from dead matter, but they could not describe the way in which this could have occurred or provide any experimental proof. They were to some extent absolutely limited by the resolving power of their microscopes and by their rudimentary chemical theory. They thought of primitive life as the featureless *protoplasm*, intrinsically capable of growth and reproduction. The conditions under which this protoplasm could have been formed were left deliberately vague. It is now recognized, owing to the development of biochemistry and of electron microscopy, that protoplasm is by no means simple, and it remains a great problem to explain *its* origin and its complexities. At that time, according to their temperament, the scientists thought it easy or impossible to explain, while a few recognized that the problem was beyond the actual knowledge of the time to solve and that it was better not to be dogmatic about it. One consequence, however, was recognized: at this level of minuteness there could be little to choose philosophically between an account of special creation and one of chance occurrence.

The last of the early theories on the origin of life were based essentially on natural historical observations. Their authors were concerned more with the apparent forms, seen with the naked eye and in the microscope, with organisms and with studies of their life histories. Their view of organic nature was limited to morphology and physiological functions. None of the nineteenth-century pioneers could really treat the question of origin they had so definitely raised, for at that time the essential chemical knowledge about the function of life did not exist. Biochemistry is, to a certain extent, the product of physiology [44], and it was originally called physiological chemistry and drew its inspiration largely from the work of the great Claude Bernard and from that of one of the greatest of his followers, Gowland Hopkins. The chemistry, which in the main is the language in which the problem of the origin of life has to be discussed, did not yet exist. It was, therefore, most appropriate that, when the question was again brought into the forum of scientific discussion, it should be done by two biochemists, Oparin in the Soviet Union and Haldane in England. The origin and consequences of their ideas will be discussed in a subsequent chapter.

Chapter 3

Modern Views on the Origin of Life

Oparin's and Haldane's First Theories

THE impact of the development of biochemistry took some time to penetrate into the field of origins. Most early biochemists were too interested in
tracing out the actual chemical changes that occurred in animal bodies or
isolated parts of them to worry about questions of origins, which seemed
to be essentially philosophical and speculative. Nevertheless, the growing
knowledge that all life was chemically one, as well as genetically interrelated, was bound sooner or later to give rise to definite speculations as to
its origin. The first of these to strike root, and the one that has remained
the basis of nearly all modern theories of the origin of life, was that put
forward in 1924 by A. I. Oparin in his booklet *Proiskhozhdenie zhizny* [75].
Five years later, essentially the same ideas were put forward independently
and in a much shorter form by J. B. S. Haldane [50]. These basic documents
on the modern approach to the origin of life are reproduced in Appendix 1.
Both were attempts – making use of new knowledge of biochemical reaction
cycles, those of oxidation and fermentation – to explain the origin of life in
terms of the origin of the essential biochemical properties of life under the
presumed primitive conditions on Earth, particularly in relation to the
oceans or hydrosphere and to changes of the atmosphere of the primitive
Earth.

A chemical analysis of fermentation processes – beginning with the study
of the work of Buchner, who in 1897 was able to isolate a non-living ferment
from the yeast cells studied by Pasteur in 1855 – gave rise to the idea of the
existence and functioning of enzymes, molecules of an organic nature capable of carrying out specific processes of normal chemical reactions at very
much faster rates; in other words, they were organic catalysts. It was clear
to Oparin that their appearance was a necessary part of the process of the
origin of life.

He attempted to answer the objections that were raised – and effectively
raised – against the older theories of the origin of life on the Earth and to

deal with the contradiction implied in the success of Pasteur's demonstration that spontaneous generation was experimentally impossible. Pasteur had shown that life could not originate except from germs of life already present in the air. If this be granted, then life had to be as eternal as matter itself and many scientists had said so. But this, in turn, rested on the essentially Aristotelian hypothesis that nothing really changes, which was in conflict with the new, established evolutionary theory of organisms. If this assumption was dropped, the way was open to another one: that the conditions under which life originated in the first place were different from the conditions in which it existed today. This difference was essentially in the constitution of the atmosphere.

The Role of Molecular Oxygen

The Earth, alone among the planets of our solar system, has an atmosphere in which oxygen plays a dominating role. The importance of this for the question of the origin of life was recognized early both by Haldane and Oparin. It was, perhaps, the recognition of the fact that the oxygen in its present concentration in the atmosphere would prove fatal to any possibility of spontaneous generation in our time. Moreover, there is a strong case for the view that the molecular oxygen is itself a product of life. Further, if life were to appear all of a sudden by itself on our present world, it could hardly persist for long. It would be eaten and ultimately oxidized before it had reached the possibility of further evolution. That the absence of spontaneous generation here and now is no argument against its occurring in a world with a different atmosphere was already apparent even to Darwin, as can be seen from the quotation already given (p. 21).

Once life appeared it, itself, provides the strongest reason why it should not appear again. Any existing life would, in any case, tend to destroy a new appearance, but there is a stronger reason provided by a by-product of life, molecular oxygen, the characteristic of the light-requiring photosynthetic plants. The life that we have on Earth today is, in fact, divided into two great categories long recognized by mankind – the oxygen-breathing animals and the photosynthetic or light-growing plants. Animals can live in the dark, but they need air to breathe, either free air or oxygen dissolved in water. Plants do not need oxygen – in fact they produce it in the sunlight – but they cannot live and grow for long in the dark. Which, therefore, came first? Or did some other form of life precede them both? This alternative now seems almost certain. Detailed studies of the life histories, the internal cellular anatomy and the metabolism both of plants and animals show them to be divergently specialized descendants of some common zoophyte. These must have been like some of the bacteria of today that can at the same time carry on the functions of animals and plants, and act both as oxidizing and as photosynthetic agents.

Pasteur: Aerobic and Anaerobic Life

Already, in the mid-nineteenth century, Pasteur had shown in his study of fermentation that life without oxygen was possible. In anaerobic life – life without oxygen – the processes of metabolism took place by cycles of fermentation rather than those of oxidation and, as Pasteur had already divined, fermentation is a simpler, though less efficient, process than oxidation and probably preceded it. Other biochemical studies examined the reactions of fermentation and oxidation step by step, each step actuated by a specific enzyme.

It was particularly Haldane [50] who chose this primacy of anaerobic over aerobic metabolism as the basis for his notion on the origin of life. He imagined life to have originated on a planet without oxygen in its atmosphere:

As the primitive atmosphere contained little or no oxygen, the first precursors of life must have obtained the energy which they needed for growth by some other process than oxidation – in fact, by fermentation. For, as Pasteur put it, fermentation is life without oxygen. If this was so, we should expect that high organisms like ourselves would start life as anaerobic beings, just as we start as single cells.

In his original 1924 booklet, Oparin [75] did not take this view. However, when he developed the ideas it contained in a book published in 1936 [76], he wrote:

. . . at the present time it is regarded as highly improbable that free oxygen was contained in the original Earth's atmosphere. . . . Beyond doubt the molecular oxygen found in our present-day atmosphere was formed secondarily and at a much later epoch, as a result of the activity of living organisms.

These views received striking astronomical and chemical support unavailable to the nineteenth-century scientists. The postulated atmospheres without oxygen, and composed of methane and ammonia, had been found spectroscopically on the planets Jupiter and Saturn.

The Utilization of Ultra-violet and Visible Light: Ozone

If the Earth at one time had had such an atmosphere, more complex compounds would be formed from these two gases and thus the way would be opened to the synthesis of the basic biochemical substances, the energy being supplied by the short-wave, ultra-violet light from the Sun striking through these non-absorbing gases.

These short waves are all filtered out by the present-day atmosphere of the Earth owing to the presence of oxygen which, though itself non-absorbing, is changed by ultra-violet light into ozone, a powerful absorbent of ultra-violet. This notion, in turn, resolves the question of why life does not arise spontaneously on the Earth at the present time. The ultra-violet light required to produce it is no longer present. This postulated origin for the organic compounds on which life is based is eminently plausible and, in fact, has been reproduced in the laboratory (p. 28). It must, however, have been slow and inefficient owing to the relatively small proportion of ultra-violet rays in the full spectrum of sunlight. Once the more efficient mechanism for generating energy for life produced by photosynthesis using the much more abundant red rays of the Sun had been developed, oxygen was produced and with it ozone which, in turn, cut off the ultra-violet rays that had been responsible for the first stages of the building up of living substances.

Another notion introduced at the very beginning by Oparin was to play a large part in the general picture of the origin of life. It was that of the occurrence of colloidal substances. The basic idea was, in fact, an old one: the notion that primitive life occurred in some form of jelly at the bottom of the sea was already enshrined in the bathybius hypothesis of T. H. Huxley. But Oparin took it up and developed it with much experimental material from the ideas of the specific colloidal phase precipitate, the coacervates of Bungenburg de Jong. He showed that such colloidal bodies could carry on complex chemical reactions and could gradually form what were afterwards referred to as eobionts or pre-vital masses which could carry on a chemical evolution of their own. This notion of chemical evolution and even of chemical struggle for existence is to be found in Oparin's original paper and was followed up considerably in his later work.

The Virus as Half Life

Haldane, also in his first paper, showed his perception of the importance of the newly discovered bacteriophages or other viruses as a possible link between pre-life and life. He saw in the virus what he calls a half life which can only grow in the presence of a complicated assortment of molecules which now form a living cell:

27

The cell consists of numerous half-living chemical molecules suspended in water and enclosed in an oily film. When the whole sea was a vast chemical laboratory, the conditions for the formation of such films must have been relatively favourable; but for all that life may have remained in the virus stage for many millions of years before a suitable assemblage of elementary units brought together the first cell.

These ideas between them removed many of the objections that had, in the previous century, held up the acceptance of any concept of the spontaneous origin of life on Earth. However, by the nineteen-thirties, the minds of scientists, and particularly biologists and biochemists, were antipathetic to such generalized suppositions. They were too interested in the immediate problems of the mechanisms of biogenic chemical reactions and in those of genetic inheritance to occupy themselves much with questions of origin. There was, moreover, a feeling that these were not quite a regular part of science: they were philosophic and speculative and, as such, not worth the consideration of serious experimental scientific workers.

It was not, in fact, until after the Second World War that the study of the origin of life was taken up again in earnest, when several questions of interest to chemists, biologists and astronomers arose. It was soon evident, however, that the solutions proposed by Oparin and Haldane had raised more questions than they had answered. They had, it is true, laid down much more precisely than before the conditions in which life might originate, but they were far from being able to determine with any degree of precision the actual mechanisms and the reactions involved. The hypothesis of Oparin and Haldane could at one point be subjected to experimental test.

Miller's Experiment

This was first done by Miller in 1953 [67]. By exposing mixtures of methane, ammonia and water to various forms of electrical excitation, he was able to produce definite molecules of organic compounds, particularly amino acids, sugars and vegetable acids. This demonstrated that the reactions postulated by Oparin could be carried out, but did not prove that these reactions were actually taking place at the time of the origin of life.

From then on the interest in the origin of life spread rapidly; it became the subject, as it had never been before, of an increasing number of discourses by various scientists and, also, it was seriously discussed at special conferences arranged for the purpose. At last, the problems concerned with the origin of life could be taken seriously and systematically and could be the subject of experiment as well as observation. Before discussing these experiments in detail, it would be worth while to recall the major steps taken in refining the concepts and adding to them.

In the early days, the two lines of investigations, based on straight bio-chemistry and on genetics, had been pursued almost independently. In 1927 however, with the work of Muller on the productions of mutations by x-rays, genetics had moved from the formal analysis of the hereditary char-acters and their combinations, which were evolved in the days of Gregor Mendel and T. H. Morgan, and moved on to consider their origins which are much more precise and even material. Some genes were found and all were deemed to be responsible for the action of particular chemicals which, in turn, as enzymes, produced the distinguishing mark of the character, for instance, colour in flowers.

Genetic Aspects: Chromosomes and Nucleic Acids

The hereditary factors had been shown by genetic analysis to be largely located in the chromosomes and these, in turn, were found to be composed essentially of nucleic acids which gave them their characteristic absorption of ultra-violet radiation. Furthermore, the association of nucleic acids with the synthesis of proteins, which had first been observed by Caspersson [38] in the 'thirties, was, in the 'fifties, beginning to reveal its secrets in terms of the actual structure of such molecules. These molecules were found to be essentially long polymers of a set of organic bases, the nucleotides, which included sugars and essential phosphoric acids. This may be taken as the birth of the study of *molecular biology*. The unravelling of the general struc-ture of nucleic acids and the demonstration that they consisted – in the case of the nucleic acid in the nucleus, DNA – of twisted strands of nucleotides, provided at last a plausible model for a self-reproducing molecule.

The purely logical idea of what kind of molecule it would have to be to lead to identical reproduction was fairly easy to grasp. It could not be a solid molecule because there would be no way to reproduce the interior. It could not even be a plane one because the reproduction in that case would be a mirror image of the original plane. It would have to be a line. What the earlier thinkers did not see was that the line could just as well be bent as straight: in fact, its most logical form would be a helix and another helix, which had to be its own precise reproduction, was wound round it. Thus the question of the origin of life refined itself down to the origin of the self-producing molecule of DNA. At the beginning, not unnaturally, this idea was driven to death. The picture of the solitary molecule of DNA on a pri-mitive sea-shore generating the rest of life was put forward with slightly less plausibility than that of Adam and Eve in the Garden.

The source of this implausibility of the DNA molecule as the origin of life was, in fact, because it had no obvious predecessor. Before being able to think of how the DNA molecule could give rise to organisms, it was necessary to ask how it got there in the first place. The idea of the separate creation of such a molecule strikes one as even more absurd than the creation of a man or of a primitive organism. The alternative idea, that it was formed by a pure chance coincidence of atoms, although not so unlikely as that of a more complicated organism itself, can be demonstrably disproved by the laws of probability. The world is not old enough for this to happen by itself. If it were, what would happen to this molecule? In any case, it could reproduce only in a medium furnished with all the other molecules required to affect the synthesis of proteins and other biochemical reactions, as actually happens in the reproduction of virus nucleic acids.

If chance or special creation are not reasonable predecessors for the nucleic acid molecule, then, in the final analysis, it must itself be the outcome of a long chemical and biochemical evolution. It is the realization of this that gave a further turn to the arguments about the origin of life, a turn which occurred about the time of the first conference of the International Union of Biochemistry on this subject in Moscow in 1957. Neither the nucleic acid molecule nor the medium in which it operates can have existed independently. They must both have grown up as a result of some previous chemical evolution and this is what we have to trace.

Chemical Evolution

We now have, added to the knowledge derived from simple biochemistry, that of genetic inheritance. The welding together of these two sets of ideas was bound to be difficult and has not yet been completed. But it is necessary; any theory of the origin of life must now include as a major feature the origin of the mechanisms of molecular reproduction. The epoch of *chemical evolution* which preceded that of organic evolution is one which is almost completely and necessarily unknown. It has to be reconstructed logically, step by step, from what can be learned from the laws of chemistry, on the one hand, and the actual biochemical compounds found in present-day life, on the other. Although chemical evolution and organic evolution are substantially different, they must at least have some formal elements in common. One of these is the concept of the survival of the fittest, of the maintenance of one particular molecular pathway as against others for which certain material substances proved to be lacking. Thus, if a certain molecule A were lacking, the process by which A could be formed from available substances B and C would be particularly favoured. This idea, which is due to Horowitz [56] in 1945, has been most helpful in tracing the origin of the most complicated aspects of existing biochemistry, the nature of enzymes and other proteins.

The structure of these complicated polymers of amino acids was elucidated chemically by Sanger by paper chromatography sequential analysis and, almost simultaneously, by the determination of the structure of the crystalline myoglobins and haemoglobins by physical and chemical x-ray methods by Kendrew [60] and Perutz [90]. Both concur in a picture of the protein chain, on which its properties depend, as an almost unintelligible sequence of the twenty-odd amino acids. Nevertheless, if this is unintelligible for one protein, it begins to gain significance when several are compared. A comparative analysis of amino-acid sequences in proteins of different, but more or less related, species may not only turn out to be a more powerful weapon in the tracing of organic organismal relationships, but may also connect structure and function and point back to the simpler forms which preceded the protein molecules of today. We are, indeed, beginning to see what kind of precursors of present-day biochemistry derive from the simpler biochemistry existing before.

First Steps: Evidence from Meteorites

Until recently, however, this could only be done by inference – by a kind of reconstruction similar to that used in interpreting lost scripts and languages like the Linear B of Crete. In the last few years, however, we have received totally unexpected assistance through the actual discovery of very ancient carbon-containing molecules, no longer from the Earth, where the subsequent changes have been too great, but from outer space, in the form of the carbon compounds in some meteorites. These will be discussed further in later chapters: it suffices here to say that in meteorites there are complex carbon compounds some of which seem to be definite biochemical precursors, but formed at least 4,500 million years ago, not on the Earth but on some form of planetary body.

These compounds make it evident that some aspects of the origin of life may have occurred elsewhere than on Earth; in fact, they must have done so even if they have followed slightly different courses here and there. This material evidence raises the question of the generality of the origin of life, no longer the origin of life on Earth, but what may be called a more general process of biopoesis of life making.

At this point, which is roughly the one reached at present, we begin to see the processes of the evolution of life as general and necessary ones.

These processes might be viewed from two angles: one is the sequence of chemical changes required to give the complicated structures which we find in life; the other is the absolute necessity to account for the energy changes involved in the appearance of life. Life, as has long been pointed out, is a process which requires a steady and ample supply of free energy to make it go on at all. This free energy may be an expendable surplus collected at some previous time, or later it may come to be continually replenished by energy sources from outside.

The Energy Balance of Life

There is a need to explain the energy balance of life at different stages without necessarily explaining the mechanism in detail. This process of life-building falls logically into stages. Of these, the first is the formation of simple biogenic molecules preceded presumably by the absorption and fixation of free energy. The source of free energy must have been some form of radiation – either the direct photonic radiation of the Sun, or the hydrogen wind it emits, or radioactive energy. The 'primitive soup' formed in this way thus has built-in free energy. The first stage of the evolution of life from it is one essentially of the conversion of the accumulated free energy into ever more complicated molecular structures. But somewhere – and the question is 'where?' – a new source of energy appeared in the interaction with solar ultra-violet radiation, sufficient, but perhaps only just sufficient, to maintain life as a going concern. In fact, life may not always have been so maintained. Various starts may have been made on an ultra-violet-absorbing life which faded out without leaving any descendants. It is here that the processes of natural selection on the molecular scale may have taken place. We see only the successful survivors.

Once photosynthesis based on visible-light takes place, however, the argument is reversed. More energy is built into organisms than can be used in their own metabolism. Much of this is released by the action of fungi or of animals, but enough remains to form massive sources of free energy buried in fossil fuels, oils and coals.

Stages in the Origin of Life on Earth

Stage 1

These stages correspond to a rise in complexity of the molecules and molecular systems that are to be incorporated ultimately into living systems. The first stage is that of the formation of pre-organismal molecules from simple molecules like the hydrides of carbon, nitrogen and oxygen (in other words, methane, ammonia and water), which are still found in this molecular form in the free space of the cooler parts of the Universe. This first stage can clearly have occurred in many places. We know it on Earth and we know it now in the meteorites derived from asteroids and possibly also in planetary dust. It is also one that we can imitate in the laboratory; the experiments of Miller and his successors have demonstrated that. The molecules that are produced are the basic biochemical ones: some organic bases, such as adenine, which are the constituents of nucleic acids; some amino acids, which are the bases of proteins; some sugars, particularly ribose, and their phosphates; and some slightly more complicated nitrogen-containing molecules, such as the porphyrins, the bases of the oxidative enzymes and the energy carriers.

Stage 2

The second stage consists of the formation from the constituents of Oparin's 'primitive soup', largely composed of molecules just mentioned, but also of more complicated ones in the form of polymers, formed by the stringing together in linear order of similar or identical monomers or sub-molecules. In the evolution of such polymers, which are the analogues, probably simpler analogues, of the nucleic acids or proteins of existing life in the process of their synthesis, there must have occurred at some decisive stage the appearance of the mechanism of identical reproduction and replication which is considered to be by many biologists the essential characteristic of life itself. So far, we can only imagine this to have taken place in an environment something like that of the Earth: that is, a planet which has free water on it and contains many gas molecules and metal ions in solution. It is difficult to imagine it taking place on a completely dry satellite like the Moon, far less on meteorites derived from asteroids, which contain only fixed water of hydration or ice.

Stage 3

The third stage, which may turn out to be not entirely separate from the second but to merge into it continuously, is one in which the simplest conceivable organisms are derived from these elements by biochemical and structural transformations. These include the various specialized parts of cells such as mitochondria, responsible for such chemical changes as oxidation; the ribosomes, where proteins are made corresponding to the orders derived from nucleic acids; the various membranes, organelles, responsible

D

for the form, structure and activity of cells, that now go to build up what is taken to be the most primitive cells, which corresponds to the simplest autonomous form of life that we can imagine. The even smaller and simpler organisms of present-day life are not autonomous: they are the viruses, which seem to be very definitely a degenerate type of cell only capable of a parasitic existence.

Necessary or Contingent Steps in the Origin of Life

There is one major question which has to be asked, but is by no means easy to answer: it is whether the processes required in the origin of life are necessary or contingent. In other words, are the compounds or structures found at each stage the inevitable consequences of those that went before them or have they been picked on by a chance concurrence of events ? Both explanations must be true in some measure, first, because any structures widely different from those of minimal energy would be unstable and unlikely to have a long life and, secondly, because there is not only one form of life but a wide multiplicity of forms. These may vary widely in small matters, but not in basic biochemistry. The particular character of any species has clearly not the same intrinsic necessity as is exhibited in basic common biochemistry. Here there is room for various contingencies that attended the evolution of that particular form, such as the changes in their environment brought about in the course of geological evolution or by the interactions of other organisms.

We shall, in the ensuing chapters, discuss these three stages one after the other and bring out their relations to internal development and to the variation of the external environment. Many questions here have not been answered and many others probably have not been put. We do not know, for instance, at which stage in the evolution of life the crucial biochemical changes associated with photosynthesis, on the one hand, and oxygenative breakdown, on the other, actually occurred. It is quite possible that they occurred only after the third stage when a completed nucleated organism had been evolved, or they might have occurred in the third stage. We have also to consider, in the second stage, how the earlier molecules were brought together in sufficient concentration to make possible their future evolution into life. In other words, how did the sub-vital areas, the presumed indefinite areas in which biochemical changes took place before organisms were formed, come into existence.

Where so little has been done and so much is still speculative, it is difficult to give a coherent account that is at the same time soundly based in all

34

points. The account has clearly to be one of a work in progress, already out of date the moment it is written. Yet, in order to retain any intelligibility, it must be told as a reasonable, continuous, hypothetical story, a myth of the origin of life, and this will be found in the subsequent chapters.

Chapter 4

The Origin of
Biological Monomers

Cosmic Origins: From Atom to Molecule

As quoted earlier (p. 21), Darwin once wrote: 'It is mere rubbish, thinking at present of the origin of life; one might as well think of the origin of matter'. Indeed, the first chapter of any account of the origin of life, nowadays, must start with the origin of the elements out of which it is formed. We have to begin with some sketch of what is currently believed to be the history of the planet Earth and its neighbours in the solar system. This has been treated at greater length and more expertly in *The Earth* by Professor Dunbar in this series: for our purpose it is necessary to consider only those parts of the story that are involved in the subsequent evolution of life. I will pass over, to start with, the origin of the elements in the galaxies, the stars and, in particular, in our Sun which is a fairly average, rather middle-aged star and which contains in its surface layers, at least, a great variety of atoms of different elements. Many of these may be second-hand, derived from some earlier supernova explosion in our galaxy. The commonest elements, as might be expected, are those of low atomic mass, the elements of the first row of the Periodic Table, particularly carbon, nitrogen, oxygen and the ever-present, and by far the most abundant, hydrogen. The remaining common elements, though present only to the extent of some few per cent on the Earth, are those of silicon, magnesium and iron.

The Uniqueness of the Planet Earth

How the planetary system around the Sun was formed has been the object of fairly considerable dispute in astronomical circles. This dispute goes as far back as Descartes, Laplace and many other philosophers and astronomers of the past. For it had psychological and philosophical aspects as well as astronomical ones. What mattered, or seemed to matter, most was the uniqueness of the Earth. Once the Earth, following Copernicus, Galileo and Kepler, was no longer thought of as the centre of the Universe, it still remained possible, and at least desirable, to consider it as a unique planet – a unique planet in a unique solar system. There was in consequence a philosophical attraction in imagining the Earth to be the product of some great catastrophe very rare in its nature and unlikely to be repeated at any other time or place. This was the basis of hypotheses first associated with the names of Chamberlain and Moulton in 1900, later, in 1918, with those of Jeans and Jeffreys and still later, with those of Lyttleton and Hoyle. It was that the Earth and other planets were formed of a filament drawn out of the Sun by some passing star or by internal catastrophe. Since the Jeans hypothesis of the origin of the Earth has been largely discredited, we have returned essentially to the old nebular hypothesis of Kant and Laplace, in which it was postulated that the planets arose from a primitive Sun which had spun around it a disc of dust and gas. This had subsequently divided into rings each of which had ultimately condensed into a single planet, a system of which the prototype existed in the rings and satellites of the planet Saturn. Indeed, it is from this analogy that the whole notion of the Kant-Laplace solar system originated. For a while this did not seem very satisfactory in its original form because it was found impossible on a mechanical basis to explain how so much of the angular momentum of the whole system came to reside in the outer planets. Jupiter accounts for more than half the momentum of the whole solar system.

Modern Versions of Planetary Origins

This outwardly displaced angular momentum was indeed one of the strong points of the Jeans solar filament theory, in which the momentum was created by the effect of the other star which drew the filament out. It was, indeed, difficult in Newtonian mechanics to devise a method for such a transfer of momentum. This was one of the reasons why the filament theory had such a long life despite its lack of astrophysical plausibility. However, following Alfvén [4], we can now postulate an early stage in which most of the nebular disc belonging to the Sun was composed of plasma, that is, of ionized atoms. Their movement was consequently quite different from that of Newtonian, gravity-controlled, electrically neutral particles. The plasma moves under the influence of the magnetic field of the whole solar system, which may be sufficient to transfer momentum to the outer parts by what are called magneto-hydrodynamic forces. A solar system may have evolved in the first place as a set of magneto-hydrodynamic vortices involved in the main vortex. Later, when electrically neutralized, they condense into separate planetary bodies, each with their appropriate inertial rotation, which they are unable to lose or alter. This idea is essentially a modern electromagnetic version of the old vortex theory of Descartes in the seventeenth century. Its revival in modern times, though in a somewhat different form, is due to von Weizsäcker [117].

Such a process as this makes the origin of the planetary systems a perfectly regular and ordinary procedure which must, therefore, have occurred over and over again in the history of the Universe or, at any rate, of our galaxy. Other such systems will probably originate at various intervals. Whether they have been produced in one or several ways is not known. We have, indeed, no direct evidence of planets of other systems, but plenty of indirect evidence.

Other Planetary Systems

The difficulty of observing planetary systems around stars, even those nearest the Earth in the galactic plane, leaves the number of such systems that we need to take into account as possible sites for the origin of life, still controversial. Such evidence as does exist is based on features like the prevalence of slow rotation and stars other than the Sun. That seems to imply that they are very numerous indeed. Harrison Brown [35], using a different argument, has even calculated that all multiple-star systems, and one in every four stars belongs to them, must have planetary systems, and in these at least one planet must be in a zone illuminated to the same extent as the Earth and therefore may be a possible source of life. We are back at the same doctrine of the multiplicity of habitable worlds which cost Giordano Bruno his life in 1600.

Hot or Cold Origins

According to modern ideas, the formation of planetary systems from clouds of dust or plasma may have pursued one of two different courses. One is the formation of actual secondary stars such as those that occur in present-day double- or multiple-star systems, which may have been the origin of the larger planets such as Jupiter and Saturn. The other is the formation of minor planets from cold dust, which have never been raised to surface temperatures at which they are luminous, such as the inner planets, the Earth, Venus, Mars and Mercury, and the asteroids – the belt of small planets that reside between Mars and Jupiter – together with the planetary satellites which range in size from our Moon downwards. In addition, we have to take into account particularly the smaller pieces of the system – the comets, the meteorites (which may or may not be fragments of asteroids) and the residual interplanetary dust. The importance of the latter has only recently been realized. It has been visible but unrecognized in the zodiacal light and noctilucent clouds that are sometimes seen in high latitudes long after the Sun has set.

Planets from Dust

The agglomerative theory of planetary formation from dust is now generally accepted. This hypothesis dates back to Kant and appeared in new forms with Schmidt [105] and von Weizsäcker [117]. The primitive dust must consist essentially of the most stable compounds of the most common elements in the surroundings of the Sun. The main constituents in the solid part of this dust are silicates, particularly magnesium silicates, and also metallic iron containing nickel. This dust has largely but not entirely disappeared from the present-day solar system, but some of it still functions as the nuclei for meteors where it has been found by space probes. Such nuclei are found most abundantly in the high-flying (200 km) noctilucent clouds. There, each silicate or iron particle seems to be surrounded by a layer of ice, and ice condensed on dust is found also in the comets which seem to come from the outer parts of the solar system on long eccentric orbits. If the dust particles are smaller, they fall down so slowly from the atmosphere that they are not heated in the process as are the meteors or shooting stars and end up either on land or sea. They are difficult to distinguish from the particles of the Earth's dust in most inhabited places, but they can be found on remote Arctic and Antarctic snowfields or after sinking to the bottom in the mud of the deep ocean sediments, as revealed by cores sunk into them. Probably larger dust particles are burnt up in the atmosphere and appear as shooting stars and their ash joins the primitive dust in the form of small spheres of iron oxide, magnetite. In the solar system itself most of this dust had long ago come together to form large planets, but some has remained for the smaller planets and asteroids from which the meteorites or the larger objects falling from space are thought to be derived. As we shall see, the meteorites contain the most precious evidence of what can happen to such elements and compounds in space itself before they are moulded together into more complex forms as larger planets like the Earth (Appendix 2).

It must not be imagined that these solid particles are the only or even the main constituents of the solar system at all ages. Clearly in earlier times there was much more gas, and gas appears now wherever the Sun's radiations, which consist not only of light but also of free hydrogen atoms or ions (the so-called solar wind), strike any of these smaller objects. The presence of gas reveals itself by its spectrum. Small particles simply reflect the sunlight and give a spectrum identical with that of the Sun. Gas atoms or gas molecules can be excited and themselves radiate their characteristic lines or bands, most clearly seen in the spectra of the tails of comets. Generally these are excited by the light of the stars themselves, but this is not necessarily always so.

In recent times, by the use of infra-red methods, sets of very large stars have been discovered in the centre of the galaxy with surface temperatures as low as 800°C [73]. These stars must be composed largely of molecules which are maintained as gases at such temperatures. The molecules of circumsolar gases formed in this way have not always remained in this uncondensed state. In the outer parts of the solar system and in the earlier times when the Sun was more extended and cooler than it is now, a process of condensation of gases on particles must have occurred. There is evidence, as already stated, for the most condensable gas, water, condensing as ice, but in the outer parts of the solar system the various cyanogen and hydrocarbon gases must also have condensed. Most of them must have subsequently evaporated as the temperature rose, but during the period of exposure a certain amount must have been acted on by the particulate radiation and partly polymerized into less volatile hydrocarbon and nitrogen-carbon compounds. Independent evidence of the effect of radiations on fine particles in the solar system is provided by the presence in the carbonaceous meteorites of free chemical radicals, as Duchesne [42] has shown by a study of nuclear magnetic resonance, which must be formed by high-energy particle interactions.

It is at least a tenable hypothesis that in this form the silicate or iron particles with their organic skin would come together to form first the asteroids and then the planets. We know that the major planets, Jupiter and Saturn and probably Uranus as well, are composed largely of hydrogen, methane and ammonia and also of ice. We may reasonably think of these condensed layers of carbon-nitrogen compounds as the primary origin of those at present found in life. There is a strong presumption that it is on the highly dispersed and consequently larger area of surface of these compounds that the chemical actions giving rise to the first intermediate sized molecules arose. The relative area of the surface of flaky dust particles, of one-tenth micron diameter and one-hundredth micron thickness, is 10^{14} times that of asteroid-sized bodies of 100 km diameter and 10^{16} times that of a planet such as the Earth.

This presumption is still a controversial one: following the ideas of Oparin and Haldane, life was supposed to have derived directly from the atmosphere and oceans of a planet the size of the Earth, particularly from the watery parts of it and its atmosphere.

A Secondary Reducing Atmosphere?

The view they introduced as to the origin of life was based precisely on the hypothesis of a primary-reducing atmosphere of methane and ammonia on the Earth in contact with the smaller primitive oceans. I do not think, for reasons that will be set out later, that this is necessarily a wrong view, but I think it is definitely a partial one. Life on Earth may, but not necessarily must, have arisen in this way or largely in this way. The next implication of this now classical picture is to ask the further question – how did the carbonaceous compounds get into the oceans and the atmosphere in the first place? Were they formed there by some photochemical process *de novo* or were they relics of a previous stage in which these compounds were formed, first on small planetesimal bodies which were later agglomerated to form the planets? Subsequently, were the carbonaceous and nitrogen compounds partly decomposed and the remainder sweated out to the surface through geological processes of consolidation?

This question, which I will not attempt at this stage to answer, may be one that it is not of very great importance to answer owing to our general lack of knowledge of origins of planetary bodies. We could, if we liked, take the starting-point of life at any stage along the line, especially as the kinds of compounds we are now discussing cannot be claimed by any extension as alive. They are definitely pre-life. Nevertheless, in contrast to what we find on Earth, the carbonaceous compounds on meteorites or meteoritic dust are themselves evidence of what can be formed in the solar system without the pre-existence of large planets with oceans on them and so offer valuable confirmation of the possibility of independent formation of complex compounds which definitely point towards life. Starting from the atoms, we must try to trace the development of simple molecular compounds to the next stage in the origin of life, in which we consider their polymerization or joining together into larger units.

The Origins of Simple Molecules

We have here two kinds of evidence, each of which, though being incomplete, helps to support the other in a general picture of the origin of the complex process. We know that life does exist here on Earth, but we also know that its first stages must have been so distorted by subsequent geological and biological processes that they are extremely difficult to find. On the other hand, in scanty meteoritic material derived from other parts of the solar system, we find evidence of molecules which may or may not be similar to those which generated life, but which are uncomplicated by subsequent changes, as in the case of a particular compound like adenine, which occurs both in contemporary life and in meteoritic debris. There is a strong presumption that the two facts are connected, and links between them have been provided by laboratory experiments, beginning with those of Miller, in which compounds such as adenine are produced. This throws light both on their genesis in the primitive solar cloud and on their subsequent role in the genesis of life on Earth.

The Elements of Life

Before we discuss the formation of these early life-generating molecules, we must discuss that of the elements from which life is built. Life, as we know it on this Earth, consists essentially of water in which is found a variety of complex carbon and nitrogen compounds. As already stated, *life is an epiphenomenon of the hydrosphere*. The elements which form life are unique in two respects: first, they are among the commonest stable elements in the Universe, particularly in the stellar system; and, secondly, they are small, reactive elements of the first row of the Periodic Table. Their abundance is a necessary property of the composition of their nuclei and refers to the original order of the formation of the elements in stars, in which the elements of small atomic weight must precede those with large. The process starts with the commonest element of all, hydrogen. To be major, life-producing elements, they have to be, on the one hand, very abundant, a nuclear property, and, on the other, capable of forming complex compounds, an electronic property; the light elements meet both these conditions. These light elements are peculiar in the small number of electrons they contain and in the corresponding range of possible molecular structures to which they can give rise. Of the four principal elements in question – carbon, oxygen, nitrogen and hydrogen – carbon holds a unique place due to the multiplicity and complexity of the compounds it can form with other carbon atoms and with atoms of hydrogen, nitrogen and oxygen as well. The identity of so-called organic chemistry as the chemistry of substances derived from living creatures, on the one hand, and as the chemistry of the compounds of carbon, on the other, brings this out very clearly.

42

TABLE I

Atomic Abundances of Some Elements relative to Oxygen [115]

Element	Sun	Earth's atmosphere and oceans	Earth's igneous rocks
H	1,100	2	4.4×10^{-2}
C	0.57	$*2.1 \times 10^{-2}$	9.1×10^{-4}
N	0.105	3.4×10^{-3}	1.1×10^{-4}
O	1	1	1
Mg	2.75×10^{-2}	9.4×10^{-4}	3×10^{-2}
P	2.4×10^{-4}	5.8×10^{-8}	1.3×10^{-3}
S	2.2×10^{-2}	5.0×10^{-4}	5.6×10^{-4}
K	5.5×10^{-5}	1.75×10^{-4}	2.3×10^{-2}
Ca	1.55×10^{-3}	1.8×10^{-4}	3.1×10^{-2}

★The carbon abundance is that of the sedimentary rocks relative to oxygen in the oceans The abundances of the mineral elements in sedimentary rocks are similar to those in igneous rocks.

sources: Sun: L. Goldberg, E. A. Müller and L. H. Aller (1960), *Astrophys. J., Suppl. Ser.* 5:1-138. Earth: K. Rankama and T. G. Sahama (1950), *Geochemistry*, University of Chicago Press, Chicago.

Hydrogen and oxygen atoms, as distinct from the molecular oxygen, O_2, in our present-day atmosphere, exist principally combined in water, H_2O, or hydroxyl, OH, as a basic constituent of planetary matter long anteceding the appearance of life. It is also the major element determining the properties of the associated soluble hydroxides and acids. Where nitrogen replaces carbon, it gives rise to an electro-positive or basic character of the compounds it enters into.

These properties in the simpler molecules are intrinsic: they depend on the quantum numbers of the electrons belonging to the atoms of atomic numbers 6, 7 and 8. The very abundance of these elements, combined with the great variety of compounds they can form and their capacity to form multiple bonds, indicate that they are most likely to be used as the main elements of any kind of life. They are certainly those of terrestrial life, their formation must depend very largely on the properties of the universal matrix, water, of which life largely consists to this day and from which we may reasonably assume it originated. The physical states of water also fix the conditions under which life could start and thrive, lying between some 10 to 40°C, that is 283 to 313°K.

This in turn fixes the limiting dimensions of the planetary body or bodies that can sustain life, namely, those sufficiently large to retain liquid water on or near their surfaces and such that the mean velocity of escape of the water molecules will prevent its evaporation in geological time. To satisfy at the same time the thermal and hydrological conditions implies that the planet must be at a distance of between 100 and 200 million miles from our present Sun. On a closer planet the water would escape: on a further one it would freeze. Similarly, a large planet would favour water retention in some form or other and a smaller one would permit its evaporation and escape.

In our planetary system, the conditions are now fully satisfied only by the Earth. Mars is too cold and dry. The recent Mariner photographs of Mars at close range show it, unexpectedly, to have a surface like the Moon's, with a number of circular craters and no evidence of the presence of water. Venus is probably too hot; how far it actually is so remains to be seen. All we know is that it may be at almost any temperature, if it is covered by a cloud layer, the lower levels of which may be heated by a kind of greenhouse effect through the atmosphere, which may retain infra-red radiation. However, if the planet surface is actually mountainous, as it appears from some radio observations, there might be conditions suitable for life in the upper valleys. The Moon is too small and dry; Mercury far too hot and dry. The outer planets are far too cold. These limitations, however, need not be absolute [30]. Any planet liable to internal heating to a high temperature – and this applies to planets and asteroids of down to 100 km in diameter – must possess, not far below their surface, a zone having the temperatures required for the existence of free water and hence the possibilities of life, except for that condition absolutely essential for life on Earth, the availability of sunlight.

The dictum, for which I was once responsible, that 'life originated in outer space, but underground', is really more a *jeu d'esprit* than a real possibility, because only the very first stages of the formation of complex molecules can have occurred in the absence of light. Within these limits, however, light could be replaced for the purpose of synthesizing more complex molecules by the radiations from radioactive bodies, but these are present in too small quantities and are of too short-range character to effect much synthesis in the short time of formation of the asteroid or planetismal.

Similar considerations hold even more strongly for smaller bodies such as particles of meteoritic dust or elements of cometary tails, rich as they are, as we know from spectroscopic studies, in carbon and nitrogen and probably water or ice. Here the very fixity of the atoms in crystals or glass prevents that interchange which would be necessary to go further and produce living forms. Nevertheless, even if the occurrence of carbon, nitrogen and oxygen compounds on meteorites can give little or no evidence as to the further developments of life, they offer invaluable clues to its earliest sources. Combined with the synthetic efforts which Miller began in 1953 and which have been followed in greater detail since then by such workers as Terenin, Pavlovskaya and Pasynskiï, and Oró, they show something of the kind of substances and the kind of reactions that would occur whenever a system of simple gases were subjected to various types of excitation. Indeed, the work already done, particularly that of Ponnamperuma, C. Sagan and Mariner [99] [100], goes far to answer the question raised earlier, whether the origin of life is a matter more of intrinsic necessity than of contingency.

The frequency with which specific life-forming molecules such as the base adenine, the pentose sugar, ribose, and its phosphates, the amino acids and the lipids can be formed in synthetic experiments, suggests that this is by no means accidental but depends on the particular stability of these compounds as the necessary consequences of the putting together of primary constituents. The limited number of basic monomeric molecules taking part in biochemistry has been noticed by biochemists and the so-called alphabet of these monomers has been given by Wald [118]:

It turns out that about 29 organic molecules are enough to introduce the bare essentials. They include glucose, the major product of photosynthesis and major source of metabolic energy and hydrogen; fats as a principal storage form of metabolic energy; phosphatides as a means of circulating lipids in aqueous media and for their remarkable structure-forming proclivities; then the 20 amino acids from which all proteins, including all enzymes, are derived. Five nitrogenous bases (adenine, guanine, cytosine, uracil, thymine), together with ribose or its simple derivative deoxyribose, and phosphoric acid, form all the nucleic acids, both RNA and DNA. These 29 molecules give students a first entry into the structures of proteins and nucleic acids, the coding of genetic information, the structures of enzymes, the composition and general properties of cell structures, and bring them to a point from which they can begin to explore the complexities of energy metabolism. That this is not the whole of biochemistry goes without saying; the extraordinary thing is that it makes so good a start. Yet this alphabet of biochemistry is hardly longer than our verbal alphabet.

The reasons for this restricted list are probably not simple. On the one hand, experiment has shown that they are particularly stable though reactive molecules. On the other hand, it may be that they are simply the residue of a far longer list which appeared at various stages in the origin of life and has been reduced by a process of natural selection of molecules in a way that will be discussed later.

The quasi-identity between compounds extracted from carbonaceous meteorites and those formed by synthetic processes from the simple gases, methane and ammonia, are, taken together, strong evidence that this first stage of biopoesis was everywhere present and by no means confined to this Earth. The latter stages, right up to the formation of organisms, however, seem necessarily thus confined owing to the need of all present-day organisms for water and sunlight. This restriction may, indeed, be an artificial one due to our lack of experience. It has indeed been claimed that such dry organisms could exist and even that they have existed and can be found in meteorites.

Organisms in Meteorites?

Such recent claims, if substantiated, might have seriously upset all the old theories of the origin of life on the Earth (Appendix 2). Thus the claims by Nagy and Meinschein [72], of apparently biogenic hydrocarbons in the carbonaceous phase of the Orgeuil and Ivuna meteorites, led to the idea of life having existed on their parent bodies, presumably asteroids. However, hardly had the controversy of this claim begun to die down, when a further claim was made of finding actual organisms in these meteorites which, in turn, gave rise to a heightened controversy. This has been mainly concerned with authenticating, or not, the supposed organisms. Some of these have been shown conclusively to be contaminations by terrestrial organisms which are introduced into the meteorite either in the field or in museums and laboratories, after its fall. Others, according to Mueller [71], have been shown to be, essentially, mineral aggregates which he calls microchondri. The controversy is still not closed, but the views of most of the critics are that there are almost insuperable difficulties in accounting for any way in which such presumed organisms could have come into existence or even maintained themselves on the dry surface or in the damp interior of an asteroid.

If, as it has been claimed, they are unicellular algae, they would require water to live in and light to provide the necessary photosynthesis. This would seem to require the existence of a planet large enough to maintain the free water on its surface. This, in our solar system, absolutely excludes the meteorites as the origin of life and limits it to the larger of the minor planets. How material from any of these planets ever got into the meteorites remains a mystery, although Urey has proposed the very ingenious solution that such meteoritic material originated on the Earth, was carried first to the Moon and then back to Earth again [114]. If the controversy about organized elements in meteorites is resolved in the negative sense, no further problem remains, but as long as it remains open it will certainly lead to much further research from which a deeper understanding of the origin of life is bound to arise [25].

Geological Metamorphism

In some ways we can get more information about the early constitution of the Earth from the meteorites than from any study of the Earth today. For the meteorites, though small and perhaps because they are small, can be studied through and through, whereas with the Earth we can only scrape the uppermost levels, and we know that the processes of geology, both the quiet processes of erosion and deposition and the more violent ones of mountain building and vulcanicity leading to melting and metamorphism, have altered the outer layers of the Earth almost beyond recognition. This is also true of the isotopic composition of the elements that we find on the surface of the Earth. Practically any geological process, whether biological or abiological, alters the relative concentration of these isotopes. These are agencies of change much more powerful than those to which the meteorites have been exposed since their first formation, about 4,500 million years ago. The study of isotope ratios, however, is still in its infancy and no doubt much more can be found out by a thorough investigation.

It is true that meteorites, or at least parts of them, have been exposed to the superficial bombardment of the hydrogen wind from the Sun, which has certainly modified their composition, but in a predictable way. Thus, the nuclei of several atoms have been altered by a process known as spallation – producing helium 4 and helium 3 – and this, in fact, can be readily detected in two ways. The first is, on account of its nature, now well known to radio chemists, and the second because of the location of the altered nuclei in the meteorite. The penetrating power of these radiations, even of the strongest of them, the cosmic rays, is limited in solid material, and so the effects of spallation may extend for the first few centimetres from the surface of the detached meteoritic fragment and do not in any case produce any large changes in the bulk of the meteorite.

The meteorites, especially, but not exclusively the carbonaceous meteorites, contain variable proportions of water. How they manage to contain water, however, after journeying through space for millions of years, is explained by the fact that the water is in the form of mineral hydrates, such substances as Epsom salts, magnesium sulphate hexa-hydrate or hydrated silicate minerals. However, there is evidence that these have been subject to some alterations, for the water they contain is much richer in heavy hydrogen than any water that is found on Earth. This would seem to indicate that the water in meteorites is part of much larger amounts of water, possibly in the form of ice, which has slowly evaporated leaving a greater proportion of heavy hydrogen than in terrestrial water. There is also evidence that the comets themselves – or at least their heads – are made very largely of crystalline or amorphous ice originally formed in the outer limits of the solar system. Ice can take a considerable time to melt or decompose. Water, or at least hydroxyl, is by no means limited to our solar system; it exists wherever oxygen is to be found, and has been shown to exist in the galactic centre.

Limitations of Life-forming Elements

We must not allow ourselves to be prejudiced about the elements which form life by the fact that they are the elements of life on this Earth, for everything seems to indicate that our Earth is not at all unique in this respect. We have, indeed, little reason to suspect any other elements as being the main chemical basis for life. No elements, other than those of the first, or possibly the second row of the Periodic Table, would have the necessary chemical versatility. Furthermore, no elements, except those I have already named and the two secondary elements of sulphur and phosphorus, which form an intrinsic part of living systems, occur in any notable abundance in the Universe. Nor do we know of any in the nuclear reactions that give rise to so many peculiar stars [47] (p. 40). It is difficult to prove a negative in this field, but, until someone provides a plausible picture of the kind of life that could be formed by such atoms and how they could be formed in quantity, it is better not to waste time thinking about them. This, of course, is not at all the same thing as saying that exactly those compounds formed by carbon, nitrogen, oxygen and hydrogen that are found in terrestrial life are the only ones that could be found there. Other compounds could occur, formed under slightly different circumstances and, in fact, there may be more than one kind of life. But, although there are many million species of different organisms on Earth, they all form part of the same system of biochemistry.

This is not to say that the elements named are the only ones which are needed for life – by no means. First we have to consider the alkalis, sodium and potassium, which are not so abundant as those already named, but on account of their solubility are omnipresent in the watery medium. Of these potassium is the alkali that seems to play the most important role, for it is found in every cell, whereas the lighter and more abundant sodium is only found in special organs, or in organisms of marine origin. The presence of sodium in the higher vertebrates' body fluids, the blood, sweat and tears, has already been claimed as evidence of these organisms having come out of the sea, but the implication of the wider distribution of potassium indicates that it is associated with life at a much earlier stage. I have myself proposed [15] that it is the very poor adherence of water to the potassium ion that provoked its association with clay particles in the very earliest stages of the thickening of the primitive soup.

One other element, calcium, is also involved in life, but in a clearly later and more derivative way than potassium. The deposits of calcium in the form of shell or bone which gave rise to most fossils does not seem to have occurred much earlier than the Cambrian period, about one aeon ago.

There are, however, other elements which, though occurring very rarely indeed, measured in parts per million or per hundred million – may have been absolutely essential to originate life. This is because their bonding characteristics (such as, for instance, those of the transition elements, including iron) form an essential part of many widespread enzyme systems.

Availability of the Rarer Elements

However necessary they may be, they are found sufficiently well distributed in primitive Earth and, for that matter, on any primitive planet, for them to be found in any form of evolving life. For instance, such rare elements as vanadium, molybdenum and niobium, are necessary for the essential respiratory pigments in certain tunicates, sea squirts, who are rather distant relations of ours. Such trace elements, as they are called, are essential to the growth of nutritious plants and their absence would doom the stock feeding on these plants to various forms of deficiency disease. The fact, however, that such elements are necessary for the highly sophisticated biochemistry of living things today does not mean that they need necessarily have taken part in the earlier stages of life. It might well turn out, for instance, that niobium and vanadium are in this category, though iron is certainly not.

The Function of the Trace Elements

The ability of an element to take a part in the process of life will depend on two or three factors: first of all and most important, its chemical capacity in itself on account of its unbalanced internal electronic structure and hence its capacity to form complexes with other elements chemically; secondly, on its effective abundance in the areas in which life first arose; this depends, thirdly, on its geochemical properties, that is, its belonging to the atmosphere, hydrosphere and upper or lower lithosphere.

Each element needs to be examined on its merits and we now recognize the importance of such elements which are known as trace elements, of very decisive value in the flourishing or lethality to livestock of districts which have less than a certain minimum of them. We are not yet at the end of this study, but the important point to realize in connection with it is that a

E

trace element does not need to be abundant. Only those elements which have to be abundant may appear as the decisive elements of life of which the two most important are nitrogen and phosphorus.

Nitrogen is rare because of its ease of escaping and the extreme stability of the N_2 molecule, which means that much of the nitrogen in the Earth has settled down over the years in the atmosphere as molecular nitrogen. The processes that exist and existed in the past for breaking up this extremely stable molecule and joining it to the normal metabolism have still been only partly solved. They are of intense practical as well as of scientific interest and they may have many surprises left for us; the importance, for instance, of the enzyme ferredoxin, which may be a decisive one in fixing nitrogen at an early stage and certainly stresses the importance of iron, also a trace element, in the nitrogen metabolism of life.

The other important element is phosphorus: phosphorus is more than ever now recognized as a key element. N.W. Pirie objects [95] that this is because we have studied phosphorus so much more than sulphur, but I am inclined to think that both are due to the same cause: the reason why phosphorus has been studied is because it is so important, and not because we have not got a suitable way of estimating sulphur as we have phosphorus. By and large, however, phosphorus is not a very abundant element on the crust of the Earth and its liberation from the rocks, on the one hand, and its fixation in organisms, on the other, determine the total rate of life activity on this globe.

Much may depend on the various forms in which the phosphate ions were first liberated from the basic mineral, apatite, $Ca_5(PO_4)_3F$, and even on the detailed texture of this mineral, because it would appear that the activity of an apatite, as it yields up the phosphate, is itself a function of the imperfection of its individual crystals. The various dislocations which may occur in apatite crystals may be actually the way in which the phosphate radicals appear in pairs as metaphosphates and thus enter for the first time into biological combinations, because the orthophosphates are at once very little soluble and very stable compounds.

The Role of Iron

Other trace elements of great importance are those of the iron group and of its neighbours, manganese, iron, cobalt, nickel and copper. These are needed for mutual assistance in the formation of the most important of the iron oxygen carriers, the haemoglobin molecule itself. The presence of cobalt is required for the existence of vitamin B_{12}; that of copper for the ceruloplasmin needed for the formation of the red blood corpuscles, and we know this now because these elements are precursors of the substances in actual life. The question arises as to whether they were also their precursors in the evolution of that life, and the evidence on the whole is in favour of their being so. There is not likely to be any shortage of these elements in sufficient, that is, in very small quantities, on the primitive Earth, and here it is not their quantity so much as their presence that is required.

The effectiveness of the elements depend on their finding suitable organic compounds to pair with, usually nitrogenous bases or porphyrins, and the similarity of these co-ordination compounds does suggest very strongly a common origin. This is the case with vitamin B_{12}, with its central cobalt atom attached to a porphyrinoid group which lacks one carbon atom and looks as if it were originally a true porphyrin that had been altered by the presence of the cobalt, with its different set of valency states from those of iron.

Life has, in fact, shown itself capable of dealing with almost any element that it finds in the sea or in the soil. Poisoning by elements is usually overcome in some ingenious way by making use of the element which would have poisoned it in the past, very much as the various living poisons have been dealt with by antibiotics.

Planets Formed of Fragments

The existence of a number of asteroid bodies, or fragments of them in the form of carbonaceous meteorites, has a definite bearing on the question of the origin of life on a large planet like the Earth [25]. If we accept the hypothesis, which is now the most favoured one, that the larger planets are made of the small fragments which had agglomerated separately – the so-called planetesimals – then each of these will make its contribution of carbonaceous compounds to the general agglomeration. To what degree the differentiation of the carbon compounds has occurred on the planetesimals is essentially irrelevant here (Appendix 2). What matters is that we have here a source of carbon and nitrogen for the whole planet. In the core of the planetary body the temperature will rise to such an extent that all the carbon will be reduced to pure carbon, graphite, and then or later be dissolved in the metallic iron, forming a weak iron and nickel carbide such as is found in the iron meteorites and also, we believe, in the Earth's core.

Sources of Carbon and Nitrogen

However, the very large volume of carbon compounds that is found near the surface would never have been heated to this extent except locally in volcanoes. Here we might expect the persistence, essentially unchanged, of the kind of molecules or molecular aggregates that are found in the carbonaceous meteorites. In addition, some of the carbonaceous and nitrogenous materials in intermediate depths will, so to speak, be squeezed or distilled out of this level to the upper levels in the form of gases, vapours or liquids, which would contribute to the secondary atmosphere, and also to the bituminous materials, which are now found in igneous intrusions, the so-called tucholites. These materials should furnish sufficient sources of carbonaceous substances before life could take root on the Earth or possibly on Mars as well. Insofar as they are soluble, they will furnish materials from which the primitive soup, which we were discussing in Chapter 1, could have been derived. It seems to me, though it is not generally accepted, that this is a more likely source for the complex carbon than the process, limited to the Earth's hydrosphere and atmosphere, originally put forward in the Oparin-Haldane hypothesis.

Miller's [67] first experiments in 1953 were crucial in one respect in that they served to demonstrate that it was possible to synthesize fairly complex organic molecules by the action of the silent electric discharge on mixtures of gases that would occur spontaneously in secondary planetary atmospheres. They did not at this stage, however, make it any easier to see how the synthesis of these molecules occurred or what particular molecules would be formed and in what quantities. Similar syntheses were later shown to occur under almost any conditions of excitation but, obviously, the conditions determined the proportions of the various end products formed. Nor were the pathways of the synthesis at all clear. These gaps were to be partially filled in by later work by Oró and Kimball [84] [85], by Ponnamperuma, Mariner and Sagan [99], Pavlovskaya and Pasynskiĭ [88], and others.

We now have a fairly complete picture of the ways in which such molecules can be synthesized. They are comparable with the analysis already carried out on the carbonaceous material from meteorites. The difficulties of analysing the latter arise from the very small quantities available, which prevent there being a close agreement between the experimental and observed results. Yet, even with these few and imperfect analyses, it is obvious that they are part of a similar, if not the same, process. Nor is the method of synthesis of the compounds on the meteorites yet clear – in fact, it is the basis of considerable controversy. The composition of the carbonaceous phase of meteorites does, however, make clear something of the conditions in which their synthesis could have taken place. The synthesis must, in the first place, be a low-temperature one, down to about 200°C: at these temperatures the actual products are found to decompose. Nor can their formation depend on enzymes or any catalysts other than a few possible inorganic catalysts largely based on iron.

The Sources of Chemical Evolution: The Primitive Soup

It is, however, by no means necessary that we should know all these things to draw certain conclusions at this stage. It is enough to know that there exist in the confines of the solar system methods of synthesizing compounds of the complexity of some twenty-four carbon or nitrogen atoms and that more complicated compounds probably exist as well, including some which are polymers, but there is no evidence so far of regular polymers. It is within these broad limits that we can specify the composition of what has previously been called in the histories of the theories of life, the *primitive soup*.

As the evidence accumulates, it appears more and more that the products of the early synthesis of the molecules of simple hydrides, appear of necessity and, correspondingly, would occur whatever the circumstances. There is nothing peculiar about them, characteristic of a particular place or a particular time. The 'proteinoids' produced by Fox [46], for instance, by heating to a temperature of 170°C a mixture of simple amino acids containing sufficient aspartic and glutamic acids are not, according to him, essentially dissimilar, except for their random order, to those that occur in organisms (p. 125). The path to organic biochemistry can well be considered intrinsic and laid down in advance.

The facts, experiments and observations referred to in this chapter go to show that the existence or the synthesis of fairly complex chemical compounds is likely to occur in the neighbourhood of any star where there is sufficient dust and gas to act as raw materials. The first stage, therefore, which was not so much the origin of life as the preparation for this origin, started from materials provided by normal astronomical processes and continued along normal chemical lines, not in themselves involving any new principles but already preselecting the kind of molecules that would later form living things. The processes occurring in the first stage would, therefore, to some extent have the power to advance the path of biosynthesis and they are to that extent dependent on the peculiar conditions on planets like the Earth, the only one in the solar system which we know to have oceans on its surface. The subsequent changes involving the first stages of chemical evolution, which in my opinion must have preceded actual organismal life, will be dealt with in Chapter 5.

Stage Two of Biopoesis –
The Origin of Biological Polymers

IT IS at this stage that we approach the essential problems of the genesis of life. This is also the most difficult stage for its explanation and where we are most at a loss for observations or experiments to help provide them. In the first stage, as we have seen, we have had experiments to guide us as well as molecular examples from other parts of the solar system. In the third stage, as we shall see, we have the final product, the organisms, to study in order to understand their genesis. Here we have only logic to guide us to a plausible account. Only later can proof or disproof emerge.

At the beginning of this stage, we can now assume there were on the Earth, or rather in its seas, a number of molecular species which have subsequently been found in living things, particularly the nitrogenous bases, the sugars and the amino acids. At the end of this stage, we have the ordered polymers, the nucleic acids, the proteins and at least some of the complex and varied processes by which the latter are produced from information contained in the former. What we have to discuss and attempt to explain here, is the origin of the processes of exact *reproduction* or replication of highly complex molecules. This touches on the latest additions to our knowledge of biochemistry and biophysics, work which is at present in full activity and from which the results are not, by any means, sufficiently complete to build securely on them. Hence the extremely provisional nature of anything that may be said at this stage.

Yet, if we say nothing, we are leaving the problem of the origin of life entirely undetermined and not even proposing a basis for further speculation. Earlier biochemical speculation and definitions of life such as that of Perret [89]:

Life is a potentially self-perpetuating open system of linked organic reactions, catalysed stepwise and almost isothermally by complex and specific organic catalysts which are themselves produced by the system.

however admirable as biochemistry, effectively evaded the essential question by covering the novelty of molecular reproduction in six words, referring to enzymes as 'molecules themselves produced in the system'. At the time they were written, these words expressed all the knowledge there was on the question, in fact, none. But it is gradually coming to be recognized that the essential feature of life is the precise reproduction of molecules, which, at least so it seems to me, must long have preceded any reproduction of organisms.

How this actually occurs in organisms is being investigated, however imperfectly, by modern techniques based on the model of the reproductive elements of deoxyribonucleic acid – DNA, ribonucleic acid – RNA, and proteins, and is now based on the Watson-Crick hypothesis for the replication of a two-stranded helix of deoxyribonucleic acid. Here we have to examine how it would be possible for such a complex mechanism to evolve spontaneously from simple molecules. This is not merely a matter of simple polymerization, but of directed, complex and ordered polymerization, because neither nucleic acids nor the proteins are simple polymers, as are, for instance, cellulose (polyglucose) or polythene (polyethylene). The nucleic acids and proteins require the joining together of molecules that are different from each other, though all of the same general character, especially in their manner of linking. They are heteropolymers rather than homopolymers [65].

Conditions for Ordered Molecular Replication

First we have to consider the possible ways in which such polymerization could have occurred at all. Then we have to consider how order could have introduced itself into the sequence of the monomers along the polymer chain and, finally – and this is the crucial question – how the order, once established, was copied and recopied from chain to chain, and copied almost but not always quite identically. For it would appear that the slightest permutations of that order may determine the appearance of new proteins, a mutation, and even a new species of plant or animal.

The very form in which these questions are put implies a general acceptance of the Watson-Crick hypothesis. According to this the determining factor is the order of the four nucleotides in ribonucleic acids or deoxyribonucleic acids, RNA or DNA, which, in turn, determines the order of the amino acids in the peptides that help to build the enzymes responsible for all the chemical actions in life. The Watson-Crick dogma, in its first stage, was so formulated as to imply the impossibility of anything but a circular answer to this problem. For it laid down that the amino-acid sequence in the enzyme was determined by the existence of a previously formed template of polymerized nucleotides in a specific deoxyribose acid, DNA. This polymerization, however, had to be effected through the action of an enzyme, polymerase, which itself was a specific protein. Now, such proteins, in turn, could be produced only by specific pre-coded nucleic acids, so that we are back at the impossibilities of the chicken and egg situation on a far lower molecular level. However, experience has shown us by now that apparent logical impossibilities in the field of biology and even in the field of molecular biology are not, in practice, absolute. All we have done is to state the problem slightly incorrectly and we have, therefore, failed to find a solution, even the solution already found for us in nature. Here we will find that the most probable solution is that poly-amino-acid enzymes and the nucleic acids, as they polymerize, evolve in the history of the origin of life together from simpler antecedents.

Chemical Evolution

However, to succeed in finding out precisely how this was done or, less precisely, how it could be done, would be at the same time to find out how to build up life artificially, and that we are still very far from doing. We need to try and trace the general lines of the chemical evolution of molecules from a limited number of monomers to the achievement of complicated and self-reproducing polymers. Clearly, there must first exist the necessary basis for polymerization itself, and this is adequate concentration of the original monomers. This requires, in the first place, a reconsideration of the actual physical and chemical state of the primitive soup from which the polymerization occurred.

The absolute size of water-covered areas on the globe in early times is still in dispute. Some scientists, basing themselves on hypotheses about the growth of the actual size of the Earth, postulate rather small oceans or, effectively, only pools of water added to in the course of time by the further escape of steam from volcanoes. Others take the more common-sense view of Lyell that the oceans were originally formed about the same size as they are now. There is evidence that they were at least that size in the earliest times that we can trace in the fossil record, that is, in the late pre-Cambrian, about 900 million years ago [53] (p. 104). It is, however, a matter of relative unimportance whether the size of oceans were less or about the same as they are today. To bring about polymerization would in any case require some further concentrations, but it would be sufficient if that concentration were local.

Thickening the Primitive Soup

What we may reasonably expect to have to start with are a certain quantity of nitrogenous bases of purine or pyrimidine type, some sugar molecules of the ribose or generally pentose type, readily associated with phosphate or metaphosphate groups, and some amino acids. All these would initially be in solution, and fairly dilute solution in the primitive ocean, however small that primitive ocean may have been.

The first requisite for any kind of polymerization to occur is that the dilution of the organic molecules in the oceans should be diminished; in other words, that we deal with more concentrated solutions in which further combinations may occur. This will not affect the nature of the combinations but may produce an enormous shortening of the time needed to produce them. The most obvious form of this concentration is by evaporation. If it occurred in small pools, it would have been, by its very nature, liable to be of limited effectiveness, as the contents of each pool would have to be deemed to evolve life separately.

Adsorption on Mud

I, myself, suggested some years ago [12] [23] that another fairly obvious method is by the adsorption of these molecules on mineral particles, largely microcrystals, of clay or platy iron hydroxides, which could be found in a finely divided state on beaches and particularly in estuaries. That is to say, I postulated the origin of the further condensations that were to lead to the origin of life as occurring not in open water but essentially in mud or soil. The soils of today are effectively organically produced, the primitive soils, marine or terrestrial, could not have been so by definition: they would have had to be derived directly from products of rock detritus or rock meal. But this would still have the capacity for adsorbing on the active surfaces of the minerals already mentioned. Experiment has shown that the monomers that we are discussing are specifically attached to the surfaces of clay minerals like kaolinite and montmorillonite, in which they occur sandwiched between silicate layers [66] (plate 1). Most of the oil deposits now being worked are deemed to be initially of this clay-adsorbed nature.

This hypothesis of mineral adsorption has not met with much favour because of the impossibility of producing supporting evidence dating so far back and also owing to the intrinsic objection that the major elements concerned in clays – silicon and aluminium – do not occur in biochemical forms in most present-day organisms. Silicon occurs only in grasses and aluminium mostly in ferns.

The Drift of Foam

Later, I proposed [23] that the concentrations in estuarine clays might have been due to a progressive separation of the most dilute surface active organic constituents from sea-water. The present-day organic content of the sea-bed is predominantly the remains of planktonic organisms (plate 2). These, when they were alive, were provided with mechanisms which kept them at a certain depth in the ocean, but, after death, they temporarily floated to the top and ultimately sank. Those that do the former form a very thin surface layer of a higher degree of organic concentration. Such surface layers inevitably drift with the wind and are concentrated in the foam of breaking waves, found particularly in surf. Sea-foam is essentially organic debris in this surface layer, some of which lies on the beaches or is piled up in the estuaries, and the rest is carried away by the wind in the form of sea-mist which settles on the land and makes it particularly rich for pasture owing to its high content of nitrogen and potassium. In this way, the surface active contents of an ocean, however big, are concentrated at first on the surface, a factor of a hundred or a thousand, and later on a coastline, a factor of another thousand or so. The most dilute solutions of such organic molecules will end up as very concentrated ones, especially in the mud of the estuaries. In one way or another, therefore, there should be no great difficulty in postulating a highly concentrated solution of such molecules, and it is in such a medium that further polymerization may be expected to occur.

The processes just described could have occurred prior to the oceans as we have them now. In default of organic debris, the concentration on the surface would apply to any form of abiogenic surface-acting material, as witness the oily debris spread on our beaches due to discharge from ships. The origin of such carbonaceous residues was discussed in the last chapter; they might have come in the first place from the kind of synthetic compounds mentioned earlier as being formed in the meteorites or on cosmic dust. Far larger quantities were, however, derived indirectly from such materials being, so to speak, sweated out of the rocks in the process of the formation of the larger planets and had accumulated naturally in the oceans without ever having been exposed to high temperatures. The precise mechanism by which the pre-organismal debris of molecules may be deemed to have accumulated may not, at this stage of our knowledge of the origin of life, be of any great moment. It will be sufficient to postulate that this did occur, because it is from such concentrated solutions that the further steps of the polymerization must take place.

The need for the concentration of primitive carbon compounds in the ocean has now been put in question by synthetic studies by eminent biochemists such as Calvin and Oró. Processes of condensation of monomers of bases or amino acids have been devised and tested in the laboratory. They involve cyanic derivatives which will affect the condensation of the monomers in dilute solution. It remains to be seen whether these processes are likely and to determine whether the conditions in the primitive ocean could have been such that concentrations of these reagents could have been built up by any conceivable means.

Segregation

This next stage may appear to be a very puzzling one and it contains real difficulties. But it also presents imaginary difficulties such as those of segregation, which are imagined to be so only by those whose acquaintance with chemistry is mostly on the biological side. The mineral chemist, on the other hand, has already accepted such processes as part of the workings of inorganic nature. The relative abundance of the natural elements which occur in the Earth varies enormously from the 27·7 per cent of silicon to the 0·00005 per cent of mercury and the 0·0000005 per cent of gold. Nevertheless, man has found these elements concentrated in certain minerals and veins and has made use of them since the earliest times, as shown by the coinage metals – copper, silver and gold. This is because, everywhere in the crust of the Earth, a physico-chemical and crystallographic process is taking place which tends to bring like elements and like compounds together. If the atoms of a particular element have a stronger affinity for each other than they have for some particular other element, they will come together however dilute the original mixture was. To take an example from modern industry: power-stations use remarkably pure water in their boilers, containing only few parts per million of any kind of impurity, such as the copper impurities derived from the wearing away of the washers of the pumps which circulate the water. Yet these impurities are able to agglomerate together to form balls of several pounds weight of pure copper.

The reasons for the coming together of atoms of rare elements to form rare minerals in the Earth are now beginning to be better understood. They do so by a process of crystallization, that is, when the size and shape of atoms and groups of atoms happen to accord and fit together well in space, they have a lower energy and so separate from the other atoms. If atoms or ions of two different elements have very much the same shape, size and charge, they will replace each other; for instance, as gallium and aluminium do, which have the same charge and approximately the same radius.

Similar considerations determine the occurrence of the most stable compound of phosphorus found on the Earth. This is pentacalcium triphosphate, $Ca_5(PO_4)_3F$, the mineral apatite. Because of the size of the respective ions of calcium and phosphate, a peculiarly well-fitting ionic compound can be made of these proportions, five of calcium and three of phosphorus. The imperfectly, quasi-regular structure of the mineral apatite has probably another effect in providing the generally insoluble element phosphorus just where it is needed as part of a catalyst. There is evidence that the apatite functions in this way in that its mineral imperfections happen to release phosphate-containing radicals (p. 61). But with this arrangement the charges do not quite balance and there is, in addition, a hole which is not occupied and consequently is filled with a singly charged negative ion, usually fluorine in the depth of the Earth, a hydroxyl near the surface. Calcium, being a relatively abundant element, therefore ensures the presence of concentrations of phosphate in this mineral. It is also a major source of the rather rare element fluorine.

We may expect similar selections and segregations to occur among the molecules of the primitive soup if they are sufficiently condensed. This preliminary coming together of the molecules of the same kind or of closely related kinds should make the further process of polymerization to form the homopolymers and heteropolymers much the easier. The coming together of atoms to form biologically significant molecules by pure chance is, however, not a universal occurrence but rather the exception than the rule (p. 136). What we have to look for is the preferential coming together of certain groups.

The segregation of organic molecules follows the same rule, but without the restrictions that are placed on the crystallization of inorganic salts. We do not know enough about the principles of the quasi-crystalline segregation of organic molecules to lay down such sharp distinctions as can be done in the mineral world. But such separations as do occur in substances with fatty constituents, that is, molecules covered with carbon and hydrogen groups, as against those with oxygen and hydroxyl groups, are very familiar in the immiscibility of oil and water.

In tracing the sequences of syntheses of molecular aggregates and polymers, we have not the same material clues as were provided in the first stage of the formation of such simple molecules from the primitive atmospheric gases. In default of these clues, we must fall back on analogies from the structures we can observe in living organisms. The main difference between the syntheses carried out in living organisms and those of the laboratory is that, in life, low-temperature reactions are taking place in relatively dilute media, mostly water-based.

In existing life, these reactions conform to the general conditions laid down in Perret's definition of living, which is really a definition of metabolism (p. 54).

Molecular Conditions for Metabolism: Enzymes and Coenzymes

Among these reactions we may distinguish three basic functions: the *enzyme* function, now carried out exclusively – or almost exclusively – by protein molecules; the *coenzyme* function, now carried out largely by simple or double, and usually phosphate-containing, nucleosides or flavonoids; and, thirdly, the *information transferring* and storage mechanisms contained in the varieties of nucleic acid. These are deoxyribonucleic acid, DNA, for *storage* of information; and ribonucleic acid, RNA, for *transferring* that information and utilizing it in processes of life. Some of these, the so-called messenger nucleic acids, mRNA, are found to be responsible for taking amino-acid molecules, one by one, and uniting them to form protein chains under the direction of another form of nucleic acid, transfer nucleic acid, tRNA.

The chemical function of an enzyme is to promote energy exchanges and the building up or breaking down of molecules involving energy-liberating steps, which would occur spontaneously in any case, but at a very much slower rate than they do in life. They are specific but not completely so. They are responsible for the making or breaking of carbon and carbon-nitrogen bonds among a certain restricted set of molecular types.

High-energy Phosphate Bonds

The coenzyme function is one of supplying or, in certain cases, of taking away energy in quantum steps in reactions that are carried out under the direction of enzymes. They are by no means as specific: each operates over the whole range of reactions. The most important coenzyme system is that of adenosine triphosphate, ATP. This molecule, by turning itself into diphosphate, ADP, or monophosphate, AMP, is able to give energy, locked up in the so-called energy-rich phosphate bond, to molecular reactions involving electron or proton transfers. By reversing the process, it can absorb energy and lock it up in further ATP. The so-called energy-rich phosphate bond owes its unique position in the processes of life to its intermediate character as an oxygenating compound. This is effected by electron transfer and oxidative phosphorylation. The element phosphorus finds itself in the Periodic Table lying between the element sulphur and the element silicon.

The P—O—P bond is consequently intermediate in energy between the Si—O—Si bond and the S—O—S bond. It is also intermediate in electrical character, the S—O—S bond being strongly acid and the Si—O—Si bond almost neutral. The intermediate P—O—P bond is therefore of an easy, changeable, labile character. Silicates are too stable and tend to form silica gels in which there are four Si—O—Si bonds round each silicon ion. It is very difficult to arrange the S—O—S bonds themselves in a series, as in the pyro-sulphates. Phosphorus, however, is able to make a great variety of short bonds of linked ions, for instance, in the mono-, di- and tri-metaphosphates of adenine such as AMP, ADP and ATP.

Proto-enzymes and Proto-coenzymes

The sophistication of the actions of enzymes and coenzymes, as well as the complexity of the molecular structures which carry them out, would seem to indicate that their place must have been filled at an earlier stage by simpler molecules acting in simpler ways. Proto-enzymes must have preceded the enzymes of today, and proto-coenzymes the coenzymes. It is not very difficult, even with our present knowledge of organic chemical reactions, to see something of what these precursors may have been. Enzymes, after all, are only specific organic catalysts. Now inorganic catalysts have been known to us for a long time and some must have been there and active from the beginning of the formation of life, because they are nothing more than complexes of some of the commoner transition elements, particularly iron and also copper, manganese, cobalt, etc. Some of the most familiar enzyme reactions, such as those of breaking up a molecule of hydrogen peroxide, occur about 20,000 times as fast when the enzyme catalase is present than when it is absent. Then the reactions will occur ten times as fast as they do in the case when a dilute solution of cobalt salts are present. Many transition elements are notable for the ease with which they form complexes with carbon-nitrogen compounds and these complexes are more active than the simple ions.

Specially successful modifications of such complexes are those of the four-coordinated, flat porphyrin type. From these, such universally active enzymes as catalase and cytochrome must have been formed. Some such primitive enzymes may subsequently have lost their original metal centre, modifying thereby, but not losing, their catalytic character.

The basic difference between the inorganic catalyst and the enzyme seems to lie in their mode of action. The action itself appears to be carried out in precisely the same way by the catalyst and the enzyme. The difference, however, seems to be in the degree of attachment. For when an enzyme is operating on another molecule called a substrate, there must be an interval of time in which the two are bound together. Now, it appears [49] that this interval is much shorter for an enzyme than for an inorganic catalyst, because the inorganic catalyst is much more firmly attached to its substrate than is the enzyme. This enables the enzyme to pick up and throw off a larger number of substrate molecules in a given time, which helps to explain its efficacy. To use an analogy which must not be pushed too far, the whole enzyme system is like a single machine tool in a mass-production factory that carries out one operation and then passes the workpiece on for the next machine to work on. The analogy with mass-production can be taken one stage further: an enzyme usually does not carry out the whole of a chemical operation, but simply one part of a chain of operations. The enzymes of the set concerned with one such total operation are linked in sequence and act, for instance, on glucose sugar, turning it successively into fructose phosphate, phosphoglycerates and pyruvate, and then through acetaldehyde into alcohol in some eleven steps.

It is just as easy to imagine, but very difficult to determine, what was the form and function of the proto-coenzymes when they first appeared in the biochemical field. The coenzymes carry out the function of transferring energy through the medium of their phosphate radicals. These are now organically bound in such coenzymes, for instance, as adenosine triphosphate, ATP. However, before this compound came into existence the operative part, the phosphate, particularly the metaphosphate, probably already existed in the form of inorganic metaphosphates and, indeed, it can be shown in the laboratory that such bodies have got coenzyme properties. We may reasonably assume them to have been present in the original watery medium. The addition of a nitrogenous base such as adenine to the phosphate complex, through the medium of the ribose sugar, must be deemed in the chemical sense to be the modifier of such electron transfer operations, analogously to the use of protein molecules to modify the behaviour of a simple transition element metal.

Coenzymes and Nucleic Acids

These remarks must not be treated as an attempt to account for enzyme and coenzyme action, but simply as a programme of possible research to see whether their prototypes can be discovered or inferred. One clue that has long struck me [20] has been the essential identity between the coenzyme nucleotides and those contained in nucleic acid. This seems to point most suggestively, and possibly conclusively, to the pre-existence of the triple molecule – nitrogen base, sugar, phosphate – as the monomer which was at an early date polymerized into a nucleic acid polymer. It is here, in the polymerization of the nucleosides through phosphate groups, that we touch the point at which life, in a true sense, may be considered to have arisen.

This key point is the origin of self-producing molecules. This implies the first appearance of self-producing molecules. They are polymers in which the monomers have a definitive order in which they will be first of all assembled and later separated to form new centres of further molecular synthesis. This is achieved in existing life through the complete and highly sophisticated mechanism of nucleic-acid-protein synthesis. Yet it is logical to suppose that it had precursors that were simpler than those which exist today and from which the present and complex forms are derived. What we have to find is first of all the minimum complexity with which a process of this sort could start and, secondly, some idea of how it developed the elaboration which it shows today.

This is now seen to be the central problem of the origin of life, and one so difficult that many have thought it effectively proves that the origin of life cannot have occurred by any spontaneous or chance process. However, considering the self-reproducing molecules to be derived from pre-existing enzymes and coenzymes, radically simpler structures, it is possible to trace something of the steps by which they were evolved. The problem has not, in fact, been solved, but we know something of the direction in which to look for its solution. There is no longer any need to assume, as has been assumed in the past, that enzymes and coenzymes were pre-formed from a chance assembly of atoms but, rather, that they were formed by a series of steps each of which was highly probable.

In biochemical as in organic evolution, we can see a process of high generality that defeats what appear to be, but are not really, the laws of probability. This is a process which proceeds from lower to higher complexity by assembling units of the lower category in space. Most present-day organisms are built of organs, built of tissues, built of cells. Most of these, as we shall see, contain organelles built of a number of different arrangements of uniform biomolecular structures such as mitochondria, as well as fibrous structures, microtubules, flagellae and cilia, all made of quasi-crystalline arrangements of identical protein molecules [37] and chloroplasts built of membranes containing proteins and lipids. The very existence of membranes implies the presence of molecules of exactly the same size, for only so can substances of minimum area be produced and acquire stability. Regularity implies equality, in fact it is the only way in which equality can be determined in nature. It is one aspect of generalized crystallography (Appendix 3). We can consequently say with reasonable assurance that all biological structures depend absolutely on the pre-existence of regular, identical sub-units.

This is the box-within-box construction first described by Charlier in 1922 in his theory on the evolution of galactic and hyper-galactic systems [39]. The apparent multiplicity and complexity of the Universe hides this relatively simple association of the orders of complexity with size and time. In the history of organic evolution, the metazoa, which are built of association of cells, succeed the protozoa, which are limited to a single cell. They are also necessarily more complicated in structure. There is every reason to assume that in the chemical evolution of life a similar process has taken place. Metazoa will, indeed, be considered as cellular polymers of protozoa.

Nevertheless, at the stage of transformation from molecules to self-producing polymers, something new has occurred, and this is the essential point we have to analyse. Once such molecules are in existence, it is easy to see how the properties of the structures they form depend on the order in which the sub-units can be joined together to form the polymers and easy to see, too, how this order can be handed down from one structure to another which is derived from it. That is the full beauty of the Watson-Crick hypothesis, subsequently amply justified by genetic information and by later studies of protein synthesis. The solution I favour here is that of the building of the longer chains with elements of shorter chains included in them, with or without variations: a kind of block polymer of polymer of polymers. Other solutions will be discussed in more detail in later chapters.

Chemical Evolution and Language

The best analogue that I have been able to find for this process is the hypothetical history of language. It is true that no-one has heard a language evolving from prehuman inarticulate cries, but no-one doubts that it did so evolve. However, some of the internal evidence may be relevant here. New words rarely evolve independently: they are usually either modifications of old words that derive different meanings by different pronunciations, or they are compounds of old words. Putting two words together gives a meaning which is different from that of the two taken separately. The same process may have occurred in the evolution of moderately long nucleotide chains. Its analysis is at present very actively in progress but, whereas the analyses of the sequences of amino acids in proteins are well known, those which produce the proteins – the tracing of the nucleotide sequence in nucleic acids – has proved to be a much more difficult problem and has recently been achieved in one case [55].

Building the Code

When this has been done for a sufficient number of cases, it will be possible to see whether the code of the nucleic acids determines the proteins with a three-to-one correspondence between triads of nucleotides and individual amino acids, or whether there is a great deal of ambiguity and redundance. Once this is cleared up, we shall be able to check by mathematical analysis the order in which these chains have been built up from shorter chains, and, finally, from single nucleotides. By tracing the process backwards we shall be better placed to reconstruct how it was in the first place derived sequentially forwards (pp. 147f).

In any case, any step in the chain order development must have been significant. Through its links with the corresponding order of amino acids in proteins, it would then follow almost as a logical necessity, the nucleic acids would evolve *pari passu* with the proteins that they helped to code. At the moment we can experimentally see and test the process only in one direction, from the nucleic-acid order to the protein-amino-acid order; but it is not excluded that it might also work in the other direction, that a certain variety in the protein order plays back to the corresponding order of nucleotides in the nucleic acids, though how in fact such a connection can be made we do not yet see. At the moment we are not entitled to claim that it is either a one-way or a two-way process.

The type of research attempting to answer such questions is now the centre of biomolecular studies: it is effectively the study of the critical stage of the chemical evolution of life. Its study is advancing very rapidly by the use of modern methods of analysis, tracers, electron-microscope studies and sub-cellular autoradiography, among others.

We know that such chemical evolution is going on in life today and obviously has gone on through the whole of organic evolution, but it would seem logically impossible that the first stages of chemical evolution did not occur before the building of the elaborate intra-cellular structures which themselves required the pre-existence of replicating molecules. We are by no means clear yet as to the principles on which such evolution would operate and have to make use of analogies from chemistry on the one hand, and from organic evolution on the other. Wald [118] writes:

Wigner [121] has recently remarked upon 'what appears to be a miracle from the point of view of the physicist: that there are (living) structures which produce further identical structures.' Fortunately, no such miracle occurs. If it did, heredity might seem to work better, but natural selection would not work at all. Wigner offers a calculation to show the quantum-mechanical impossibility of keeping the information coded in the genes from growing increasingly disordered as it is transmitted. The point is that the genetic message is continuously disordered by mutation; but that the selective process as continuously prunes it back to orderly, and indeed toward optimal, sequences. Wigner's calculation can be turned to positive account; it provides some assurance that any molecular genetic code must continually produce such random variations as natural selection demands. Order in living organisms is introduced not beforehand, by preconceived design, but after the fact – the fact of random mutation – by a process akin to editing. We are the products of editing rather than of authorship.

An analogy from chemistry may be drawn in the case of the formation of polymers, whether regular or irregular. This is now seen to be an extremely common process in nature and the actual existence of inorganically formed catalysts, such as the Ziegler catalysts, would provide a means of building straight-line polymers of a great variety of compositions but not necessarily of a highly complicated character, because the operations of such catalysts are likely to be of a serial kind, producing the same kind of combinations over and over again. This may be an error due to the possible existence of replicases such as those cited by Lwoff [65], but proto-replicases of great complexity are not likely to occur.

Natural Selection in the Molecular World

To get from such a simple polymer the complicated polymers which are needed to code the nucleic acid part of protein synthesis, may be a matter of appealing to the biological side, particularly to the analogy of natural selection. Horowitz [56] suggested in 1945 that the various proteins were selected out of the general chaos of an equilibrium mixture of organic synthetic molecules through a mechanism by which those that provided for a substitute for an element or molecule which was difficult to find, would be favoured at the expense of the others. In this way a highly complicated set of molecules might be evolved in a straightforward way, by a kind of molecular selection or survival of the fittest. Horowitz's ideas were expressed in advance of the Watson-Crick hypothesis, however, and can be modified and actually improved by means of it. But this is still a controversial issue and something more will be said about it in Chapter 8. Meanwhile, whether by natural selection or by controlled catalytic synthesis, we must assume that polymers of this sort can have occurred and can at the same time have reacted together to form the dual relationship between nucleic acids and proteins.

Another question this raises is whether it throws any light on the state of organization of the medium in which these polymerized molecules were interacting. At present, such reactions occur only in a cell, and not only in a nucleated, eukaryotic cell, but also in the non-nucleated, prokaryotic, bacterial cell containing the fragmentary genetic material. For much of the information about the code is derived from the study of the bacteria-destroying viruses – the bacteriophages – which seem to inject into the cells they infect only chains of DNA. At first sight it would seem simplest to assume that the original nucleic-acid and protein evolution occurred in such cells. This, however, seems to be most unlikely for reasons already given, because the structure of even the simplest cell would imply an already fully developed mechanism (plate 3).

Life before Organisms?

If the mechanism of nucleic-acid-induced protein formation did not originate in cells, we must postulate an earlier stage when it was evolved in a medium which did not contain any divisions which would interfere with the passage of small molecules, at least, by diffusion. Diffusion, however, would limit the travel of these molecules so that high concentrations of them were limited to small volumes, effectively dividing the space into regions in which one or other set of reactions predominated. A hypothesis which I made some years ago [12] [20] was that *life* had existed before separate *organisms* of any kind. It was not well received because it seemed to contain a contradiction in terms. In any case, it is not easy to imagine life occurring without any of the present-day functions of the primitive cell. But this is also implied in the original Oparin hypothesis that the primitive cell, or 'eobiont' of Pirie [93], was a somewhat indefinite coacervate blob not furnished with any constituent organelles or parts.

However, here, again, we are faced with intrinsic difficulties, for the hypothetical coacervate cell is a complex gel of at least two kinds of polymers – in the classical case a protein and polysaccharide (albumen and gum arabic) – which both require considerable synthetic mechanisms and hence an advanced stage of organic evolution to produce. I, myself, would assign the production of coacervate-based cells to a somewhat later period of chemical evolution: that in which the fully developed nucleic-acid-protein synthesis mechanism already existed.

The Synthesis of Identical Molecules

Such sequential syntheses now occur in the specialized organelles of the cell, the mitochondria; the synthesis of the individual specialized protein enzymes is left to other organelles, the ribosomes. However, it may not be either necessary or, in fact, possible at this stage to decide the question of the priority between separate organisms and indefinitely extended synthetic mechanisms. At any rate, a consideration of each can be carried on independently of the other. Consequently, we shall regard as the central features those elements of mechanism which lead to the building of *identical* molecules. This aspect has undoubtedly logical priority over the formation of organisms. Molecular reproduction is also the antecedent of organic reproduction and is now, as we see, absolutely essential for the processes that we call metabolism and which characterize life.

Identical or quasi-identical molecular structures must have identical or quasi-identical chemical functions. The 'quasi' is introduced to cover the possibility of variations, the mutations of genetics. It would appear that what actually reproduces in life is not the identical molecule but a part of a nucleic acid which corresponds to a prescription of an identical protein molecule. The satisfactory production of all the enzyme molecules of an organic system implies the production of the means of carrying out all the ordinary processes of life in a controlled way. Fermentation, oxidation, photosynthesis, digestion, excretion are all controlled by specific identical enzyme molecules. These molecules, however, as we now know, do not reproduce themselves; the primacy of the proteins has now given way to the primacy of the nucleic acids. These molecules are also required to be identical, or nearly so. But their identity is secured by the actual reproduction of helical molecules of nucleic acids (Appendix 3).

The Incorporation of Function in Molecular Structure: Prescription

This necessarily produces a time-fixed structure for all living things. They no longer exist only as given material things or processes in being only at the moment they are examined, but carry in themselves their whole past and are not fully intelligible apart from their ancestry. This extended time requirement of all living things is the real characteristic of life which distinguishes it from the inorganic world. The structures life gives rise to, including the organisms themselves, are more expressions of this inner, prescribed molecular character of life. Indeed, as we see it now, the notion of *prescription* is the unique characteristic of life on the Earth. Life in other parts of

69

the Universe is likely to be prescribed too, but not necessarily precisely in the same way.

It is the varieties of prescription due to slight variations in the order of the molecular reproduction process which give rise to a whole multiplicity of evolved life forms. This idea of a *prescription* of life is the exact opposite of the notion of Aristotle of the teleological nature of life. Although his teleology itself was derived from the study of prescribed life forms, it was conceived on the analogy of the artist and his creation, the observation and description of the object preceding the creation of its form out of matter. The lesson of Darwin is that a life form has to be effectively functional, at least in some environments, though not necessarily in many. The same applies to the molecules whose self-production generates the different forms of life: most bad prescriptions, mistakes in order of some character, will not work and will, in consequence, not be perpetuated. This is essentially the idea of *internal* selection of the fittest, stressed by L. L. Whyte [119]. Only those relatively small changes which result in viable organisms can lead to further development. Of these, only those that can establish themselves in normal competition with the other organisms can be the beginning of a mutant variety or species. This is the basis of the essential chemically determined conservatism of the various aspects of life, which is one of its major characteristics.

The Energy Balance of Early Life

Something should be said here of the application of the energy balance at the primitive stages of life. As already indicated, the chemicals produced in the second stage of biopoesis may all be energy-rich compared with the simpler molecules from which they were formed. This implies a finite time for this stage, because once it was completed there could be no new source of energy and the system would have to come to a stop. If more energy is fed into it in the form of long ultra-violet rays from the Sun, this might provide the permanent source of free energy. However, how far this may occur must be determined by careful measurements and calculations. In the absence of atmospheric oxygen and, consequently, of atmospheric ozone, which cuts off ultra-violet radiation, the flux of ultra-violet radiation is likely to be large. If it were too large, especially on the short-wave side, this radiation would itself effectively prevent the occurrence of the more common polymerizations that have been dealt with in this chapter (pp. 55ff), or actually break them up.

On the other hand, on account of the complexity of the structures involved, I am inclined not to believe that effective long wavelength photosynthesis occurred in this stage and hence the oxygen-rich atmosphere was not produced. This early preorganismal stage of life can effectively consist only of anaerobic reactions, less energetic than the ones we observe now in aerobic forms, but this would be of less importance as there would be no competition from such aerobic forms. In fact, a long continued and slow anaerobic synthesis would be likely to lead to greater and greater accumulations of matter that either was living or had passed through the stage of living without being decomposed, since most decomposition consists of oxidative reactions which, by implication, could not have existed at that stage.

The Early Earth's Surface: Sub-vital Areas

The Earth's surface, only in the period just before the occurrence of separate organisms and cells, must be imagined as very like it is now with all the geological phenomena occurring largely as they do now: with seas, rivers, atmospheric circulation and sea border phenomena, such as sands and muds in estuaries, except that somewhere on and in this mud would be what I have called the 'sub-vital' areas [20]. More complicated and interlocked sets of reactions would take place in these areas. These reactions would be limited by the diffusion of active molecules in relatively viscous layers of a colloidal nature, conditions which also emphasize the proposed slowness of reactions of that time. This picture expresses the conception of a hypothetical biochemical stage of life which preceded any separate physical form of organism.

It is postulated that, in this chemical form, the whole set of reactions involving the production of identical protein molecules and the self-reproduction of nucleic acid molecules would take place, controlled only by diffusion, there being no possibility and indeed no need for organisms at this stage. This also implies the absence of any movement or sensation and the limitation of means of communication between one part and another to purely chemical ones controlled by diffusion. Objection may be made that the picture is not a clear one and we have no actual evidence for such a state, all the arguments for it being indirect ones based on the illogicality of postulating organisms before biochemistry. Some of these arguments will be dealt with in a later chapter.

Membranes and Lipoids

The transition from the segregation of the uniform sub-vital areas, controlled only by diffusion, to the sharply divided volumes that determine the occurrence of actual separate organisms seems logically and historically to be effected by means of membranes, essentially the lipid membranes already referred to.

The membranes we know at present in organisms are all composed of two elements: a protein element, not necessarily different from those of the ordinary structural protein and, therefore, depending only on the production mechanism of such linear molecules; and the lipoid element. It may well be the latter that are the most characteristic of cellular life.

We know that molecules with long-chain hydrocarbons tend to lie parallel to each other and form two-dimensional extended sheets. However, all such sheets that we actually observe in cells, usually with the electron microscope the so-called unit membranes, are sheets of uniform thickness, that is, usually, two lipoid sheets of the order of 40 Å units thick, tied together with a protein sandwiched between them and sometimes on each side as well (p. 85). This implies, further, that the lipoid hydrocarbon chains making these sheets, together with their phosphate or carboxylic heads, are of the same length. Consequently, the existence of sheets implies a mechanism for making hydrocarbons of definite lengths, usually of sixteen, eighteen or twenty atoms.

Unfortunately, we know nothing about the mechanisms which limit the polymerization of methylene groups to such numbers, but we have two interesting indications. One is an observation on meteorites of Nagy and Meinschein [72], already alluded to, that such odd or even hydrocarbons occur in alternating abundance in the meteorite hydrocarbon fraction and, the other, an observation by Bassett and Keller [8] that artificial hydrocarbons of the type of polyethylene commonly crystallize in layers of which each layer is of a thickness which is constant and does not depend on the actual length of the hydrocarbon chain, which is several thousand Å in length (plate 4). It is shortened by a process of folding where the hydrocarbon chains over most of their lengths are packed side by side. They tend to fold themselves backwards and forwards like a hank of thread, the length of each loop depending on an external factor such as the temperature. Apparently, paradoxically, the higher the temperature the longer are the loops:

It is apparent that a crystalline polymer consists of distinct, morphologically defined crystals. This is in sharp contrast with the traditional concept of a random arrangement of crystalline micelles. A gradual departure from the traditional picture has been in progress for some time ever since the importance of the crystalline morphology, or for that matter, the existence of such a topic, has been recognized. Even so the crystalline entities which now emerge appear to be more

distinct and come closer to the familiar idea of a crystal than one might have anticipated. Even if problems concerning molecular configuration, the nature of the
cement which holds the crystals together, and the geometry of crystal packing are
not yet settled, observations such as presented here place a crystalline polymer in
the category of a usual polycrystalline solid from the point of view of observable
texture [59].

Factors like these may have helped to generate membranes at quite an
early stage in biopoesis. If they did so, the hypothesis of the sub-vital areas
may have to be modified in favour of a proto-membraneous arrangement.
It is evident, as is shown in the next chapter, that the membranes have an
absolutely decisive part to play in the structure of the actual cells, prokaryotic and eukaryotic alike.

The extension of crystallography (Appendix 3) to cover the arrangements
which involve only one-dimensional regularity, and that in a helical or
spherical form, goes far to explain the kind of ways in which the association
of pre-existing monomers can give rise to a structure in which order can be
constructed in a regular sequential way, and thus to the first stage of the
origin of the regularities and morphologies of life.

At the outset here, however, we are faced with a fundamental divergence.
Were linear polymers formed in the first place, in the systems that gave rise
to life, as long polymers with irregular association of monomers, whether of
nucleotides or amino acids that, later on, by a process of natural selection,
turned into ordered polymers? Or, alternatively, were short lengths of polymers formed in a disordered way at the start and gradually associated together into longer, ordered polymers? At the present moment it does not
seem to me that we have enough evidence to decide absolutely between
these two views. The first is the one held by Oparin [81]:

When polymerization of mononucleotides is carried out in their pure solution,
it results only in the production of peculiar aggregations of polynucleotides, which
under natural conditions would create only deposits of these substances resembling those of ozocerite or some other organic mixture of homologs. But if this
polymerization occurs in the presence of other polymers, for example, polypeptides (which seems to have taken place in the case of the primeval soup), the polynucleotides arising would necessarily produce polymolecular complexes with
these polymers. These complexes, once separated from the surrounding solution,
seem to be initial systems that interact with their environment in the process of
evolution and give rise to primary living beings endowed with metabolism.

I, myself, think that the latter view is slightly more probable on present
evidence (p. 128). This is because I give more weight to the chemical aspect

73

of the formation of life than to the physical forms. Long simple or disordered linear polymers are all that is required to form colloidal structures, the coacervates of Oparin.

I think, on the other hand, that the chemical aspect of the action of a specific oligomer with few monomeric constituents is an essential feature of the synthetic properties of coenzymes in the first place, and only later of peptides and proteins. I note the importance of one dinucleotide enzyme, nicotinamide adenine dinucleotide, NAD. The process of polymerization may occur in two ways, either by adding the monomers one by one to a chain – a process which tends to form simple homo-polymers – or, alternatively, by the polymerization of blocks of dimers, trimers, etc., with definite, specific activity of their own, implying a complex polymerization ordered, to some extent, from the start.

If we consider, in the first place, only the polymerization of nucleotides, there is some evidence that this pre-ordered polymerization actually takes place for, in the so-called 'code' that determines the transfer of information from the nucleotides to the proteins, sets of three nucleotides in succession are needed to determine the sequential order of the twenty-odd amino acids in the proteins (p. 331).

It should be apparent from this discussion that the key question of the origin of life – the order of monomers in polymers – is just now acutely controversial, but the situation is very hopeful and new experimental results are appearing almost day by day. By the time this book is published, I may want to revise this part of it radically. It is therefore quite futile to attempt to make strong argumentation at this level of knowledge. Here is a case where the provisional nature of current science is most clearly to be seen.

The importance of the helical shape for the genesis of reproduction, or rather replication, the central feature in the origin of life, is becoming fairly obvious. Topologically, a helix is a straight line containing only one element of order – the sequence of the units along that line. By coiling up, however, helix elements separated by two or three or four in order of the line come together and may be expected to react or at least to influence the reactions of the whole (figure 8, p. 149). It is thus possible to imagine the specific and reproductive activities of even such a small amount of a nucleotide polymer as one containing three or four nucleotides, and it is here, on a limited scale, that I envisage the first truly self-reproductive elements in the life-forming process.

The situation becomes far more manageable when a double helix rather than a single one is considered for the nucleic acids. The basic innovation of the Watson-Crick hypothesis is this double helix, which permits the two forms of nucleotide base – the single-ring, pyrimidine, form (thymine, cytosine and uracil) and the double-ring, purine, form (adenine and guanine) – to pair with one another and thus to ensure that any particular sequence is exactly reproduced by another.

The Genesis of Order

In this chapter, which is the main one of the book, I have stated and discussed the essential problem of the origin of life which, as seen now in the light of molecular biology, is: at what stage was order introduced into polymer chains? Unfortunately, it cannot be said that this problem has been solved as well as it has been stated. Put into quasi-mathematical form, as we now are forced to put it, it has indeed been shown to be much more difficult than had previously been imagined. However, I do not think, as some writers in this field do, that this is a metaphysical problem outside the range of experimental science. I only say that at the moment we do not know what the answer is and we must be content not to know it for some time longer, but it is quite possible to devise the type of experiment that would resolve it and to carry out the *experimentum crucis*, namely to construct such an ordered system out of completely disordered molecules. The process is formally analogous to crystallization, although it is only crystallization of one dimension. This subject is one to which I will return in Chapters 8 and 9, where I deal with objections to the theory, and in Appendix 3 on generalized crystallography.

Difficulties and Prospects

I realize that this chapter of the description of the possible origins of life is the most difficult to understand, as well as to write, of any in this book. This is, in a sense, because it represents the advances of the last few years, which have made the problems more precise and, consequently, rendered their solution more difficult. It was relatively easy in early days to indicate how certain things, such as the origin of polymers, could have occurred, without knowing enough to make the particular difficulties appear. Now it is much more difficult and, what is more, it is liable to much more rapid changes. That there will be essential gaps in any account of such an important transformation as the origin of life is inevitable, otherwise the problem would not exist. I think it is better to present these as difficulties rather than claim, prematurely, that they have been solved.

The fascination of the modern studies of biomolecular order is that they are at the very centre of scientific interest today. We recognize that the

75

evolution of life itself now depends on the more purely mathematical question of in how many different orders several disparate objects can be arranged. We know, also, what an extraordinary variety can be generated from a small number of units. In a sense, the pattern of life is a linear message in the same way that a book is a linear message containing words, paragraphs and chapters, representing the chromosomes and the order of the genes in them. This in itself is an enormous intellectual advance; but to determine how the book is written and what it means is a much more difficult question which, even with the rapidity in which advances are being made, may still take many years and much genius to solve.

The Central Position of Chemical Evolution

This chapter has also been primarily biomolecular, dealing with the chemical changes which preceded the appearance of life. It is consequently a whole which is determined by the nature of its content; it does not follow necessarily that these were the sequence in which the whole of life developed, because the interaction between the chemical events and the physical events which surrounded them were not always apparent. By treating them separately in different chapters it should be possible to see them in their full context. What I am trying to say here is that for me the chemical evolution of life and its physical evolution, particularly its morphological evolution, are not to be considered as separate stages of development. They are necessarily interrelated at every stage but, logically, it is easier to follow them separately than together because we have here two problems, the logical chemical order and the logical physical order; and from these arises a third problem, the relation of the first two problems. This third problem will be dealt with subsequently and a provisional solution sketched out, but it is here that the greatest field remains open for speculation. It is essentially the same kind of problem that baffled the historians as they have developed a more precise but more varied account of human history, as political history, economic history, religious history, history of ideas. These can be treated separately, but they quite evidently react at every stage, and it is in this reaction that the full richness of human history appears; but so also does the incompleteness of our knowledge of it at any stage.

Provisional Conclusions

So far, our knowledge, if interesting, is inconclusive because essentially it is advancing so rapidly. The picture will be clear in one respect, but may appear covered and obscure in others as we penetrate deeper into the problems raised by the origin of life. We are here trying to settle the question of a different character from those of the rest of science; it is not merely a description, because here we cannot describe things not directly visible or even indirectly traced by any kind of marks or fossils, but an attempt to carry out an intellectual reconstruction based on assumptions of inner logic themselves drawn from experimental science here and now. Just because the picture is inconclusive at the moment, my tone in dealing with it is bound to be apologetic. This is not because there is any serious doubt as to the general nature of the origin of life, but there is very much doubt as to its details. The fact is that these details are being elucidated more and more rapidly, so that the fact that anything written now can be shown, or may even have already been shown, to be out of date, adds to the temporary uncertainty.

Nevertheless, it is not a basic uncertainty, but simply, on the one hand, uncertainty of detail and, on the other hand, of aspect. We cannot or dare not assume that the account that we give now, that anyone can give now, is going to be substantiated immediately by further research. It may be substantiated; it may be completely reversed; in any case, we are bound to learn. But, to introduce it to someone who is not acquainted with this field, is now in danger of becoming more and more confusing. I hope, to some extent, to have avoided this confusion and that I can present a story that is at any rate internally coherent if not always in line with the latest discoveries of biological science.

Chapter 6

From Molecule to Cell

THIS chapter covers what I have taken to be the third main stage in the origin of life, that is, in the origin of life as we find it now on Earth. From what has been said earlier it can be taken that in my opinion – which is somewhat heterodox – the origin of life may have preceded the origin of any particular species of closed organism. But for those who take the origin of life as the origin of the cell, it is necessary to trace the steps which lead from an extended structure having the biochemical function of life, including the property of reproducing active molecules such as enzymes, to the self-contained units with definite internal structures that we find everywhere in cells, even in the simplest. This chapter is also a most complex and difficult one: complex, because it necessarily involves a knowledge of the internal structure and functions of all types of cells, one of which I can lay no claim; difficult, because the subject is advancing very rapidly and any conclusions reached now may require revision in the near future. We have to rely more on the present and less on inferences from the past than in earlier chapters and at the same time we have to be sure that the picture is a coherent and rational one.

To do this without some descriptions of the internal structure of cells, a knowledge of which is only now beginning to be found out, is impossible. Any full description, however, is beyond my own competence and would risk appearing tedious and inaccurate to those who know, and incomprehensible to those who do not. Nevertheless, I will attempt to set out a summary description of what I think is this *last* stage in the origin of life. Indeed, of course, to many it may be considered as the *first* stage : all that has been discussed so far, in both Chapters 4 and 5, may appear to be not so much a discussion of the origin of life as an examination of pre-life because none of the kinds of structures, even in the sub-vital areas dealt with in the last chapter, would be dignified as life by the more strict biologists such as N.W. Pirie. The whole subject is highly controversial and can only be treated more as a matter of persuasive inference rather than one of conclusive argument. There are so many detailed features in organismal structure which are being revealed on the molecular scale by modern methods that seem definitely to point towards the consequences of chemical structures, that it appears almost inconceivable that they have not got such an origin, but it is still very difficult to *prove* that they have.

Imitating the Visible Forms of Life

To a scientist of the last century speculating on the origin of life, the first task as he saw it, was to produce something that gave the forms of what seemed to be characteristic of primitive life; to imitate life by means of various precipitates of inorganic or organic substances; to show that even silicates could produce globular and filamentous forms which mimicked many of the features of life as did, for instance, Leduc's algae and mushrooms. The alternative notion of the very primitive, formless and organismless life is also one of the early nineteenth century: it is that of the bathybius of Huxley first put forward as early as 1868. To some extent the earliest work of Oparin himself shows a tendency to repeat these earliest speculations. The second main feature in his *Origin of Life* – but not in Haldane's – is the formation at a relatively early stage of separate coacervate drops which, though morphologically formless even on the level of the electron microscope and composed of unspecified proteins and polysaccharides, could be deemed to be the progenitors of better organized cells. I do not accept that view, even as modified in later work of Oparin, but this is not the place to discuss it, it will be discussed in conjunction with other variants to the scheme of the origin of life in Chapter 8.

The First Cells

The discovery that all the larger organisms, animals and plants were composed of cells was a great landmark in the history of biology. It was effectually completed by Pasteur when he showed that all cells, even the smallest single-celled bacteria, are produced by other cells. It was then nearly inevitable to conclude that to explain the origin of life meant explaining the origin of the cell. But this is now turning out to be a far more complex task than when it was first seen. We can recognize a unique biochemical foundation for all life but instead of a unique structure for cells we find an enormous variety which furnishes a rich field for observation and experiment, particularly since the advent of modern methods, especially that of the electron microscope. It is becoming evident that the cells that are best known, those of the higher organisms, must have in themselves a complicated pre-history which can be unravelled only by detailed studies. The

79

task is, first of all to describe, secondly to classify and thirdly to put in order of genesis, the different types of cell that build up living organisms. When we reflect that the classification of organisms, particularly the simpler organisms, the bacteria and protozoa, were made before the advent of the electron microscope or of modern ultra-microscopic biochemistry, we can see that we cannot depend on the existing classification. This is a crucial difficulty in trying to account for the origin of life: the first thing is not just to define what life is in the philosophical sense, but what it is in detail.

In dealing with this stage in the origin of life, we can more easily attempt to proceed backwards from what is actually observed in existing cellular organisms – even the simplest, such as bacteria – and to infer from these observations in what order they occurred and how one led to another. Such reconstructions are by no means straightforward and are full of pitfalls. If we take the cell of the simplest protozoan, but not that of a bacterium, we can at once realize now, from studies with the electron microscope, that it is extremely complex and contains a number of quite different kinds of sub-particles, the so-called organelles. Clearly, it has behind it the most elaborate history.

Some of the main features of the history of cells are now becoming apparent and leading to a new classification based essentially on intra-cellular structure as revealed in the electron microscope. I have made use here of the nomenclature and ideas of Stanier [106b] and Van Niel, modified by Lynn Sagan [104a]. They divide existing single-celled organisms into two categories, the *prokaryotes* and the *eukaryotes*. The former have no distinct nucleus, with the elaborate mitotic mechanism which characterizes the other, more advanced type of cell, the eukaryotes. In the eukaryotes, the DNA molecules are associated with basic proteins to form complex chromosomes. In the prokaryotes, the carrier of inheritance is the haploid genome, composed of a single (double-stranded) DNA molecule. They are still, probably, the most numerous types of cells on the Earth, including all varieties of bacteria and various other micro-organisms. In their present form, however, they are represented by the anaerobic bacteria, depending on various fermentations, photosynthesis and chemical oxidations for their metabolism.

With the first appearance of prokaryotic cells, the decisive step towards separate organisms was passed, presumably very early in the evolution of life, perhaps as much as three aeons ago. It can be taken that pre-organismal evolution, chemical evolution, had already produced the essential mechanisms of metabolism and of the replication of molecules, the DNA-protein synthetic apparatus. The essential new elements that were added in this

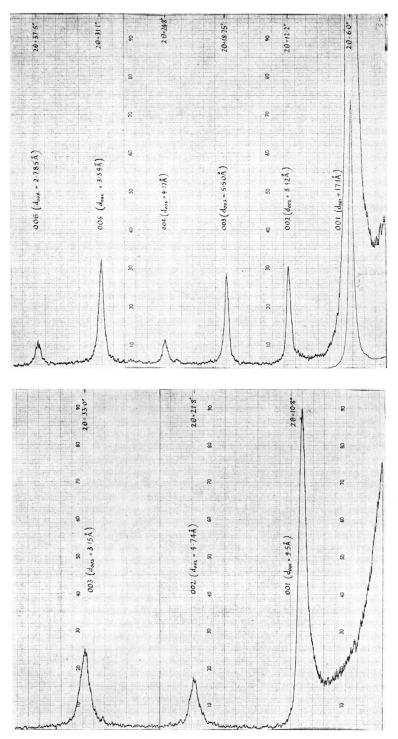

1. These X-ray diffractometer traces show the effect of an organic molecule (ethylene glycol) when it is adsorbed between the layers of clay silicates in montmorillonite. It can be seen that the main layer spacing is increased from 9·5Å to 17·1 Å. (Top) The montmorillonite with interlayer ethylene glycol. (Bottom) The same specimen after heating for four hours at 300°C to collapse the lattice by driving out the glycol. It should be remembered that in X-ray diffraction increased distances imply shortened layer intervals, and vice versa.

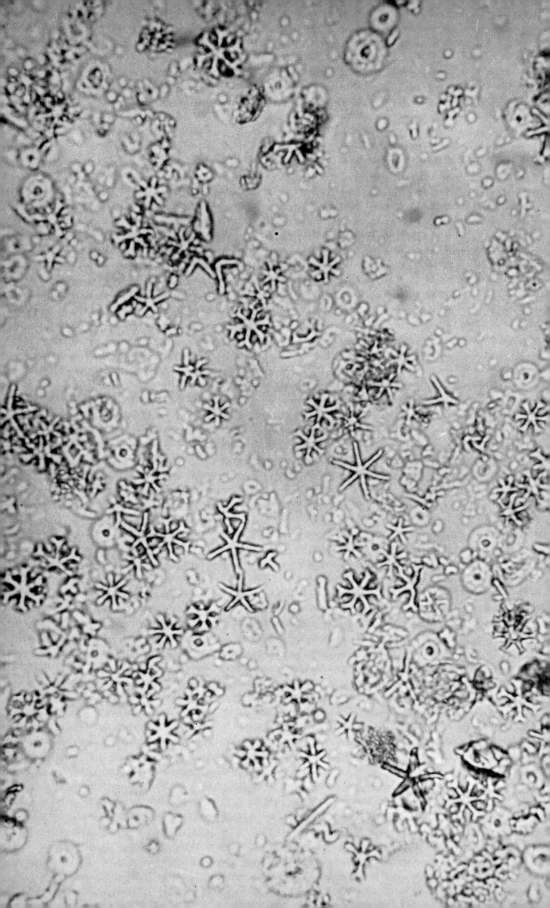

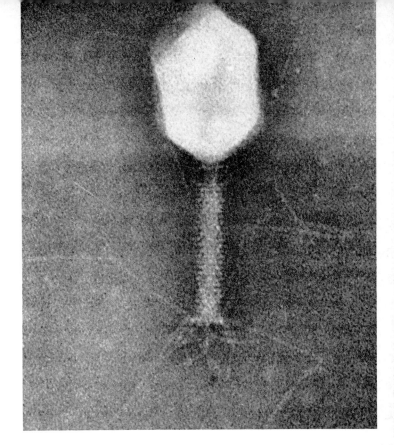

2. (Opposite) Micro-photograph of calcareous deep-sea sediment of middle Miocene age, composed dominantly of discoid coccoliths and dis-coasters. Magnification: ×1050.

3. (With diag.). Electron micrograph of a T4 bacteriophage. Note the unretracted tail. Magnification: ×370,000.

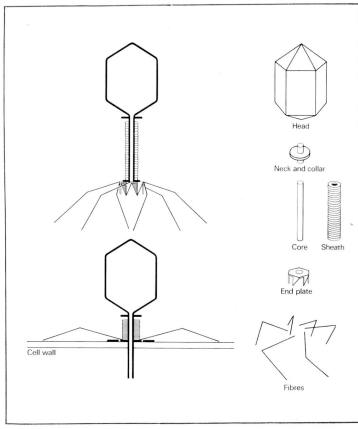

Head

Neck and collar

Core   Sheath

End plate

Cell wall

Fibres

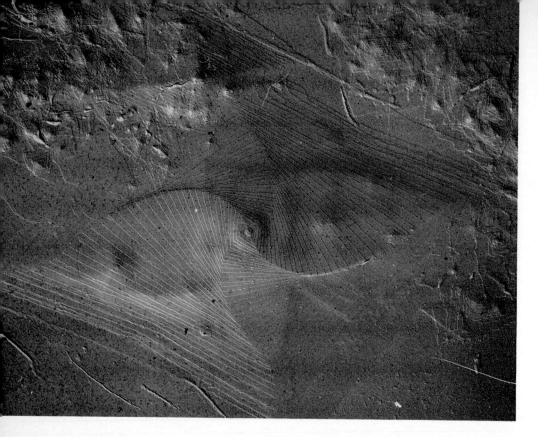

4. Crystalline polymers. (Top) Electron micrograph of multilayer polythene crystal where consecutive terraces are rotated with respect to each other always by the same amount in the same sense. Magnification: ×6,300. (Bottom left) Electron micrograph showing splaying multilayer aggregate from polyethylene crystallized at 129°C. Two apparent monolayer half crystals are also visible near the edge of the field. Magnification: ×11,000. (Bottom right) Microphotograph of branched polythene drawn 4·5 times, after thirty-five hours' nitric acid treatment at 85°C, showing longitudinal cleavage. Magnification: ×6·6.

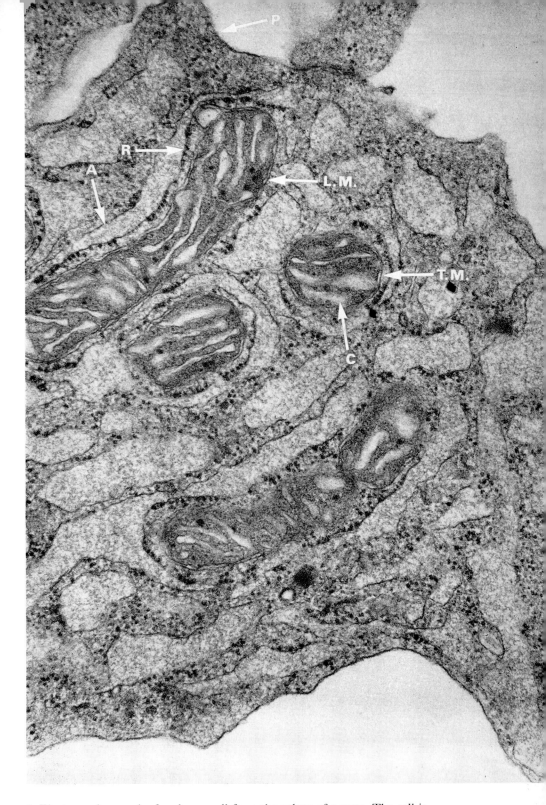

5. Electron micrograph of a plasma cell from the spleen of a newt. The cell is responsible for the secretion of antibodies which are stored in the cell. LM = longitudinal section through a mitochondrion; TM = transverse section through a mitochondrion; C = crista; R = ribosomes; A = antibody protein secreted by the cell; P = plasmlemma. Magnification: ×54,000.

a　　　　　　b　　　　　　c　　　　　　d

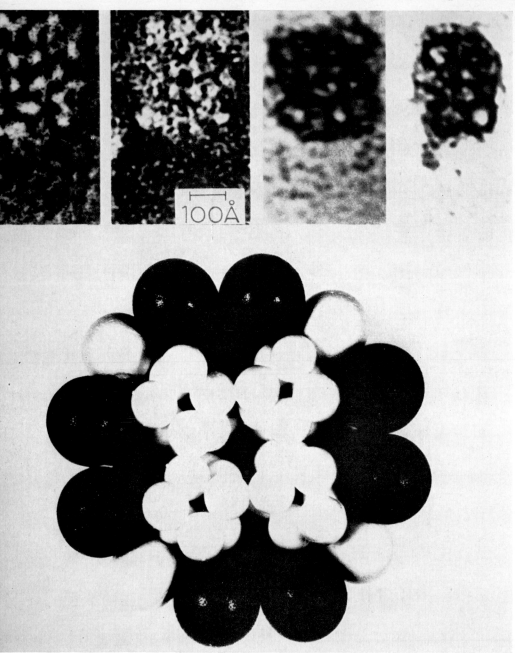

100Å

e

6. High-resolution electron micrographs of *Escherichia coli* pyruvate dehydro-genation complex from mitochondria (from left to right): (a) Reconstituted complex negatively stained with phosphotungstate. Magnification: ×950,000. (b) Native complex showing four central subunits and associated structures. Magnification: ×950,000. (c), (d) Complex positively stained with 2 per cent uranyl acetate. Sub-unit structures show in different orientations. Magnifica-tion: ×950,000. (e) Model of *Escherichia coli* pyruvate dehydrogenation complex from mitochondria based on the results of correlated electron microscopic and biochemical studies.

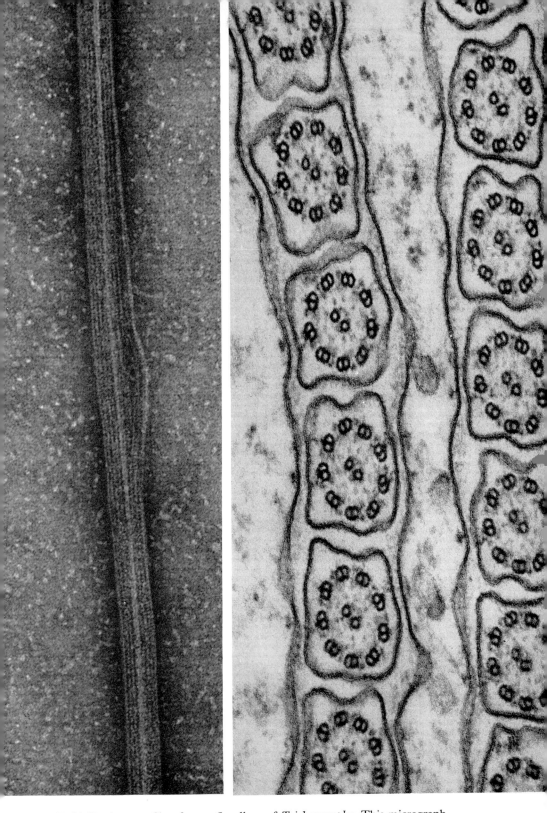

7. (Left) Single outer fibre from a flagellum of *Trichomympha*. This micrograph shows well the 50 Å beaded filaments which make up the walls of the hollow fibres (or tubules). Magnification: ×134,000. (Right) Transverse section of Type A flagella. Magnification: ×212,000.

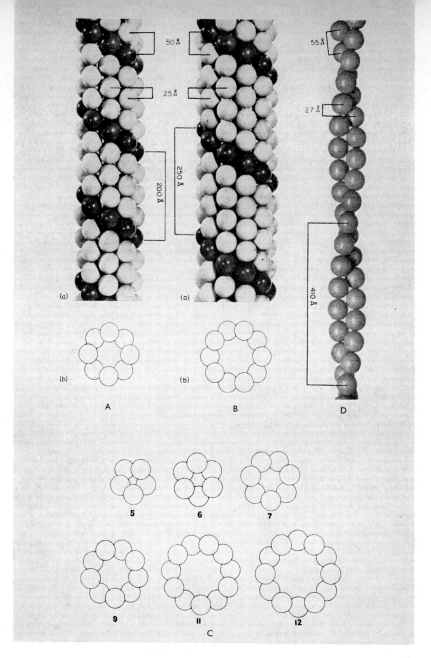

8. Models of globule arrangement in type A flagella. A: *Ps. rhodos, Pr. vulgaris, Salm. typhimurium.* B: *Ps. fluorescens.* These models are based on electron microscope results. In the case of *Proteus* and *Salmonella* (A) there is meridional X-ray diffraction evidence for the proposed model; the *Pseudomonas* species have not yet been examined by diffraction methods. Other models also consistent with electron microscope and diffraction data are discussed in the text, but those proposed here are the simplest. The end-on views are intended only to show the arrangement of the globules at the periphery; the flagella are not necessarily hollow. The effective diameters inside the cylinders are about 58 and 85 Å in A and B respectively. C: End-on views of flagellar models with various numbers of longitudinal strands. D: Model of an actin filament showing a helix pitch of 2×410 Å. In negatively stained preparations, actin filaments have a different configuration with a pitch of 2×350 Å. However, it is possible that these filaments in intact muscle have the configuration shown above.

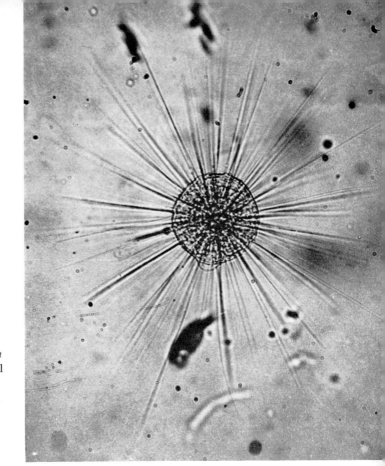

9 (a). Living *Actinosphaerium* (Heliozoa). The spherical cell body possesses numerous slender axopods which reach lengths of 400 μ. Each contains a birefringent core, or axoneme. Magnification: about × 170.

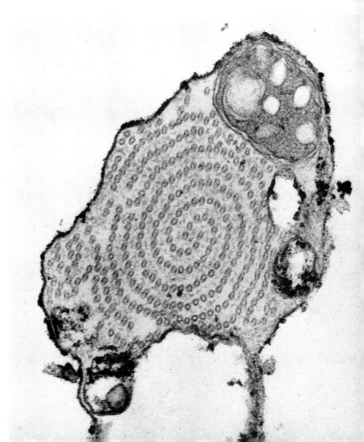

9 (b). Transverse section through an axopod of *Actinosphaerium*. The axoneme, central to the axopod, is constructed of a double-coiled array of microtubules. The tubules are individually approximately 240 Å in diameter and each is equidistant from its nearest neighbours. The total number of tubules in an axoneme near the base of an axopod may be as great as 500. The axopod is limited by a thin membrane which is continuous with the membrane covering the cell body. The compact double array of tubules is the underlying structure of a relatively stiff gelatinous rod, essentially the skeletal element of the slender axopod. Magnification: × 58,500.

10 (Right). Centrioles from human lymphosarcoma. One of the centrioles is cut transversally, the other longitudinally. Magnification: × 114,000.

11 (Below). Electron micrograph of transverse section through one flagellum of a paralysed mutant of *Chlamydomonas reinhardii* showing a 9 + 0 arrangement of fibres. Note the presence of some disorganized material in the centre of the flagellum. Magnification: × 287,000.

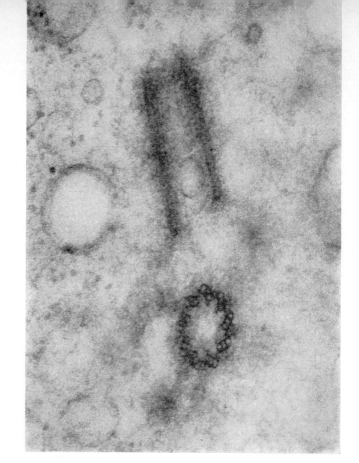

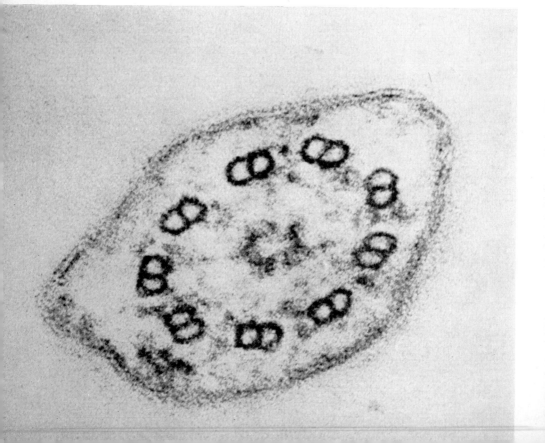

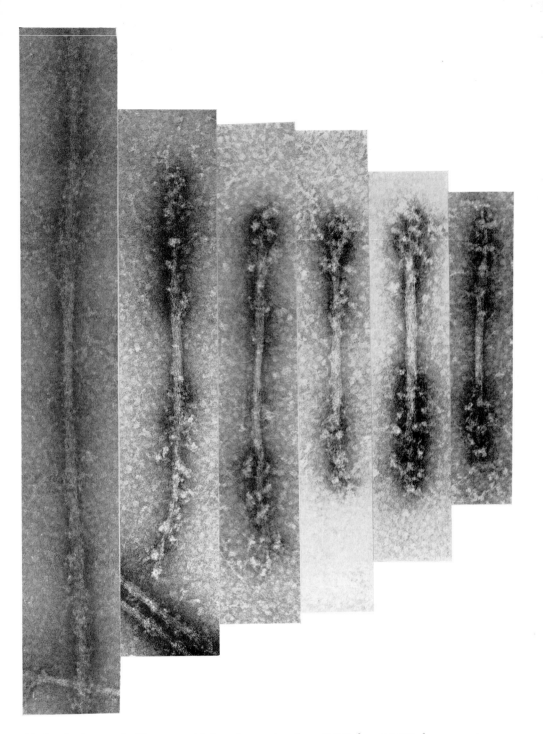

12. Synthetic myosin filaments with lengths varying from 5,000 Å to 14,000 Å. All of these show the same characteristic pattern on a bare central shaft and projections all the way along the rest of the filament. The appearance of the projections is rather variable, perhaps due to them clumping together in some cases. Magnification: × 126,000.

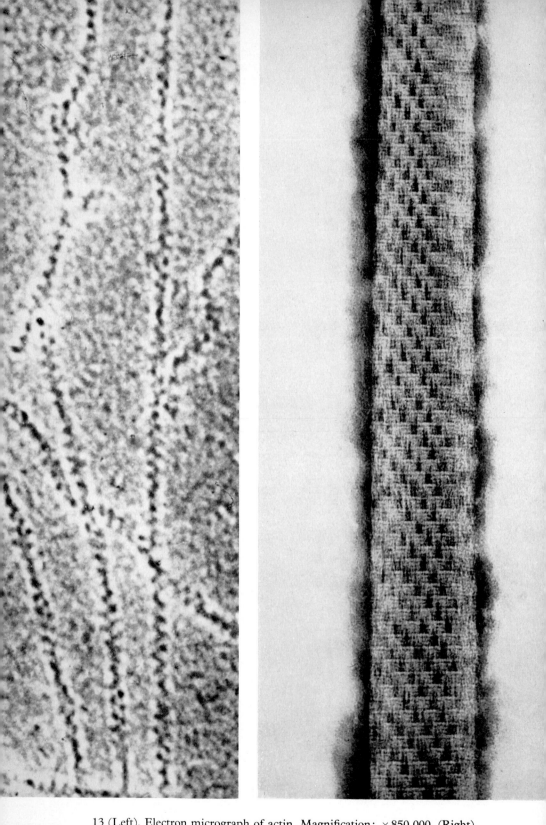

13 (Left). Electron micrograph of actin. Magnification: ×850,000. (Right) Electron micrograph of paramyosin. Magnification: ×230,000.

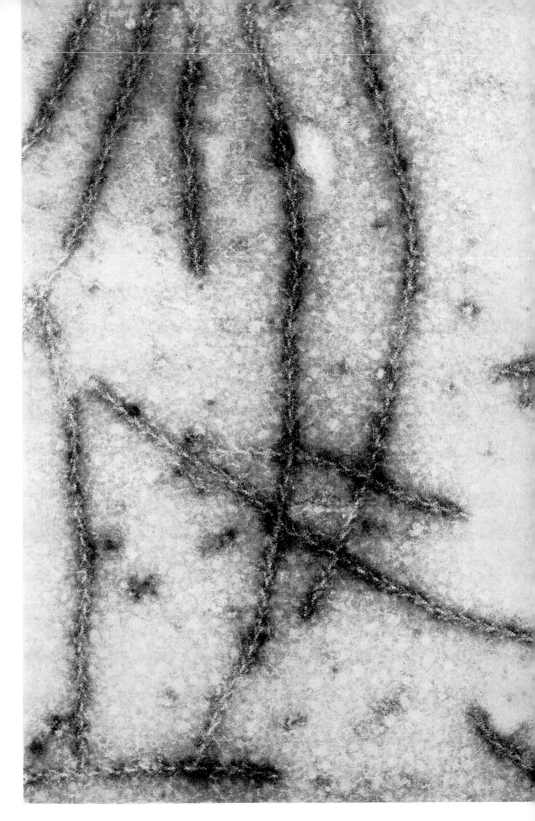

14. Filaments of *F*-actin, treated with a solution of heavy meromyosin. The filaments show a well-marked structural polarity ('arrowheads'), which has the same sense all the way along any given filament. Magnification: ×131,000.

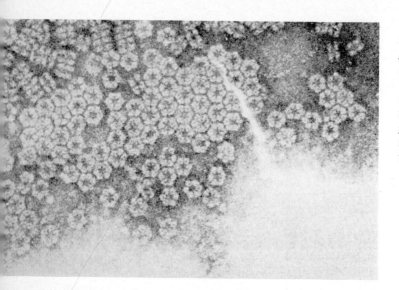

15 (Left). Electron micrograph of *Spirographis* chlorocruorin. Magnification: ×250,000
(Below). Electron micrograph of *Helix pomatia* α-hemocyanin molecules. Magnification: ×315,000.

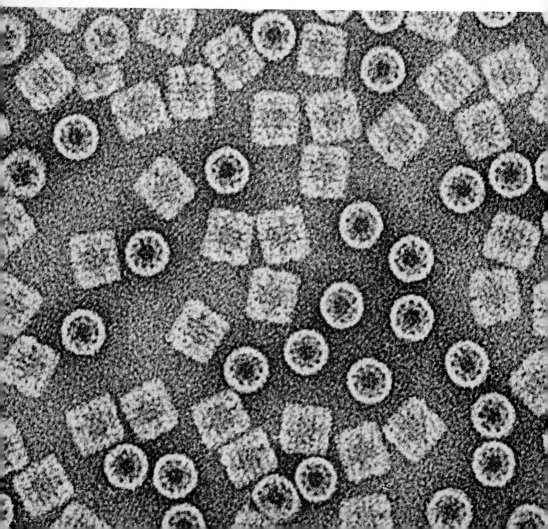

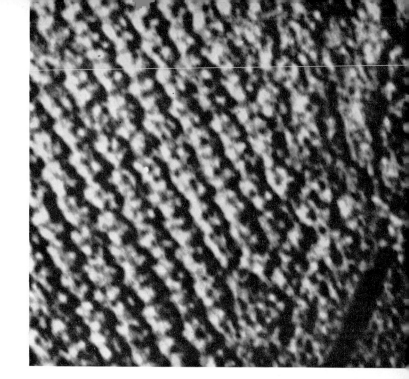

16. Electron micrograph of chloroplasts. Magnification: ×455,000.

17. Electron micrograph of lecithin micelles embedded in thin phosphotungstate film showing typical periodic arrangement of the biomolecular lipid layers. Magnification: ×800,000.

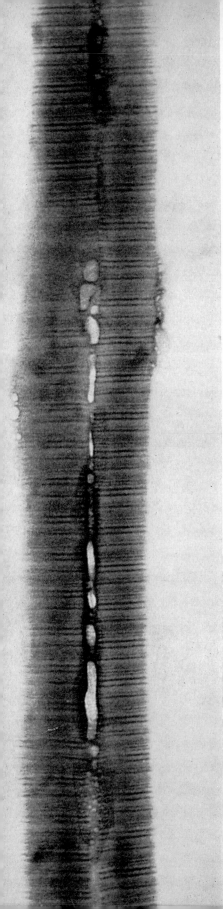

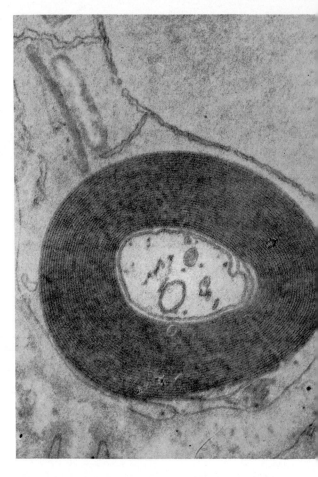

18 (Above). Human cutaneous nerve surrounded by myelin sheath arranged in a spiral and derived from the Schwann cell which can be seen surrounding it. Magnification: × 42,000.

19 (Right). Myelin sheath. (a) High-resolution micrograph of myelin sheath segment from transverse section of frog sciatic nerve demonstrating concentric array of dense and intermediate layers. Magnification: × 380,000. (b) Low-angle X-ray diffraction pattern of fresh rat sciatic nerve recorded with Finean camera. This pattern features a fundamental period of 178 Å, with characteristic alteration of the intensities of the even and odd orders.

20 (Left). Electron microscope transmission photograph of collagen, showing regular transverse striations unsymmetrically related to the direction of the fibre. Magnification: × 156,000.

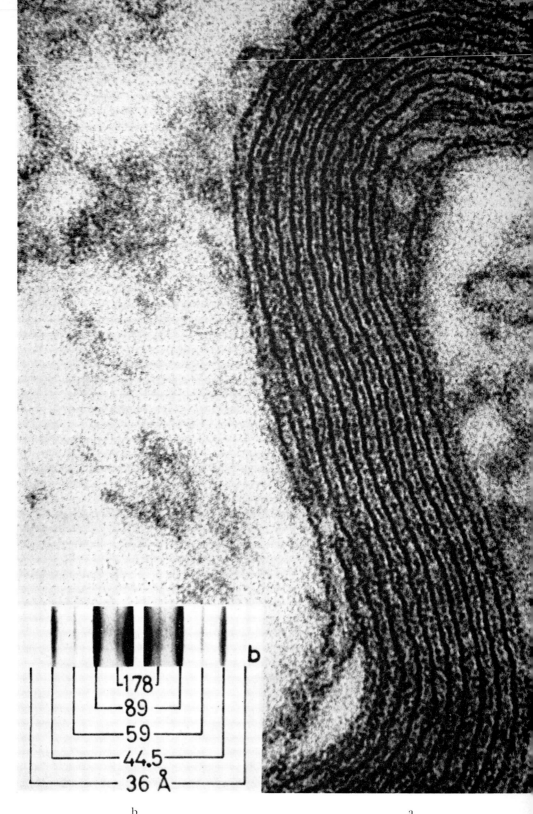

L178J
89
59
44.5
36 Å

b   a

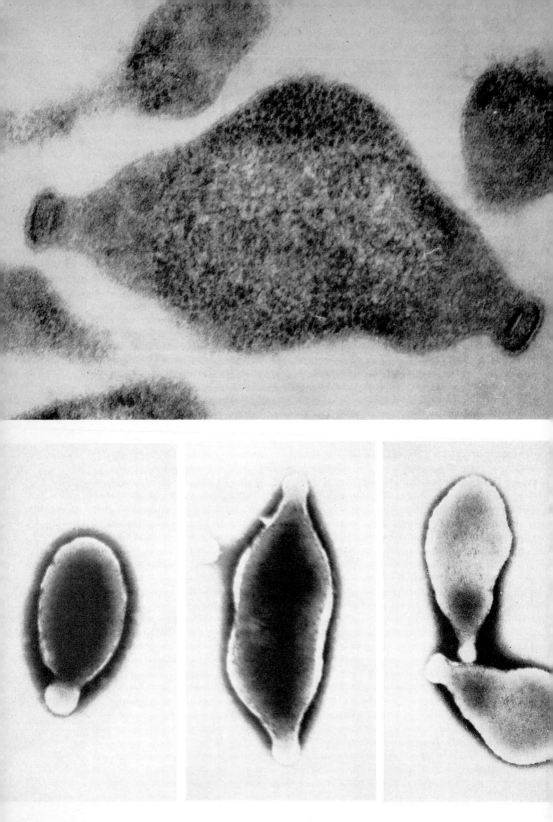

21. Mycoplasmas. Magnification: about ×122,000. (Top) Electron micrograph of a dividing cell of *Mycoplasma gallisepticum*. (Bottom) Single cells in various stages of the division cycle.

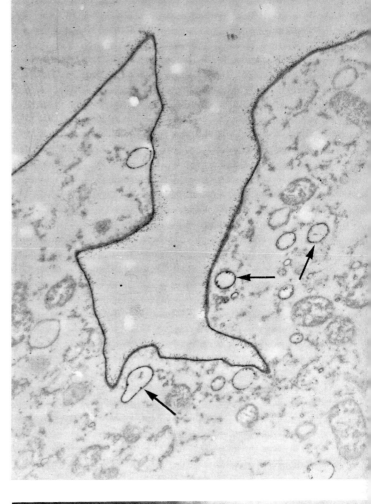

22. Amoeboid pinocytosis.
(Top) Electron micrograph
of *Amoeba proteus*, showing
pinocytosis channel and
vacuoles (at arrows). The
mucous coat appears as fine
fibrils, and the same material
is visible with the vacuoles.
Magnification: ×9,000.
(Bottom) Phase contrast
photograph of single pseudo-
pod, bearing a fully developed
channel. The pinocytosis
takes place through the
channel. Magnification:
×1,100.

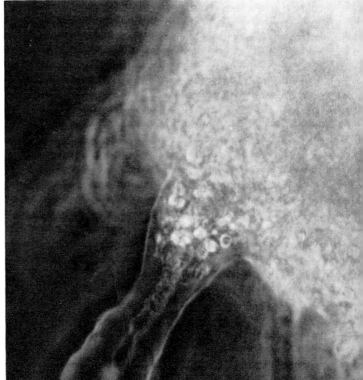

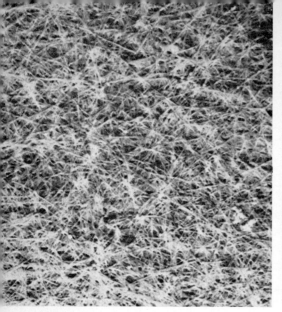

23. Electron micrographs of the cell-walls of the alga *Valonia ventricosa*. (Left) Shows the first random arrangement of cellulose fibrils as they appear on the otherwise naked protoplasm surface of freshly formed *Valonia ventricosa* aplanospores. Magnification: × 12,000. (Right) Shows the condition of the mature wall, emphasizing that there may be three directions in successive layers. Magnification: × 16,000.

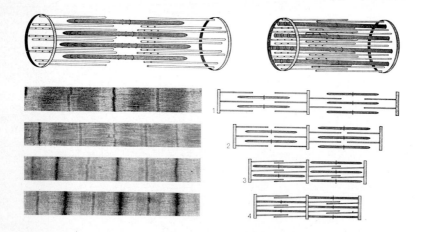

24. Contraction of muscle entails change in relative position of the thick and thin filaments that comprise the myofibril (top left and right). The effect of contraction on the band pattern of muscle is indicated by four electron micrographs and accompanying schematic illustrations of muscle in longitudinal section, fixed at consecutive stages of contraction. First the *H* zone closes (1), then a new dense zone develops in the centre of the *A* band (2, 3 and 4) as thin filaments from each end of the sarcomere overlap.

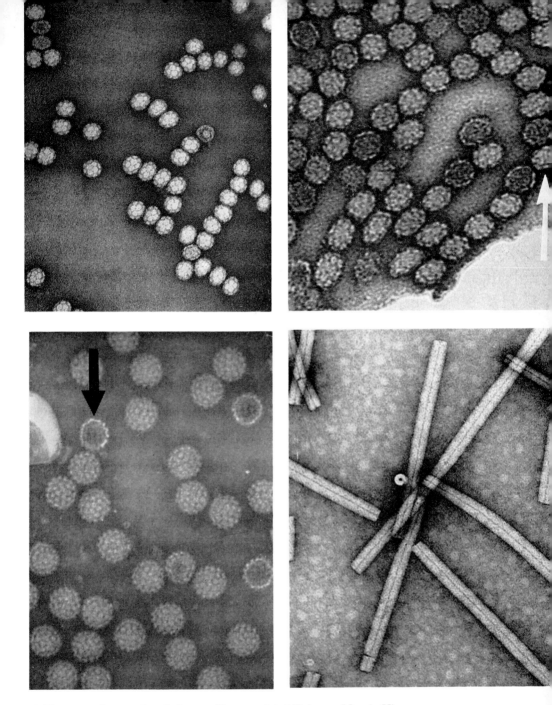

25. Electron micrographs of viruses. (Bottom right) Tobacco Mosaic Virus,
showing piles of plates and central tube. Magnification: × 182,000. (Top) Turnip
Yellow Mosaic Virus, showing polyhedral structure. Arrow shows empty particle
containing no RNA. Magnification: × 228,000 (right); × 180,000 (left).
(Bottom left) Human Wart Virus. Arrow shows empty particle containing
no RNA. Magnification: × 157,000.

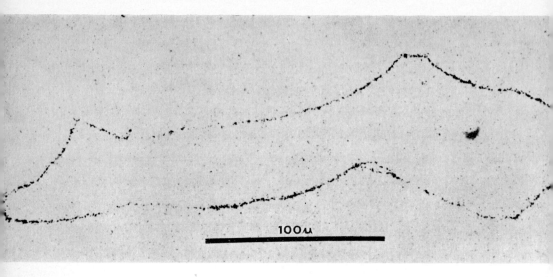

26. An autoradiograph showing the DNA in the single loop chromosome of the bacterium *Escherichia coli*, labelled with H-thymidine and extracted by digestion with the enzyme lysozyme. Some regions of the molecule are not completely extended.

27. Reef of *Conophyton* in the Pharusian, Pre-Cambrian of the Hoggar, Central Sahara.

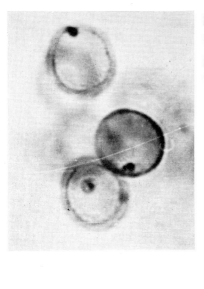
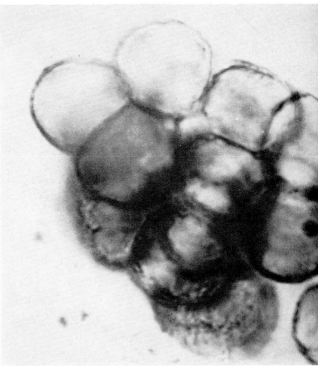
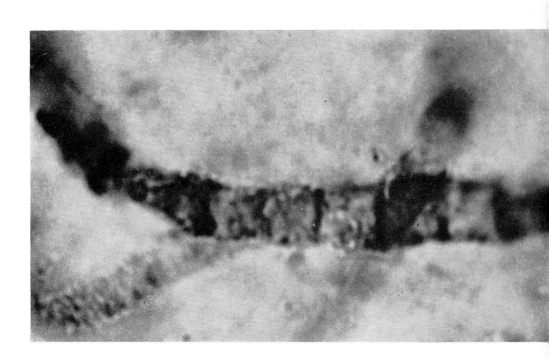

28. Photomicrographs of actual fossils (preserved in the Gunflint formation, Lake Superior, Canada), nearly the earliest we know, of living organisms dated about 2,700 million years. Magnification: ×2,500 (top); ×4,200 (bottom).

29. Photograph of Mars taken by *Mariner IV* from a distance of 7,800 miles. The large crater that fills most of the picture is about 75 miles in diameter. The clearly defined small crater on its rim is about three miles across. The sun is shining on the surface from the north, which is at the top of the picture.

stage were the functioning membranes, which blocked off parts of the living space and made them relatively isolated. It is difficult to reconstitute the original cells: they clearly cannot have existed in their present form. The bacteria must be their highly evolved descendants, but something of what their original nature would have been can be seen from their persistence in other cells, particularly in the eukaryotic cells, as organelles.

The Place of Organelles

So far the general assumption has been that the transition from a sub-vital area stage to one in which definite cells were formed occurred in one jump, even though it was a complex one that may have taken a very long time. An alternative has now presented itself with continually growing insistence, that is, of the interposition of another definite stage, that of independent organelle life. The evidence for this idea is still all of an inferential character. No independent organelle has been found existing as a free organism, but the structure of all cells down to the bacteria is found to contain organelles. Further, these organelles seem to have an existence of their own and often to be largely independent of the central genetic control of the reproductive organism. They seem to behave as if in some way they are a kind of foreign element introduced into the organism, and several in eukaryotes have marked resemblances to free-living prokaryotic cells. Blue-green algae are sometimes almost completely indistinguishable from 'plastids'.

Now, it is generally admitted that the viruses are not in any way primitive organisms. One might say they know far too much about the cell and its mechanism to have evolved independently of them. Nevertheless, one might learn much about the hypothetical independent organelle from the behaviour of the really dependent viruses. The organelles seem to belong to two major classes, the particulate and the membraneous, and in some cases to a third which is a combination of the first two.

Ribosomes

The universal particulate organelle is the ribosome, itself made of two parts, the so-called 30s and 50s. It is here that the process of protein synthesis is carried out under the complex direction derived from the DNA in the nucleus or other DNA-containing structures. We still do not know the structure of the ribosomes, but it is evident that they are very primitive because they occur in all free-living cells, including the simplest of the independent existing organisms, the mycoplasmas.

G

Enzyme Biosynthesis

The main function of the ribosomes is in connection with messenger RNA to synthesize the enzymes. According to the view of the origin of life here presented, the essential parts of this process took place very early, even before the formation of organisms. The enzyme proteins are not separate *ad hoc* creations, but seem to be closely mutually related and to have evolved by a process of multiplication and specialization, controlled at all stages by natural selection. For advanced or sophisticated life, that is, life of eukaryotic organisms, higher than the simplest bacteria or their analogues elsewhere, a single enzyme system is not sufficient – different but related enzymes have to link together in chains and cycles. But there are already hints that such building of enzymes in chains actually occurs out of the disposition of sets of ribosomes as so-called polysomes. Some of these polysomes may be working together to produce just one type of enzyme, but others may be producing the enzyme sequences of a cycle of transformation, such as those of cellular oxidation carried out in the mitochondria. The ribosomes themselves seem to be the universal agents for making proteins or enzymes. The particular proteins they make have their character determined by the order of the constituent amino-directing acids under the direction of messenger RNA, which itself is copied from DNA molecules of the nucleus or nucleoid, where there is one, or the genome, where there is not, in the way already described (p. 80) (plates 5 & 6).

The study of the origin of enzymes and other proteins on the systematic scale throughout living organisms is only just beginning, although it has already acquired a name – chemical paleogenetics. It is beginning to be possible to trace the origin of proteins back to different species and find at what point the various changes occurred. From this alone, it is possible to see that chemical evolution has not ceased and has continued by successive modifications of previously laid down proteins and enzymes.

Microtubules and Cilia

Far more complicated than the ribosomes are the organelles that seem to be built of simple protein molecules. The simplest form of these are the newly discovered microtubules from which the more complicated bacterial flagella (plates 7 & 8) and the cilia seem to be derived. The microtubules are formed of protein units arranged in a helical network on the surface of a cylinder. These are found in many different types of cells, both prokaryotic and eukaryotic. They are beautifully illustrated in the rigid rods of protoplasm of the primitive heliozoa which are composed of parallel bundles of simple microtubules arranged in a double spiral (plate 9). These micro-tubules appear to have the same kind of structure as that of the nine outside hollow fibres of the cilium. The ciliary organization itself appears to be a special arrangement of microtubules and its universal distribution indicates that the microtubules themselves belong to an even earlier era of organelle evolution. The first stage of this seems to be that of the bacterial flagella. The next stage in the evolution of fibrous organelles would appear to be a cilium and its derivatives. The cilium consists of a structure containing nine double or treble hollow fibre bases in a circle, and another pair, more or less similar, in the centre (plate 10). Furthermore the cilium in its function as a centriole and its relation to cell division shows how deeply it enters into the whole existence of the cell, at least of the eukaryotes. Here the ciliary function seems the older: they were ciliary bases before they became centrioles.

The fully formed cilia are found in the higher eukaryotic organisms from protozoa to animals and plants. In fact, as will be seen later, the cilium is obviously a late and highly evolved organelle system, each separate fibre in the cilium is like a microtubule composed of a tube of separate helically ordered protein molecules fitted together.

The essential feature of the flagella of bacteria, the microtubules and the cilia of the higher organisms is that they appear to be self-reproducing, that is, they have associated with them their own nucleic-acid-protein mechan-ism independent of the general protein mechanism of the cell as a whole. This has been shown by the discovery of a single gene-operated mutation which destroys the motility of the cilia by affecting their two central fibres (plate 11).

Contractile Fibres

Probably in this class also are the contractile fibres of myosin and actin, together with other similar contractile substances such as paramyosin, which is responsible for the permanent contractions which occur in some invertebrate muscle (plates 12–14). I treat with these the complexes that build up the oxygen-carrying macromolecules of molluscs and crustaceans – the chlorocruorins and the haemocyanins (plate 15) – where a definite number of oxygen-active protein molecules join themselves together to form less diffusible compound units or finite crystals, parallel in action with the actual membrane-covered corpuscles of the blood of the vertebrates. These invertebrate particles resemble viruses, or, rather, virus coatings, for they contain no RNA, though they probably need an RNA mechanism for their formation.

Membraneous Organelles

The membraneous organelles seem to be part of the general membraneous structure of the cell and, of these, the most important are the mitochondria and the chloroplasts, one responsible for the general metabolism of the cell, particularly its phosphorylation, oxidation and energy-transfer mechanism, and the other for photosynthesis. Although the biochemical action of these organelles has been elaborately studied and largely elucidated, its connection with their structure has hitherto only been guessed at. Nevertheless, it seems to play a vital part in their dominance of cell biochemistry. Both mitochondria and chloroplasts seem to contain two kinds of membrane, outer and inner. The outer membrane seems to separate the organelle from the rest of the cell fluids. In this respect it resembles the membranes derived from the cell itself that are found to cover a number of the larger virus particles (pp. 95f). The inner membrane, on the other hand, seems to belong to the organelle itself and appears in the characteristic folded or indented patterns of the chloroplast grana, or of the cristae of the mitochondria (plate 16).

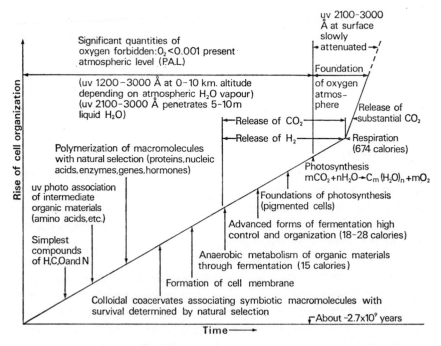

Figure 2. Diagrammatic visualization of evolution of the simple living cell [10].
(*After Bernal, Calvin, Hoering, Oparin, Rabinowitch, Wald, and others*).

84

Morphologically, and perhaps chemically as well, the cell organelles fall into definite groups. Some of them are particulate, as are the ribosomes and the more complicated centrioles and ciliary bases, already discussed, as well as many granules whose function and structure have not as yet been elucidated. Other intra-cellular components are derived from membranes (p. 86).

The Function of the Membrane

I have chosen, though without any conclusive evidence for the choice, the appearance of membranes as marking the first stage of the separation of elements from the sub-vital areas into forms that may lead to the present forms of cell. My main reason is that a biological membrane, as a surface of separation, is one of the most constant features of all cellular structures, both externally and internally. One of the most striking features is that all

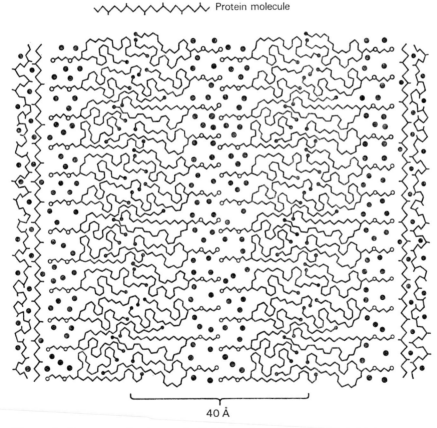

Protein molecule

40 Å

Figure 3. Structure of unit protein-lipid membrane [33].

these membranes seem to have the main basic structure of the unit membrane, consisting of two layers of fatty molecules and one, two or three layers of protein sandwiched between them (figure 3). Their existence would therefore seem to be contemporaneous with the first synthesis of fatty molecules of about sixteen to twenty carbon methylene groups. Whatever is responsible for the production of hydrocarbons of this length and even longer, it should suffice to produce membranes. These long, thin molecules aggregate into sheets spontaneously, but it is only when they are of the same length that these sheets can have any parallelism and stability (p. 72).

Apparently many if not all the membranes in cells find their origin in that part of the cell already membraneous, one which contains folds of various lengths, the so-called Golgi apparatus which is present in nearly all cells containing an endoplasmic reticulum.

The mechanisms by which movements of polymerization proceed to a certain number and then stop, are not well understood. They are probably genetically controlled, but they are certainly less complicated than those which arrange a number of heterogeneous sub-molecules into a complex polymer, as is done in the formation of the nucleic acids. The two-dimensional lipoid sheets that are formed in this way are not by any means necessarily occupied by the same lipoid. Experiments show that they can be penetrated by other molecules of similar but not identical character, such as the sterols. Further, as most biological lipoids are phospho-lipids, they can also be penetrated by ions. It appears that many of the characters of the sheets of lipoids in living systems depend on the relative ease of penetration of the different ions, such as those of potassium, sodium and magnesium, which are responsible for the behaviour of most active systems both sensory and motor, such as muscle and nerve. Some membranes in cells appear in simple spherical forms, such as the digestive vacuoles and the excretory lysosomes, while others are folded structures, such as the cisternae of the ergastoplasmic systems, the Golgi apparatus and the folded cristae of the mitochondria. In some of these, the folds are multiply repeated, building up a pattern of piles of membranes at regular intervals (plate 17). This is particularly the case in organs concerned with light, either photosynthetic, as in the grana of the chloroplasts, or sensory, as in the rhabdomeres in the eyes of invertebrates and the rods and cones of vertebrates. A similar system of repeated layers, but this time cylindrical and not flat, is produced in the myelin sheaths of nerves (plates 18 & 19).

Still another form of organelle is based on fibres, such as in the collagen fibres, which are produced inside cells, essentially as an excretory product, and which also have striations at regular intervals, as have corresponding fibres in striated muscle (plate 20).

The Origin and Function of Organelles

These structures can be considered from two points of view – their formation and their function. As will be discussed later, the existence of highly folded membranes is one indication of the higher complexity of the cell, and is due to the need to preserve a suitable ratio between surface and volume when the cell volume as a whole increases (for the same reason, for instance, as we have convolutions in the brain or in the intestine). The folding in the case of the inner cell particles, however, is much closer and indicates the effective forces holding the folds together, corresponding to the long-range forces, which will be discussed later (p. 127). The scale of the inner structure of these organelles, particularly that of the grana of the chloroplasts, is related to their chemical function in determining the possible range of the set of separate chemical reactions, which are fixed absolutely by the distance that the reagents, including electrons, can travel, which here is of the order of 100 Å. A slightly larger distance seems to hold in the case of the mitochondria, but here there seems to be some evidence that there is an inner structure, not yet fully resolved, of particles maintained on stalks which carry out similar processes to the regular layers of the grana.

Until the fundamental question as to the origin of the method of reproduction of the organelles in the cell is solved, it would be dangerous to dogmatize on how far they are really independent of the general control of the genetic mechanism of the cell, but that control may be exerted in an indirect way, and it is worth following up the idea that the organelles represent independent units that were only at a later stage grouped together to form the complex that we call the cell.

From the point of view of the origin of life, we may consider that there was possibly an intermediate stage, represented very largely by the formation and activity of the membraneous endothelial reticulum, which brought a certain number of organelles together and enabled them to function as a complete cell. This transformation from prokaryotic to eukaryotic cells, which may have occurred rather late in the evolution of life, may, indeed, not have occurred all at one time but spread over a number of millennia or aeons. One decisive change was the occurrence of photosynthesis, liberating free oxygen and requiring appropriate biochemical changes of which the replacing of fermentation by oxidation is the principal one (p. 27).

Animal and Plant

The eukaryotic cells must, however, have been fairly complete at a very early stage of organic evolution before there was any clear separation between the modes of life of animals and plants. The eukaryotic plant cells seem definitely to be of multiple origin, engulfing and maintaining photosynthetic plastids, originally free prokaryotic organisms. The difference between the two, which was obvious in the later and larger examples of organisms, was not always so; in many cases we have the greatest difficulty in distinguishing between single-celled animals and plants. The essential difference is functional rather than structural, namely, in their mode of feeding. Supplied as they are with organic molecules from the photosynthetic apparatus, the plants have no need to take in already formed molecules as the animals have to do and, therefore, have no need of motility or other means of engulfing other organisms whole, with what this has implied for the development of sense organs, muscles and neural apparatus.

The transformation from the prokaryotic to eukaryotic organisms must have meant also a drastic reorganization of the species existing on the Earth. Many, if not most, prokaryotic species must have disappeared (pp. 80f). What they were like we can only study indirectly in their relics in the organelles of the eukaryotics, and as these have been the major objects of study in biology, we are more informed about them anyhow. The chief characteristic picture is the karyon or nucleus containing most of the DNA of the cell as a whole, that is, all except what belongs to the organelles, and ensures their reproduction and codes for genetic pathways which were indigenous to them and hence never could have been taken in by the nucleus.

Many-celled Organisms: Metazoa

In the many-celled animals and plants, the metazoa and metaphyta, the nucleus contains all the elements that look after the control, not only of the cell itself, but of the organism of which it is part. It is walled off by a double nuclear membrane most of the time, but it loses that membrane and fairly obviously reverts to a former simplified state when it divides under the influence, presumably, of the impulses from the specific ciliary base organelles, the centrioles. In the first stage of division, the prophase, the nuclear membrane disappears and only appears again after division. Two nuclear membranes then cover the two cells into which the original cell had divided.

It is evident that here we have attempted to go too far – and further than I am competent to do – into details of cytology, but enough has been said, I hope, to make it clear that the existing eukaryotic cell is the product of a very elaborate history. As what we are concerned with here is a question of the origin of the cell from its pre-cellular but vital ancestry, it should be sufficient to record these facts and observations and to look for the origins of these in central parts of the structure, in the organelles and viruses composed as they are largely of assemblies of protein molecules and of membranes directed by separate nucleic acids, DNA or RNA.

Viruses and Mycoplasmas

We can go further and proceed to look among living things for something simpler even than organelles, and we find it in the viruses which do not seem to have any more in them – at least in the simplest of them – than specific protein particles and chains of nucleic acids, some containing ribose, some deoxyribose. It is tempting to treat the viruses as primitive, but there are many reasons to suppose that they cannot be so. It seems more probable, the more they are studied, that viruses are degenerate. A parasitic mode of life has led them to do without most of the structures necessary for free living in organisms. Next to the viruses we find the simplest organisms we know that do live independently or at any rate can be cultivated on cell-free materials, the so-called mycoplasmas (plate 21), of which that of bovine pleuropneumonia has been the most studied [70]. The fundamental difference between the bovine pleuropneumonia and the larger celled organisms is the comparative absence of folded membrane structures; ribosomes and DNA particles are present as well as one unique kind of particulate organelle. The absence of membraneous organelles may be simply a consequence of the small size of the mycoplasmas and, consequently, of the need to maintain the maximum ratio of surface to volume since they can achieve it without folding, whereas even in the smallest nucleated cells, the ratio of surface to volume can only be maintained by increasing the surface of the internal parts by highly folded membranes such as the internal cristae of mitochondria or the folds of the endoplasmic reticulum and of the Golgi bodies.

Normally, however, these organisms are parasitic and may, indeed, have simplified their structure accordingly. Yet, we may accept them, if not as very primitive organisms, as at any rate marking the degree of simplification possible while maintaining independent, viable potentiality. When we do this, we notice at once that the elaborate structures, particularly the multiplex foldings that occur in all cells, are here absent; there is not room for them and, strictly speaking, there is no need for them either.

The Membrane-divided Cell

Once membranes can be formed, the way is open to dividing any organic communicating material, such as that postulated for the sub-vital areas into separate, only partially communicating boxes. These occur, first of all, as groups of nucleic acids, as genetic material, then organelles and cells and then separate organisms, although the exact order in which these appeared is still uncertain. The organelles may be specialized sub-assemblies of more or less uniform organisms, or the organism may be formed by the coming together of a number of already pre-formed organelles. I incline to the latter view essentially for two reasons, first of all because in nucleated organisms, eukaryotes, the organelles themselves are not, or appear not to be, dependent on the cellular genetic mechanism for their multiplication but each has its own particular genetic mechanism. The second reason is that each type of organelle has a much wider range than the species of cell or organism in which it occurs and seems therefore to have an independent existence with possibly independent and common origin. This view is strengthened by the self-sufficiency of the organelles, which, in eukaryotes, can be separated by centrifugation or other physical means from the cells they occur in and continue as such to carry on their biochemical activities. A nucleated cell, at least, seems quite comparable to a symbiotic organism like a lichen, which is composed of fungus and an alga.

The elucidation of the relations between organelles and the cell in which they take part is obviously going to be a very complicated process. The activities and even the growth of some organelles seem to depend on the general nucleic-acid directed, genetic control of the whole cell and a part depends on the nucleic-acid-protein formation provoked by the organelle itself. There seems to be evidence that, however the association started, it is now well established, that it occurs in most living organisms both plants and animals. The mutual relations between the organelles and the host cell have been thoroughly integrated and their original separation can now only be inferred.

Co-ordination: Endoplasm and Endolymph

Although most of the organelles and intra-cellular structures can be seen clearly in the electron microscope, how they arise and multiply was for long a mystery, because of the difficulty of checking its occurrence in fixed sections in the electron microscope. Now, however, there seems to be some evidence that mitochondria undergo binary division, apparently determined by their own genetic material. The major membraneous organelle with its associated ribosomes, the endoplasmic reticulum, probably does not divide but forms as an extension of other membranes in the cell, possibly in the Golgi apparatus. It seems to divide the cell itself into two regions: one which contains the ribosomes, the so-called *rough* side of the reticular membrane belonging to what I have elsewhere called the *endoplasm*, as it seems to resemble more a gel than does the other region which faces the so-called *smooth* side of the endoplasmic reticulum and which I have correspondingly called the *endolymph*. The endolymph is perhaps the part of the cell that is in communication with the outside of the cell, which, in the case of the single-celled organism, may be the actual liquid in which the organism floats or, in the multi-celled organisms, the tissue fluids. It is not identical with the tissue fluids, however, as there is a process by which the outer fluids communicate with the endolymph by a process of bulging in and invagination to form internal vesicles. This is the process used, for instance, by the amoebae in feeding and drinking, and is referred to as pinocytosis or engulfing (plate 22).

The limiting organelle, that can be called so, is the cell membrane itself, the surrounding membrane which defines the cell and divides it from the external medium or from the rest of the body in the case of the metazoa. The cell membrane has many features resembling those of the internal membranes, but it has another which is characteristic, namely, that it has deposited on it products of the cell which are used to strengthen the membrane and fix its shape or give it particular properties such as mechanical strength as, for instance, cellulose in plants and keratin or horn in animals. This may be considered a special case of utilizing solid material excreted from the cell (plate 23).

The characteristic function of the outer cell membrane varies enormously with the kind of cell. For motile cells, it is obviously a hindrance for it to have any structure more solid than that of the internal membranes because it has to be able to move; for static cells, however, such as those in plants or the various hard parts of animals, the cell surface is essentially intended to have mechanical strength and, therefore, to preserve the shape of the organism.

Cell Growth and Division

The reproduction and growth of cells occurs essentially by division or, the equivalent, budding. Both involve the creation of new external membranes, either as an intermediate membrane as a stage in division or as a separated membrane in budding. The division of the eukaryotic cell is the one act which involves the directing effect of the special organelle, the cylindrical ciliary base or the centrioles already mentioned. This appears to multiply, not by splitting, but rather by the formation in its neighbourhood of another ciliary base situated quite close but at right angles. This is formed *de novo* by some special nucleic-acid mechanism contained in the ciliary base, whose function is to turn out the kind of protein molecules that can be associated together to form automatically a replica of the original ciliary base with its arrangement of fibres. The two sections of a dividing cell, at least in the metazoa and higher plants, seem to pick up their organelles more or less at random; the organelles themselves do not participate directly in the cell division.

Some clues as to the origin of cellular life can be found by discussing the different kinds of cells found in existing organisms. It is best to divide these into three categories of different levels of complexity. The first two of these we have already considered, the prokaryotic and eukaryotic cells (p. 80), which differ primarily in their reproductive mechanism, the first not really having a nucleus, the second being controlled by a nucleus containing chromosomes. It is clear that the eukaryotic cells are more developed morphologically but less developed in the varieties of the chemical reactions that they can carry out and in their reproductive activity. Chemical evolution is more active in the prokaryotes than in the eukaryotes.

In the third category are the cells of higher, many-celled animals and plants, the metazoa and the metaphyta. In this case, starting from the same primitive eggs, we have a great variety of specialized cells that are differentiated according to their function in the total organism, apart from cells devoted to reproduction. Among animal cells, for instance, we have some that are mainly concerned with the chemical processes of the body – digestion, excretion and internal transport, as in the oxygen-carrying red blood cells. In the higher organisms some are concerned with external and internal communication, such as nerves, some with sense organs and others with mechanical movements of effector organs, such as muscle cells. These cells are generally so specialized that one particular component of protein predominates over all the others and the rest of the cell is relegated to providing growth for nutriment and repair, as far as it can go, for this part of the cell. Other cells again are essentially concerned with structure; they are producing some organic or inorganic material which will give the organism as a whole its appropriate form, such as the cells producing collagen for connective tissue, keratin for skin and hair, and secretions of inorganic substances for bone and shell. The remaining cells, ever more highly specialized, are concerned with the defence of the body against harmful chemicals or external organisms, as in the lymphatic system and the white blood cells.

It is in this respect that the greatest development of purely biochemical activity is shown by cells, particularly by the cells of the latest developed class in the *Phylum* Chordata, the vertebrates. This is the development of the mechanisms of immunity, the capacity which these organisms have for dealing with foreign and harmful substances, inanimate and animate, which have found their way into their bodies. This seems to be the latest and most successful application of biochemical evolution in organisms. It is demonstrated by the extraordinary capacity which cells of these organisms have for dealing with foreign chemical substances. This implies such a degree of chemical sophistication as is hardly imaginable and, in fact, it was well known to function before any clues as to how it worked had been discovered. The mechanism of immunity, in which the effect of a foreign agent, particularly of protein, is to stimulate what must be equivalent to the chemical analysis of the agent or antigen and the production of another specific agent or antibody that will react with it, must be of excessive complexity, and yet it is a necessary performance for the very survival of the organisms themselves. By contrast, the plants, with their slower circulation mechanism, can tolerate the presence of infection and virus diseases in various parts of their structure without always endangering the whole organism. The full development of immunity mechanisms are required in the higher metazoa, which have circulatory systems which would otherwise spread noxious agents all over the body in a very short time. It may also be determined by the fact that higher plants are open systems, able to grow from any part. Hence the limitation of immunity reactions. It is foreshadowed by the greater and specific adaptability of much simpler organisms to unusual chemical surroundings. Similar kinds of reactions are found in the adaptation of bacteria to circumstances and conditions which they are not used to, such as, for instance, the resistance to antibiotics. A streptococcus can, indeed, be induced not only to tolerate streptomyocin but to require it for its normal existence. The mechanism of this may be more complicated and involve elements of natural selection.

These categories give only a brief general view of the varying functions of cells. Further studies may serve only to show that it is possible from the same basic structure, by laying emphasis in one or another aspect of the generalized cell, to evolve this great variety of function, and how particular functions may be modified in the direction of greater efficiency in the interests of the whole organism. For example, in very small organisms, any motion that occurs during the change of shape or in actual movement is mainly independent of the time in which it was carried out. The movements are a quantity, slow and unco-ordinated, and can be carried out through the development of a few more or less disconnected fibres of the myosin and actomyosin type arranged more or less in parallel, as they are found in smooth muscle. But in larger and more elaborately connected organisms, reactions have to be co-ordinated in time, especially when this action has to be taken in a very short time so that the dynamic aspects of motion come in, including the inertia of the system and the viscosity of the medium, in such motions as flying, swimming and jumping. This requirement is met by arranging the myosin and actomyosin elements strictly in parallel and in step, as in striated muscle (plate 24). An even more striking adaptation, without effectively much internal change, are the nerve cells, which are essentially the same throughout the whole of the animal world (except for the great speeding-up effected by the introduction in vertebrates of myelin sheaths and their carefully spaced nodes), but able to serve for more and more complex communication systems by their mutual arrangement, just as a computer can be constructed with varying degrees of speed or memory simply by using the same kind of transistors in different ways.

In plants we have a similar but much more restricted variety; here, growth predominates over movement. In structure and growth, the production of cellulose determines the stability of the whole. There is, however, one major difference and that is the presence of the photosynthetic elements which seem to have an independence as organelles in the green chlorophyll-containing chloroplasts found in leaves. These seem to be one standard type of organelle which evolved at a fairly early stage and has been found to be so efficient that it has been retained very largely independently throughout the whole of the higher plant kingdom, the only exception being some of the blue-green and other primitive algae.

The Value of Co-operation: Ultra Cytology

The value of the studies of the varieties of specialized intra-cellular structures for the study of the origin of life is that this represents an exaggeration of some features originally present in the common cell ancestor. Protein synthesis and the presence of many ribosomes and their corresponding endoplasmic reticulum occur especially in all forms of secretory cells, whether that secretion is one which is used in other parts of the body, is stored inside the cell itself or forms parts of the mechanical structure of the whole organism as, for instance, in the formation of cell walls, already discussed.

It can be seen that there is great variety of cells of organisms based on relatively few intrinsic patterns, apparently derived from these few by modifications of the older structures to take on new functions. Some of these cells seem to be indicated as primitive and seem to belong to the period that followed the separation of separate organisms – for instance, the ribosomes (pp. 81f), which would seem to belong to the period when the whole sub-vital areas were engaged in a common metabolism. Others, such as the endoplasmic reticular folds, are evidently subsequent to the cells of which they form part.

Viruses

In endeavouring to reconstruct a possible or plausible account of the evolution of the cell, another type of cell component would need to be considered; this is, more properly speaking, an intrusion from outside, in other words, a virus. The study of viruses has thrown light on the biological structural processes, essentially because they are subject not only to observation but also to experiment. Virus particles, marked in various ways, can be introduced into cells under controlled conditions and some viruses can not only be grown but also be bred in cells. In fact, this method has been used very largely for elucidating the code of the nucleic-acid-protein synthesis. The simpler viruses, for instance, tobacco mosaic virus and bushy stunt virus in plants, the polio virus and adeno virus in animals, and the bacterial viruses, the bacteriophages – I will not discuss here the complex viruses like those of vaccinia or influenza – are composed apparently of only two parts. These are: a protein, which is particulate and identical, characteristic of the virus and even of a particular strain of it; and the specific nucleic acid, most often a ribose nucleic acid (plate 25).

The function of the protein coat of the virus is not yet fully understood. Certainly, it protects the virus: a virus with its coat can be kept under very rough conditions for years without loss of virulence; while without the coat it becomes inactive in a few hours. It may also help to detect its host and attach itself on to it. The six filaments on the base of the T2 virus of bacteria may have this function. However, once attached to the host, the proteins have no further function, they do not enter it. The entry is affected entirely by the nucleic acid and the coat is discarded. Once inside the host, the virus nucleic acid replicates a large number of times. When it has replicated a sufficient number of times, it starts synthesizing protein under the guidance, not of the host's nucleic acids, but of the nucleic acids of the virus. Finally, this protein aggregates itself around each of the new virus nucleic acids.

At this point usually the cell dies, its outer membranes dissolve or are dissolved by enzymes generated by the virus, and the complete new virus particles with their shells are liberated to carry out further infections. Several interesting facts can be deduced from this behaviour: in the first place the virus nucleic acid alone of the infected cell, without any other material from that virus, is able, in the living mechanism of the host, to carry out its own replications. Next, the same amount of virus nucleic acid can in some way manage to get control of the host's protein-building mechanism, which can now produce only virus protein. The actual metabolism of the organism is often speeded up so that it can not only produce but also assimilate more material from which to produce protein than in a healthy cell. It is the cuckoo mechanism on a molecular scale. Finally, the building of the outer coat of the virus is often a complicated matter; it is only in the simpler viruses that this outer sheet of protein molecules takes the form of a cylindrical tube or a spherical vessel in which all, or nearly all, the protein units are similarly placed. Exceptions are the protein molecules at the squared-off ends of the cylindrical forms or the pentagonal arrangements at the twelve five-fold axes of the polyhedral forms, which have slightly different co-ordination.

In more complicated viruses the structure is built out of a finite number of types of protein molecules which are placed quite differently. The greatest complexity is to be found in the T4 bacteriophage which contains DNA (plate 3); it is furnished with a tube which is operated by a kind of spring mechanism to penetrate the host's skin, as well as a hexagonal end plate, and six sensory hairs. These can be built inside a host's body in large numbers – of the order of 100 in a few minutes – and this by a mechanism which is apparently inherent in the newly made protein molecules and owes nothing to the host cell. Even more intimate forms of virus infection are known in which the virus enters into and apparently joins on to the genes of the normal reproduction of the cell. It may not destroy the cell in the first place but can be transmitted with every cell division. Much of the organism, which may be a many-celled animal or plant, can thus be infected with a latent virus and may remain in this state for many years until, on the reception of an appropriate stimulus, an outbreak occurs of the more usual form of virus multiplication with its lethal effects.

That this is so is shown by the fact that, in most cases, in addition to apparently identical virus particles containing nucleic acids, empty shells of viruses, with the same shape and packing of the same kind of crystals, are produced at the same time, the so-called inert or top layer which can be separated because of its lightness. Finally, by a suitable chemical treatment, viruses can be desegregated, the protein separated from the nucleic acid. The latter can be shown to be ineffective in the absence of the former, which can be digested away. On the other hand if, instead of digesting the protein, the nucleic acids are removed by ribonuclease, re-aggregation of the protein without the nucleic acid can be effected. The particular structure of the virus can therefore be reconstructed *in vitro*, thus proving that the construction is entirely due to the shape and mode of the attachment of the protein molecules peculiar to the virus. This may well provide a clue for the reconstruction from protein molecules of all of more or less complicated structures in cells. We already know examples of this occurring in the absence of viruses: for instance, in the transition between globular and fibrous insulin or globular and fibrous actin, a constituent of muscle. This would imply, however, that the properties of biological structures are, so to speak, built into the unit molecules from which they are built, which emphasizes the importance of the idea of *prescription*, already referred to.

The Principle of Self-assembly

So far, most of this chapter has been taken up with descriptions of recent discoveries in the micro-structure and molecular structure of the interior of cells. But we are here concerned essentially with the origin of these cells from a previously postulated complex organic mixture, aggregated or not in sub-vital areas. The sequences that are produced in this way cannot be exactly determined, but they can be fairly well inferred from what has been said about the rule of *self-assembly* of quasi-identical particles giving definite structures, and the way in which the occurrence and spread of membranes divides up the whole volume of living processes into separate sections, carefully adjusting to each other and capable of an evolution genetically controlled for the first time, that is, by the coordination of the different processes which previously occurred spontaneously and without coordination in the postulated sub-vital areas. The idea of coordination of biochemical activities is as important as the evolution of the structure of the cell itself, and the two clearly go together in the history of the origin of life.

Summary

To sum up the lessons that have been learned, if only tentatively, from these observations on viruses and from the study of the micro-structure of cells with the electron microscope, we are fairly safe in assuming that once a mechanism for building identical protein molecules with specific properties from the corresponding nucleic-acid system has been evolved, the appearance of cells will almost inevitably follow, beginning with those of exposed

membranes, particularly when there are possibilities present of further complicated folding producing structures built of such membranes. Those
giving rise to independent structures that can carry out metabolism on their
own will tend to wrap themselves in membranes and function as micro-
organisms, like the mitochondria and, to a certain extent, the ribosomes
themselves, which contain not only ribose nucleic acid but also protein enzymes. They may be called – without stretching the term too far – living
macromolecules and, in common with such macromolecules surrounded by
membranes, will correspond to the idea, formed logically in trying to account for the origin of life, of the first living things or *eobionts*. These may
be further complicated by putting several different kinds of these macromolecules together in a symbiotic way, each making use of the products of
the other.

Thus, we may consider the possibility, indeed the inevitability, of the
building of new organisms from molecules which have the capacity of self-
reproduction. This mechanism of self-assembly, the putting together of
identical parts, has now been observed in a very large number of detailed
structures of organisms or organelles. It may be considered the general rule
for the forming of permanent structures and goes a long way to answering
the question of the forms of nature without the necessity to postulate for
these any specific or form-generating vital forces. This is an aspect of what
I have called 'generalized crystallography', the formal aspect of which will
be discussed in Appendix 3.

The upshot of this is that, in the specific processes of the nucleic-acid–
protein-making cycle, it is sufficient to produce identical protein molecules
and these, of one or more specific types prescribed by the process, will of
themselves, without any further vital interference, build up the necessary
structures. In other words, the order of nucleotides in nucleic acids determines at second hand both the functions and the structure of life. This does
not in any way imply a molecular determinism, because only particular
structures under definite conditions are determined. Both the proportions
and the order of occurrence of different macromolecules are mutually related and are under the control of the general genetic mechanism of the
organism. The new knowledge shows something of how structures are
built up and how functions are carried out. It does not show, yet, why they
are so and what relations they have to each other. It is here, particularly,
that the greatest variations can occur and have occurred, giving rise to the
multiplicity of species of living things.

The picture I am presenting here of the origin of organisms differs widely
from the popular conception of evolution, which begins with one primitive

organism and then differentiates out into the number of organisms that we know now. Further, my hypothesis is that a large number of organisms were appearing almost simultaneously, blocked out, so to speak, from the general *living* macromolecular pre-organismal stage. The primitive organisms were in some degree separated out from their biochemical background: that was their essence. Yet they were never alone. They existed from the very start in an environment containing many other organisms, different from themselves and to some extent complementary to them. All the time, they exchanged metabolic products. Sometimes that exchange was complete as when one organism ingested another, decomposed it and used its molecular contents to build its own metabolism and provide it with energy and structural material. This is a typical animal, predatory, method of existence, and to ensure its success, the various sense organs and apparatus for movement and capture were evolved. But the interaction must just as often have been of quite a different character. Two of these proto-organisms might have come together microsymbiotically, having a common cytoplasm but separate genetic apparatus. This might sometimes have been pathological, as in the case of a virus infection or, as has been suggested here, mutually beneficial, as in the incorporation of organelles. In the extreme cases we might even take the phenomena of conjugation and sexual reproduction as analogous to such incorporation between two cells of the same species.

The stage that we have now reached, in tracing the history of the origin of life, is encroaching on the field of the evolution of organisms, which will be dealt with in other volumes of this series. It is, however, still relevant to consider the mechanisms of membrane formation and the self-assembly of protein molecules in dealing with the intermediate stage between a structureless equilibrium mixture of active molecules and the formation of the structure of even the most primitive organisms. For it is at this point that biomolecular studies, using x-rays and electron microscopes, on the one hand, and light microscope histology, on the other, begin to separate. By now the stage of chemical evolution is drawing to a close and that of organic evolution is beginning. This is a phase of macromolecular rather than of micromolecular interactions, which characterized the previous phase.

It is just in this field of cellular origins that research has been proceeding with the utmost vigour and with the greatest yield of new knowledge. It is here, therefore, that such speculations as are contained in this chapter are most liable to be altered or perhaps to be completely superseded. It seems worth while, however, to look forward, if only to say that it is possible by further observation and experiment to produce such speculative pictures and to proceed from them step by step to critical verifiable predictions.

Chapter 7

The Origin of Life in Time and Space

so far, the origin of life has been treated on a physical, chemical and logical basis, taking into account not only the general laws of science, but also the particular events which may be deemed to have occurred in the various stages of the evolution of our Earth, for instance, the postulated oxygenless atmosphere at the beginning of life. It is now worth taking into account what we know and may infer about the actual timing of these successive stages and how they link up with other facts we have been able to ascertain from sciences such as astronomy and geology.

Before trying to fix the absolute dating for the different stages of the evolution of life, it is worth trying to see what evidence we can find for their relative temporal appearance. An attempt to do this is shown in Chart 1 (p. 101). This is a modification and, I hope, an improvement of the chart which I have published in various forms in earlier years, in my book *The Physical Basis of Life* [12] and at the Biochemical Congress on The Origin of Life, held in Moscow in 1957 [20]. There would seem now to be definite correlations between different functions and structures in the origin of life.

The essential event, from which most others in the origin of life can be dated, was the advent of photosynthesis. Photosynthesis, on a scale large enough to influence the atmosphere and to fill it with molecular oxygen, topped off with ozone, correlates with the appearance of cells, not necessarily of eukaryotic cells. There were membranes, and even folded membranes, which seem to be a necessary feature of photosynthesis using chlorophyll-like compounds. This implies, further, quite sophisticated micro-biochemical reactions, involving oxidation and reduction, in particular the oxidation-reduction processes facilitated by the anomalous protein, ferredoxin. The switch-over from anaerobic to aerobic metabolism must have been the last great change in chemical evolution, involving the presence of a host of porphyrinoid proteins, particularly the cytochromes now present in every cell, their presumed function being to protect life against the poisonous effects of atmospheric oxygen. It is at this stage, also, that we must

CHART 1

Stage	Years Ago (millions)	Atmosphere and Hydrosphere	Sources of Free Energy	Location of Life or Pre-Life	Forms of Chemical Evolution	Forms of Structural Evolution
III (Chapter 6)	800 Base of Cambrian	As at present with variable oxygen content; Formation of oceans; Continental drift	Visible sunlight (ultra-violet cut off by high ozone layer)	In sea and on land; In algal reefs	Chemical evolution slowing down	Evolution of plant and animal phyla (figure 6, p. 108).
II (Chapter 5)	2,400 (gunflint algae); 3,000	Oxygen concentration growing; Ozone near surface	Ultra-violet light	In surface waters; Under surfaces of pools	Oxidation replacing fermentation; **Photosynthesis** yielding O₂, yielding S; Lipids; Polymerisation	Eukaryotes with nuclei, single- and multi-celled organisms; Folded membranes in mitochondria and other organelles, flagellae; Folded membranes in chloroplasts; Prokaryotes i.e. bacteria
I (Chapter 3)	4,000; 5,000	Formation of hydrogen; Anoxic secondary atmosphere N_2, CO_2; Simple molecules containing H, C, N and O atoms	Radioactivity? and local heating	Estuarine muds and proto-soils; Sub-vital areas; Primary soup; On the surfaces of planets, planetesimals, asteroids, cosmic dust	Nucleic acid and protein synthesis; Carbohydrates; Metal-containing proto-enzymes; High-energy phosphates as proto-coenzymes	**Separate organisms** Membrane formation; Coacervates

place the appearance of the most universal organelles, the mitochondria. Taken together, these correlations would establish an order or possible choice of orders in the development of life.

The Time Frame of the Evolution of Life

The next thing to do, clearly, is to attempt to set the whole process into an absolute time frame. We know that life exists and has existed in many forms on Earth and we may be able to infer or assume its existence on any other planets of the solar system. In its fully evolved form, including motile organisms, it is unlikely that it exists on any of the outer planets, though some of the preliminary stages of creation of some formation of pre-organismal molecules may have taken place on planets such as Jupiter, Saturn, Uranus or their satellites. This may even have taken place farther out, as indicated by molecules such as that of cyanogen and methane, or their radicals, common in the spectra of the tails of comets, which are considered to be derived from the outermost limits of the solar system. The story we have been trying to reconstruct, therefore, can be treated as leading up to the present time. But the question arises, when did it start – at least on Earth?

An ultimate limit is given by the date of formation of the atoms of the elements that are found in living things today. These, though very old, are not of endless age. The astrophysicists allow us a variable number but it is not much greater than twenty aeons – that is, 20,000 million years – dating from the particular supernova that in the beginning provided our Sun with its main stock of elements. The origin of the Sun and the solar system that derived from it is another fixed early date and this is more definitely known to be of the order of six aeons.

We have available to us at least some evidence about the primary formation of the Sun's elements. For example, an analysis was recently made on meteorites or, rather, on the siliceous chondrules contained in them. This material contains a particular isotope of the element xenon, of atomic weight 128. This isotope, in turn, is derived from an element, iodine 129, which is a primary radioactive element with a decay period of some 20 million years. It is evident that iodine was the form in which it was taken into the silicate phase in the meteorite. Consequently, the meteoritic material, and necessarily the asteroid from which it came, must have been formed within 20 million years of the first formation of the radioactive iodine in the Sun, as xenon itself would not normally be absorbed in a silicate melt, whereas iodine would.

This dates the silicate phase of the meteorites which we have here on Earth, as 150 million years from the formation of the Sun (we may give it a

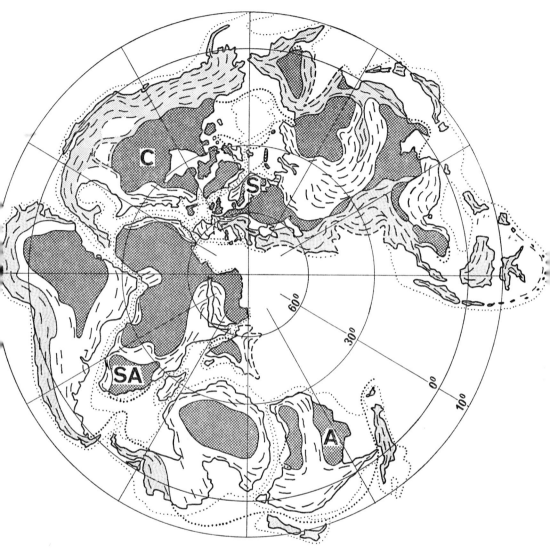

Figure 4. Grenville, Pre-Cambrian, (1,075 m.y.–o m.y.) map of the world reconstructed on the basis of continental drift, showing main shields and fold-belts. Early Grenville fold-belts unshaded; Late Grenville fold-belts dotted; cratonic regions cross-hatched. (C = Canadian; S = Scandinavian; SA = South African; A = Australian).

separate era, 150 m a.s., *anno solis*). Other dates from meteorites range in the same neighbourhood of about four and a half aeons, though the carbonaceous materials, which are associated with them, are clearly younger than the chondrules found among them [5] the latter are at least four aeons of age and, therefore, the first stage of the formation of complex carbon-nitrogen compounds must lie between these dates of five and four aeons, that is, between five and four thousand million years.

Now, these are dates far older than any that are known for most rocks on the Earth. Some of the oldest rocks in the world are found in the Canadian Shield, the Scandinavian Shield and the South African Shield; their ages approaches three and a half aeons. Recently, however, still older rocks have been found [107]: the St Paul's rocks, which occur on the Central Atlantic, rise opposite the coast of Brazil, have been dated as practically four and a half aeons old. But these are rocks of peculiarly basic character, almost pure peridotites, and seem to come straight up from the mantle. The crust of the Earth seems to be from 1,000 to 3,500 million years old, mostly of far more recent date. Compared to such dates, the evidence of organisms has been considered until recently as relatively late. The Cambrian period, which from the start contains a rich assembly of recognizable fossils, began about 700 million years, 0·7 of an aeon, ago.

This figure must now be expanded, however, on account of evidences for the existence of organized forms of an earlier period. It is very difficult indeed to draw conclusions about life on the primitive Earth from the study of igneous rocks, however old.

Evidence from Rocks of Biogenic Molecules

Out of primary sedimentary rocks have come actual biogenic remains, more or less degraded by time, pressure and moderate heat, as Abelson [1] and others have shown. Metamorphic and igneous rocks also contain such alteration products transferred to different positions. Now metamorphic and igneous rocks, especially the granites, seem to be the end product of a partial remelting of rocks that were originally sedimentary and, therefore, presumably containing traces of life, now very difficult to recognize as only the elements remain. Moreover, most of the carbon had been turned to graphite and most of the nitrogen had been expelled. Nevertheless, by systematic studies, particularly in the study of isotope ratios, it may be possible to restore these rocks into something like their original organic composition. This is definitely a task for the future.

There is a belief that the base of the Cambrian, 0·6 aeons, witnessed the first appearance of fossils with calcareous or horny shells. It may be that

Cambrian and later strata are present, and well defined thick deposits and their sudden appearance at this point may be just an illusion. However, the extreme scarcity of any kind of fossils of earlier date would seem to argue that something special occurred at this period. Berkner and Marshall [10] associate this with the production of oxygen in the atmosphere by organic photosynthesis and treat the genetic phenomena of multiple evolution of organisms as a product of chemical changes in the atmosphere. This is one of the questions which will need to be solved before we can establish an effective timetable for the origin of life.

Early Fossils

Recognizable forms of life, possibly either plant algae or animal polyzoa, apparently date as far back as 2·7 aeons from the present. A number of these are to be found described in Rutten's book on *The Geological Aspects of the Origin of Life on the Earth* [103]. The earliest of these is an apparently biogenic limestone of the age 2·7 aeons found in Southern Rhodesia. Actual fossil calcareous algae, probably later in date, are found in the Sahara as conophyton and collenia. The latter form persists into post-Cambrian time, but its origin must be placed somewhere between one and two aeons. New discoveries are continually being made; some of the most striking of these are those made in the Canadian Gunflint formation. These were first shown by Bargehoorn [7] to consist of what appeared to be single cells or filaments, sometimes multicellular. These were presumably primitive algae, and these conclusions have been confirmed by later work showing that the actual remains contain complex hydrocarbons of clearly biogenic origin [86]. They are dated at approximately between 2·0 and 2·5 aeons.

From the discussion in the last chapter, this must serve to prove that actual cellular organisms had been formed at this date; consequently, the pre-organismic period I have postulated in my account can have lasted only between one and two aeons. Though such a vast period of 2,000 million years, much longer than the whole period of organismal evolution from the point of view of life from the Cambrian period up to today, may appear long, it is no more than one might demand for the processes of the evolution of life from an inorganic start to the existence of recognizable organisms. This, then, is the time frame in which we have to work.

In a series of papers [9], [10], [11], Berkner and Marshall have studied the sequence of the absorption spectra of ultra-violet light in the components of the atmosphere – hydrogen, water vapour, carbon dioxide, oxygen and ozone – the last of which is formed from oxygen by the ultra-violet

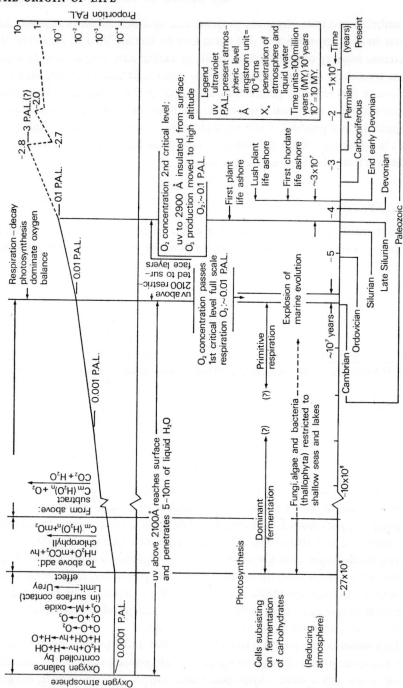

Figure 5. Tentative model of growth of oxygen in the atmosphere
(*after Berkner and Marshall* [10]).

light itself. They recognize that the formation of oxygen by the break-up of water vapour in the high atmosphere is likely to liberate a minimum of free oxygen which would not permit life based on oxidation. According to them, photosynthesis would have started when the concentration exceeded 0·01 per cent of the present oxygen concentration. At that time the ozone formed would be near the surface and, therefore, damaging effects of ultra-violet radiation would be limited to the upper layers of pools in which life forms existed. This coincided in their view with the onset of the Cambrian period (600 million years), in which life would be limited to the sea. Previously, life would have depended, as suggested by Haldane [52], on fermentation. Further, biochemical oxidation, releasing as it does so much more energy than does fermentation, led to an outburst of evolutionary activity coinciding with the appearance of complex life forms and shells of fossils. Later on, life was spread all over the hydrosphere and the oxygen level rose further until, at the end of the Silurian period (400 million years), it reached a concentration of one-tenth of the present value, whereupon life was enabled to spread to the land surface and the present forms evolved. Berkner and Marshall's work is of particular interest in that it treats organic evolution as an automatic by-product of biochemical efficiency. In other words, if the conditions are suitable, life will appear and evolve rapidly. The evolution of life is here treated as a dependent and not an independent variable.

Radioactivity and Life

There is still another way of looking at an upper limit for the origin of life on Earth. As already stated, many of the elements which were first on the Earth were short-period radioactive elements. The resulting radiations, at least earlier than between four and five aeons ago, must have made life, as we know it now, impossible owing to high radioactive dosage. It does not, however, follow that this would apply to primitive forms of life such as discussed in the earlier chapters. It is the particular delicacy of reactive systems to radiations, especially the nucleic-acid-protein cycle, that makes them so sensitive. In very early forms of life, not necessarily organismal, the sensitivity must have been much less. In fact, as has been suggested, the radioactive substances may have provided some of the free energy which brought life into existence on Earth.

The Speeding Up of Evolution

The relatively short time of 1,000 and 2,000 million years for the chemical evolution of life is undoubtedly hard to explain, because it apparently conflicts with the general law of the acceleration of the evolutionary processes

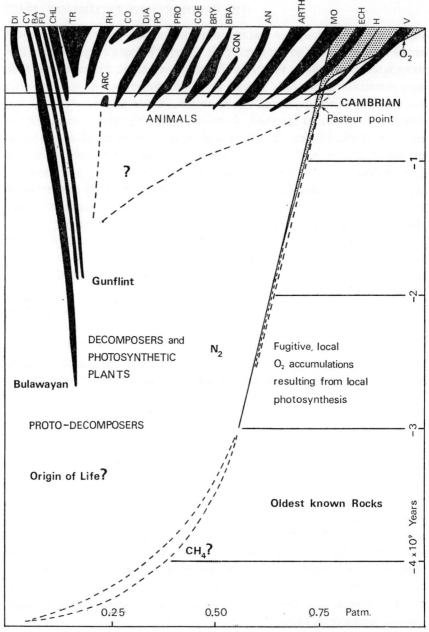

Figure 6. The fossil record, plotted on a model of the evolving atmosphere. *DI*, Dinoflagellates (incl. Hystrichospheres); *CY*, Cyanophyta (blue-green algae); *BA*, bacteria; *FU*, fungi; *CHL*, Chlorophyta; *TR*, Tracheophyta (the higher plants); *RH*, Rhodophyta (red algae); *CO* Coc-colithophorida; *DIA*, diatoms; *ARC*, Archaeocyathida; *PO*, Porifera; *PRO*, Protozoa, *COE*, Coelenterata; *BRY*, Bryazoa; *BRA*, Brachiopoda; *CON*, Conodonta (affinities unknown); *AN*, Annelida; *ARTH*, Arthropoda; *MO*, Mollusca; *ECH*, Echinodermata; *H*, Hemichordata (incl. Graptolites); *V*, Vertebrata (*after Fischer* [43].)

with time. These processes seem, as they go on, to speed up, a tendency that Oparin in particular has noted [79]. The evolution of land animals and plants scarcely required more than 400 million years; that of mammals and birds, warm-blooded animals, required some 100 million; that of the primates needed only some 4 million, and man less than a million.

In human evolution the Early Stone Age lasted far longer than the successive Neolithic, Bronze and Iron Ages. The present age of science and mechanism is a mere 300 years old. If this is a general rule, must it not also apply to the earlier stages? Is it a general principle of the older the slower? However, against this we have to consider the great simplicity of the proto-biological chemical reactions. What can be carried out in a few minutes in a laboratory, nature might have allowed as long as the same number of years or even ten times that number; but the relative importance of antiquity and simplicity cannot yet be measured sufficiently quantitatively to draw distinctions of this kind. This speeding up is another example of the kind of explosive evolution first accounted for in Berkner and Marshall's theory. The various changes in evolution, those, for instance, accounting for carboniferous coal formation, the permo-carboniferous Ice Ages and the extinction of the reptiles at the end of the Mesozoic are, according to them, the result not so much of biological evolution as of oxygen and carbon dioxide concentrations in the atmosphere.

Panspermia

The only other escape from these time-dependent limitations is that offered by putting forward once again a hypothesis which seems at first sight to be far more improbable than the relatively rapid first occurrence of organized life on the Earth, that is, that the organization did not take place on the Earth but took place somewhere else. Now, this hypothesis is twice as improbable as that of rapid evolution on Earth, for it is first necessary to solve the problem of the origin of life under circumstances outside the Earth and even outside the solar system. We must face all the difficulties presented by the arguments on the origin of life on the Earth and then try to solve the problem of transferring these living systems in an active – or, at least, in an activable – state from wherever they originated to the Earth.

Nevertheless, in spite of these improbabilities, or perhaps because of them, it is a very old way of explaining the origin of life through the doctrine of *panspermia*, put forward by the Greek philosopher, Anaxagoras, in the fifth century BC, which is really a doctrine of the effective eternity of life, all new life coming from seeds which are everywhere and always present.

The same doctrine in one form or another has been taken up by many philosophers and physicists both in ancient and in modern times. It is most associated with the Swedish physical chemist Svante Arrhenius in 1884. This doctrine then gained some support. J. B. S. Haldane wrote in 1954 [51] that it was still something to be taken into account.

I find this theory of the extra-terrestrial origin of life less and less acceptable in the measure that we understand more and more about molecular biology and its dependence on particular molecular forms. To my mind it seems to have essentially the same philosophic emptiness to say that life was especially created as to say that it came from somewhere else and that it had been there all the time. It has, also, the dubious philosophical advantage of being a hypothesis impossible to refute and equally impossible to prove until some of these eternal germs are actually found and can be examined. Until that time, it is also impossible to discuss it profitably. We must consequently consider the origin of the life accessible to us, and that is the origin of life in this solar system, but not necessarily only on this Earth.

However, it is only on this Earth that we can study the detailed progress, especially of the later stages, of the evolution of life. If, as I have indicated in the earlier chapters, we divide the genesis of life into three major stages, the first one, which depends essentially on chemical reactions of small molecules, could, of course, occur in a relatively dry medium, as is shown by the presence of molecules such as the purines and the amino acids in meteorites. It has been suggested by H. E. Hinton [54a] that this might have occurred in rapidly drying-up cracks in rocks; but I think that this is most unlikely, as the conditions in which life can evolve are likely to be much more stringent than those in which it can merely survive. The next two stages, however, those concerned with the polymer molecules capable of reproduction and their agglomeration together to form cells, could only have occurred on a planet where free water existed on the surface and the water was exposed to solar radiation to permit photosynthetic energy absorption.

Photosynthesis

According to the Haldane-Oparin hypothesis, the evolution of life on this planet involved one critical transformation which should be sufficiently important to leave its traces on the geological record. That was, the first occurrence of photosynthesis itself, and the resulting changes it brought about through the presence of free oxygen and its product ozone in the atmosphere in the first place and in the rocks in the second. This point has itself been questioned and, after careful examination of specific gases and isotopes, Rubey [102] has concluded that there is little evidence for a reducing atmosphere on the Earth and that the secondary atmosphere contained very much carbon dioxide.

Photosynthesis as we find it now is the production of molecular oxygen in a free state. It is true that in its early stages, as it is carried out in some of the blue-green algae and red and purple bacteria, photosynthesis of carbonaceous compounds as such does not demand anything more than the production of elementary sulphur; but such limited and poor-energy-yielding photosynthesis cannot be expected to have left an endurable mark on the geology or on the atmosphere of the Earth. It is quite different, however, with oxygen. Some of the most important minerals composing the crust of the Earth are readily sensible to low concentrations of oxygen in the atmosphere or in the water. Among these, the most important place is taken by the iron minerals and a similar but subsidiary role belongs to minerals of manganese and vanadium, all of which can exist in various stages of oxidation.

Now iron is, after silicon and magnesium, one of the commonest elements in the body of the Earth. It exists in the crust and the upper mantle however, primarily as ferrous iron, Fe^{++}, the ion of which has lost two electrons. Iron which appears in this combination in salts, is pale green to black in colour; on oxidation, it turns to ferric iron, Fe^{+++}, the ion of which has lost three electrons. Iron in this combination shows colours from brown to dark red – the typical colours of rust. In the interior of the Earth the ferrous iron dominates: these are rocks of green, grey or black colours. On the surface, in this stage of the Earth's history, the predominant form of iron is the ferric and these are yellows, browns and reds. As the basic rocks of the interior weather in the atmosphere which contains a large proportion of oxygen, they tend to form yellow to red sands, the reds predominating where there is more oxidation, as under desert conditions. From these sands are formed the characteristic sandstones, but they are generally of a yellow or red colour, the old red sandstone of England and Scotland, for instance, and the pre-Cambrian Torridonian sandstone.

All these forms, which are characteristic of an oxygen-rich atmosphere, might be deemed, according to the Oparin-Haldane theory of the origin of life, to have been formed only at periods subsequent to the oxygen-containing atmosphere and particularly to the origin of the photosynthetic process. Life must, therefore, be older than the oldest of these red sandstone formations.

We might hope to date the appearance of photosynthesis by the appearance of red rocks and several attempts have been made to do this without arriving at concrete figures. It is by no means certain, however, that the evidence of the red beds can be interpreted in such a simple manner. It must be remembered that these beds are usually originally of a deep-seated nature and have been exposed throughout aeons of geological time to seepage of mineralizing solutions from above, derived from upper strata produced in a later period when the atmosphere contained oxygen. So far, the most hopeful way of dating the appearance of photosynthesis has been the study of the pebbles formed of the iron disulphide, pyrites, FeS_2, at the bottoms of streams in very old formations. Rutten has studied these with particular care and reported on them [103]. Some of these minerals representing the contents of stream beds contain freshly worn pyrites crystals which have not oxidized at all, a condition which Rutten claims could not be met in an atmosphere containing the amount of oxygen that our present atmosphere does. This matter is still controversial: other possible interpretations of the appearance of pyrites have been put forward which are the inverse of those mentioned above. According to them, the alterations are produced by reducing solutions which have caused a new growth of pyrites, so that its appearance does not provide concrete evidence for an oxygenless atmosphere.

Modern methods of chemical analysis capable of detecting and measuring the smallest traces of matter, measured in parts per million of elements and even of isotopes in rocks, are the only possible ways of tracing the early stages in the origin of life on a measurable time basis. Some results have been claimed for them already, notably in a study on the variations of the ratios of the isotopes of the element sulphur. Thode [109] has shown, for instance, that the ratio between the two sulphur isotopes ^{32}S and ^{34}S was about 22·1 in the period more than 1,000 million years ago, and that this ratio changed over 22·3 or higher in more recent times. He takes this stage as indicating the predominance of oxidized sulphur over reduced sulphur. However, these can be only the first stages of what must be a systematic study of the distribution of isotopes of all the elements in all the rocks of ascertainable date, for even the rarest of them may give the most valuable information. When this is done and well interpreted, it will provide us with the quantitative measure to take the place of the various speculative inferences contained in most works today on the origin of life.

Two similar lines of investigation can be deemed to contribute to this dating problem, one is the study of the successive enzymic mechanism in cells, stressed by C. Sagan [104], and the appearance of such enzymes as catalase are taken to indicate the protection of the cell from excess oxygen and therefore to date later than the appearance of oxygen and the effectiveness of photosynthetic processes. The other, stressed by Calvin [36], is the presence in rocks even 2·7 aeons old of small quantities of hydrocarbons of polyisoprenoid character such as phytins, supposed to be essential for the further photochemical process itself. We have other reasons to believe that in this state cellular life was present and photosynthesis was already occurring.

All such investigations, however, require to be criticized very carefully. It has been found that complicated compounds of the nature of the vanadium porphyrins are, in fact, being formed abiogenetically from igneous rocks. The vagueness and the uncertainties of such interpretations make it all the more necessary to avoid dogmatism in this stage of tracing the origin of life on the Earth. While it gives us hope that such tracing can be done, I would not like to put too much weight on the very partial observations that exist at present as marking positive and definite evidence of the early stages of life on this Earth.

Nothing that has been found, however, is incompatible with the theories that have been put forward, particularly with the central Oparin-Haldane hypothesis of the origin of the present biological molecules from those occurring on an Earth lacking an oxygen atmosphere. Indeed, apart from photosynthesis, it is difficult to see how such a high concentration of such an active gas as oxygen could persist for any measurable time. If life was abolished on this Earth today – which does not seem an entirely impossible hypothesis – an amount of ferrous iron derived by weathering from the existing basic rocks would be sufficient, in a matter of a million years or so, to remove from the atmosphere the oxygen now present.

In the absence of any fixed point on the scale, all that we can do is to introduce an ordinal scheme, referring to Stage 1 from an indefinite beginning, whether on the Earth or on primitive planetary bodies, right back to four or five aeons; taking Stage II as the stage of polymerization and molecular reproduction up to the formation of sub-vital areas, say, another aeon, ending it at three aeons ago; taking for Stage III only one more aeon, up to two aeons before now, as indicated on Chart 1 (p. 101). The advent of photosynthesis would occur, therefore, at or soon after that date. I would put the origin of photosynthesis and that of membranes with chlorophyll in parallel layers at around three aeons ago, two aeons for the end of the evolution of the first organisms, leaving for organic evolution proper the rest of the time between then and now. This timetable may require drastic alteration in the light of the theory of Berkner and Marshall (pp. 105 ff.); it is obviously a very provisional and guess-work scale for the time of evolution of life on Earth.

Life in the Universe

We have already had some discussion on the distribution of life in other parts of the Universe. At the moment we can have positive evidence only for the solar system and little enough of that except for the first stage, which must have gone on practically everywhere in it. Somewhere, there is a certain amount of mixing, as the evidence for carbon and nitrogen compounds in cometary tails and meteorites shows. Some of the further synthetic processes may even have occurred in the major planets, in Jupiter and Saturn, for instance. The red spot in Jupiter seems a persistent part of an extremely gravitationally compressed atmosphere and has a colour which cannot be due to any heavy atom but which must represent some simple carbon or nitrogen compounds [30]. Its appearance will not be easy to reproduce as it seems to change colour from time to time and, therefore, whenever clear it shows as red, but it may be covered over at some times by a whitish film, making it appear as a pale yellow.

The critical Stage II, involving the evolution of a self-replicating biochemical mechanism, as has already been stated, in my opinion can only have occurred on a planet containing some kind of hydrosphere; this, in our solar system, limits its occurrence to the Earth or to Mars. Further, Stage III, involving the appearance of organisms, may have occurred only on the Earth. What we observe telescopically, in the way of spring and autumn vegetation on Mars, may only be that of sub-vital areas in which some form of photosynthesis occurs. The first close-up observations of the Martian surface, the most extensive study of the new space era, showed a surface sparsely covered with circular craters more like that of the Moon than the Earth, without folded mountain chains and, presumably, without oceans or life either. However, as this is only the beginning of the study, I will avoid more speculation at this point.

As to life outside our solar system, we can only indulge in pure speculation and the celebrated but treacherous principle of 'sufficient reason'. On the strength of this we can assume that where the conditions of size and degree of irradiation of another planet anywhere resembles those on Earth, the same stages in the evolution of life will also appear; for the basic life-building elements will be the same everywhere. We may expect from the laws of general probability and those of astronomy, including Bode's Law and its close analogues, that there would be one or two planets within the range of temperature and irradiation suitable for the origin of life. With a more powerful or hotter sun, these may be found further out but at least one planet ought to fulfil the conditions. Whether they would also fulfil the condition of size, enabling a free hydrosphere to be formed, is less certain but a substantial proportion might be expected to do so. The occurrence of water is likely in any case, as water is about the commonest molecule in the Universe.

Underground Water

There is increasing evidence that those planets or asteroids which contain water may have preserved it under layers of what is effectively permafrost or frozen mixture of dust and ice that forms a self-sealing layer preventing evaporation. At the bottom of the permafrost layers may be found even some liquid water, similar to that found at the bottom of some of the static glaciers in Antarctica. Water may indeed be found beneath many lunar craters and the future investigators of the Moon will probably be able to detect it by using scientific methods. Such pools, however, deprived of any method of intercommunication as well as of photosynthesis owing to the darkness in which they are formed, do not seem to me a suitable site for the evolution of life. Harrison Brown's calculations already referred to (p. 38), indicate that there are some thousand visible stars that are each capable of carrying planetary systems with, on the average, two planets within the life zone! In our galaxy this gives a very large number of planets suitable for producing life, and of this we may be reasonably sure. Even if the conditions for the spontaneous occurrence of life are more severe than has been indicated just now, it has the chance of occurring at least ten billion times in our galaxy. It must happen millions of times more often in the other galaxies.

We cannot tell now, but hope we may be able to do so in a few year's time, what is the distribution of these life-generating planets in time, depending as they do rather narrowly on the age of the stars that gave rise to them. The Hertzsprung-Russell diagram, which shows the age of stars as a function of their luminosity and mass, might help to determine the ages of stars capable of having planetary systems. If, again, we use the principle of 'sufficient reason', we should not take our own position as in any way special. Now we know stars both older and younger than our Sun and, consequently, those of them that had planets would have some form of life process much before us and others much later or only starting now.

Going over a range of time equivalent to galactic ages of some twenty aeons, we should expect to find samples of life of a great range of ages. We might therefore expect to find evidences for life at each stage before that reached on Earth, evidences of the type I have tried hypothetically to reconstruct (chart 1, p. 101). Beyond that we are far more in the dark because we do not know and cannot know from our own experience, what are the states of life later than those which we have observed on Earth. It is at least permissible to think that the phenomena of consciousness would be likely to evolve, if only in the first place to permit predatory feeding through an internal correlation between sense-organ analysis and ensuing action. The further development of a social life, which has occurred more than once in the evolution of animals on Earth, seems to be in itself only a consequence of the improvement of the limited reproduction and the corresponding appearance of parental care and with it the possibility of learning and passing on the traditions, consciously acquired, from generation to generation. Civilization seems a logical consequence, but the forms of such civilizations are likely to be beyond our imagining.

One place might be much more likely than others for such emergence. By analogy, one can see that the evolution of multiplicity of species enjoying a kind of commensal relation with each other might be a natural end-product and there is no reason, in itself, why it should change as a whole, though any part of it might go through the cycles of evolution and extinction. We have seen that on Earth, not only individual species but whole groups of species like the reptiles of the secondary period have mainly disappeared (p. 109). It seems very much as if, once life has appeared on the Earth, the evolution of successive groups capable of exploiting its possibilities to the full come with it. What we cannot say *a priori* is whether the sensory-motor correlation which has occurred in every branch of life on Earth up to very different levels, has also occurred elsewhere, and whether this will lead to social co-operation and the emergence of what Teilhard de Chardin [108] has called the noösphere or conscious social existence in the history of the evolution of man.

The sequence of events in the evolution of life on Earth that might be put down to chance has been so complex that one is tempted to consider it as unique. The particular gifts of the primates of eye-hand co-ordination might have been accident or the coincidence of trees of the tropical forest type bearing so much fruit that the small rat-like animals who must have inhabited them in the first place were not big enough for the job. This high degree of chance might seem to imply that such a production as a human being and his sequence of societies are very improbable events, and consequently a very infrequent occurrence. The number of planets having life is likely to be much greater than the number of planets having developed noöspheres. We know we have one on Earth, but we do not know whether we are the only one to have them. We think this is unlikely, but it remains to be proved or disproved, if that is possible.

Civilizations in Outer Space?

The possibilities of the existence of conscious and science-controlling forms of life throughout the Universe and of our communicating with them is far greater than our obtaining any knowledge of forms of life that have not reached this stage, because even the rudimentary apparatus that we have on Earth is capable of sending and receiving regular radio messages to and from all parts of the Universe, right to the furthest, although the power of such transmissions has to be enormous. Efforts have already been made, though discontinued for the moment, to obtain coded messages from presumably scientifically competent planets: no verified instance has yet been received. But this need not mean that none have been sent nor do we know if any of the messages we have sent have been received elsewhere. It may be purely a technical matter – of whether we have sufficient threshold of sensitivity for such messages – or a psychological one – of whether it has occurred to people in other planets to send them.

There is a possibility [106a] that the oldest and most advanced civilizations on distant stars have in fact reached the level of permanent intercommunication and have formed, as it were, a club of communicating intellects of which we have only just qualified for membership and are probably now having our credentials examined. In view of the present chaotic political and economic situation of the world, it is not by any means certain that we would be accepted.

This is, of course, the wildest of speculations but it has a definite *a priori* probability. For that reason it is not by any means a waste of time to keep on searching and reaching out to see whether we can find any trace of such intelligences existing, much as the sailors of Columbus, when they found bits of floating wood carved by human hands, could be sure that men existed in the New World.

Paths of Advance

The sketch of the time-table of the evolution of life on Earth included in this chapter may seem very inadequate but it is likely to be filled in relatively soon with the very rapid advances on age determination by numerous different radioactive methods and by a more intensive study both of meteorites and of the oldest rocks on Earth, to find evidence for chemical changes that will reveal, particularly, the oxygen content of the atmosphere (p. 104). There are certainly clues to be found in the isotope ratios which have enabled much of the past to be reconstructed, even when the molecules themselves have been destroyed. Much more serious is the present almost complete lack of correlation between dates given geologically and epochs in the processes of the origin of life.

The key date of the appearance of oxygen in a serious quantity in the atmosphere and its association with photosynthesis has yet to be fixed. A relative chronology of chemical and biological processes with geochemical and geological data is still to come. At the present moment this may not matter very much because, as we have no idea of the rate at which these chemical evolutionary processes took place, we cannot assert that there was or was not enough time for them. So far, the picture seems an essentially self-consistent one; we can be fairly sure that, over the last two aeons of the Earth's development, life existed in conditions not so dissimilar from what they are now. An organic, Darwinian evolution would have full time to work itself out.

The other date is less clear. Chemical evolution can have another two aeons to play with. We are now only beginning to glimpse at the enormous complexity required to evolve for itself the processes of duplication of molecules and the co-ordination of their chemical reactions. But the fact that many of these have been reproduced in the laboratory, in what is geologically no time at all, makes it no longer inconceivable that they occurred of themselves given the aeons to work in.

Chapter 8

Alternative Pathways to Biopoesis

IT should be evident by now that the story I have unfolded about the nature of the origin of life is one which inevitably expresses my personal opinions. It is not that I can claim any originality in bringing them forward. They represent, for the most part, views already expressed by several workers and elaborated further by others. I have attempted to include all that I have been able to find of other ideas, as long as I judged that they could be fitted together into a plausible and coherent theory. I realize that my ideas of the best way to achieve such coherence have varied from time to time: as new ideas have come in, I have changed many of the older ones. The selection I have made in this book will not be to everyone's taste, but I have tried to compensate for this by giving accounts, at various stages, which differ from mine – not radically different and not departing from those which seem to have a genuine scientific backing.

The Criteria for the Serious Discussion of Other Views

In this chapter I am attempting to make up for any omissions by citing other possible and coherent pictures of the origin of life than those given here, of which there are many. I have rejected them in my account, not so much because I do not always agree with them in themselves as because they will not fit well into the picture I have given. In doing this I have not attempted to discuss or even enumerate the various mystical and semi-mystical ideas of the origin of life, for that would take me too far from my story. I have also omitted, because it might only confuse things at this stage, those reasonable accounts that cannot now be accepted because of more recent observations and which really belong to the early history of the subject and not to its present stage of active growth. There are, however, several reasonably scientific views which lie outside the main line of the theories of the origin of life and fall roughly into two categories, the ultra-imaginative and the ultra-sceptical.

Ultra-scepticism and the Improbability of Life

The latter of these is the more difficult to refute. By applying the strict canons of scientific method to this subject, it is possible to demonstrate effectively at several places in the story, how life could not have arisen; the improbabilities are too great, the chances of the emergence of life too small. Regrettably from this point of view, life is here on Earth in all its multiplicity of forms and activities and the arguments have to be bent round to support its existence.

The Appeal to the Supernatural

Faced with this difficulty, the temptation is to pass to the imaginative pole, to introduce supernatural factors, to appeal to a special creation at every difficult point. Another alternative, which in the last analysis comes to very much the same thing, is to admit total ignorance and to counsel serious scientists to abandon the search until better times when more knowledge will be accumulated. This is the path chosen by most professional biologists today. Biochemists and biophysicists tend to be more sanguine, perhaps because they do not see all the difficulties [36].

Nevertheless, the ranks of those trying – with admittedly inadequate facts and methods – to explain the origin of life continue to grow. One of the reasons why working on the origin of life is not only a difficult but a deceptive process is the very rapid advances of the subjects on which greater knowledge of the origin of life depends: astronomy, geology, biochemistry and molecular biology. Not only is it so difficult as to be virtually impossible to be competent and up-to-the-moment in all of these subjects at the same time, but there is also an inevitable inertia in setting out the new ideas of those with which we are less familiar.

An Amateur Subject

As both a new and a speculative subject, the origin of life inevitably attracts the minds of many who are overall perforce amateurs, even though they have fields of science in which they are acknowledged experts. The resulting crankiness, as much as the scepticism which I have mentioned, is very characteristic of all works on the origin of life. However, an amateur subject is also an exciting one and will in the course of time be refined down to something as safe and dull as the rest of science. Workers acquire a vested interest in a particular theory or attitude towards the origin of life and are loath to change it for another, even though it may really belong to a previous era in our knowledge of the physics and chemistry of life processes. Many of the different lines of explanation to which I will be referring are in this category. The differences between them are more apparent than real, however deeply felt.

The argument in this book has followed what might be called the central or orthodox theories of the origin of life. They derive from the Oparin-Haldane hypothesis in the main, but with alterations which have been introduced from time to time by the originators or by other workers, largely as a result of advances in biology and in the astronomical-geological background. The major, generally accepted alterations have already been described in some detail. Most of them affect what I have called Stage I and Stage II in the processes of origin. In Stage I there has been the major alteration due to the appreciation of the experimental work on the building up of the biological primary molecules from those of the simple gases.

From the first experiments of Miller in 1953 onwards, we have had a series of syntheses and chemical explanations which now furnish a very solid background of hard fact to any theory of the earliest stages of the origin of life. As chemistry, they are not open to serious criticism; what may be criticized, however, is their relevance to the actual origin of life on Earth or in the solar system. Inevitably, they refer back to what can only be a theoretical appreciation of the origin of the Earth and its subsequent development. And these, as Pirie has pointed out [94], are very insecure and changeable bases.

Alternatives in the First Stage

Many of the alternative paths in relation to biogenesis are unsure from the very beginning; as they also come together again and again at various intermediate stages, this may not be of so much importance. There is not, for instance, any complete consensus of opinion as to the origin of the Earth itself as a planet, far less of the origin of its hydrosphere, its oceans or its atmosphere. The evolution of the atmosphere is now tentatively accounted for by the Berkner-Marshall hypothesis (pp. 105ff.). This, however, leaves many questions unanswered. It is not even certain that life originated *on* Earth.

Opinion at the time of writing has gone back from the catastrophic and fiery origin of the Earth as part of a cooled-down filament drawn out of the Sun, to the original Kantian hypothesis of the Earth as an agglomeration of cosmic dust, forming initially cold primitive planetesimals or planets. This has been subsequently refined by Schmidt [105] and Levin [64] and, in a slightly different form, by Urey [113]. The latter postulates further subsequent heating, gravitational or radioactive. Such heating would decompose most complex chemical compounds formed in the first stages of reaction of gases produced by solar radiation or x-rays.

Meteoritic and Cometary Origins?

Effectively, such a process would cast doubt on any picture of terrestrial life being formed directly from meteoritic, or even from cometary, material. The view that cometary material has been one of the main sources of pre-vital organic molecules has been reached by Urey, by Oró [83] and to a lesser extent by Calvin. It is based on the presence of abundant cyanogen and hydrocyanic acid in comets and the possibility of very easy synthesis of complex organic compounds starting with them or with their derivatives, cyanamide or dicyanamide. However, gravitational or radioactive heating of the Earth seems to be mainly in the centre. It should not have affected so much the outer layers all over the surface but only certain special areas of volcanic or other geo-thermal activity.

Moreover, the degree of heating, particularly as it affected the formation of a primary and a secondary atmosphere, is still very much open to dispute. While it is generally admitted that the primary atmosphere of the Earth, composed very largely of hydrogen and rare gases, must have disappeared very early, for there is little trace of it in the present atmosphere of the Earth, the hypothetical original methane and ammonia atmosphere still has little geo-chemical foundation. It is essentially astronomical extrapolation from spectroscopic studies of the atmospheres of Jupiter and Saturn. The major recent changes in this part of the story have come from the realization that the carbonaceous compounds in certain meteorites show that Stage I, the formation of the monomers such as the amino acids and organic bases from which proteins and nuclear acids are derived, is not a phenomenon exclusive to the Earth and that some, at least, of the accumulation of carbonaceous compounds, which still does occur on the Earth, may not have been formed, as suggested in the original Oparin hypothesis, entirely in a primitive ocean but in circumsolar space.

As previous chapters show, however, my own inclination is to think that much of Stage I did occur extra-terrestrially, but I must admit that in this matter I am not following the orthodox view of the origin of life which is still held, for instance, by Oparin [81] and is supported by the synthetic experiments which are aimed at reproducing conditions on the surface of the Earth rather than those on that of an asteroid or in open space. Even the composition of the primitive and secondary atmospheres is still a subject for dispute. There are other possible origins for oxygen in the atmosphere than photosynthesis, for instance in the decomposition of water vapour in the high atmosphere and the subsequent escape of hydrogen from the gravitational field of the Earth [30].

Although there is a strong case for the postulated reducing atmosphere of the primitive Earth, due largely to the predominance of hydrogen in the solar system, what really matters here is to what degree the atmosphere *was* reducing at the time when life first originated. The question correspondingly becomes one of quantity rather than quality, a matter of estimates of the relative rates of production and absorption of molecular oxygen on the primitive Earth.

I have argued [20] that, in the absence of vegetation, the ferrous-iron compounds in the Earth's crust will remove oxygen as fast as it is produced by any purely physical mechanism operating in the extremely dilute upper atmosphere, but I may be wrong. It depends both on the amount of reduced iron that would be exposed by eroding processes on the crust and on the extent of the primitive oceans: both matters on which we can have no sure knowledge nowadays, although methods of finding them out are being developed. Rubey [102] has, indeed, argued that there is little evidence that the primitive atmosphere was not similar to the present one, in particular in the presence of abundant carbon dioxide (p. 111). This point may be admitted, as it was by Haldane and myself at an earlier stage, but it does not touch the main one which is the absence of oxygen in the primitive atmosphere. But it must be admitted that the positive evidence for the existence of a reducing atmosphere on the Earth is very slender and controversial at that. However, it is also true that some of the indications for a reducing atmosphere come from biochemical sources, namely, the prevalence of an aerobic metabolism in primitive organisms, a point which led Haldane to the postulation of a reducing atmospheric origin for life.

The necessity for a reducing atmosphere to set off the series of reactions leading to life on Earth, has also been questioned by Dauvillier [41], one of the earliest writers on the subject and, unlike most of them, at least in modern times, still adhering to the hypothesis of an Earth formed from a solar filament, and consequently starting at high temperatures. He, therefore, postulates an atmosphere, not so much of methane as of carbon dioxide, a view also put forward by myself in 1957 [20] but since abandoned. But it is characteristic, as pointed out by Pirie, that grave differences in the theories adopted for the very beginning of the Earth do not seem to affect the accounts of the later developments of life on it.

Changes in the Primitive Soup

Great uncertainty also prevails as to the hypothetical chemical situation that must have occurred in the primitive hydrosphere, what has been called the primitive soup. Until we know more about the composition of the secondary atmosphere of the Earth, the kind of reactions occurring in this hydrosphere must remain hypothetical. The organic content of the primitive soup is itself open to serious question. Its estimates vary between 25 per cent by Urey and 0·1 per cent equilibrium mixture put forward by Hull [57] [22]. The main point at issue is the degree to which this was a mixture which was subjected to the same photochemical process which produced the compounds and, subsequently, largely decomposed them, unless they were in some way protected from the action of the ultra-violet light by ozone (p. 27). I have suggested [12] that this point could be met by securing the separation of the resulting compounds by adsorption on clay which would also protect them from destruction by the ultra-violet radiation.

All this implies that there is still much room for doubt about the precise nature of the complex organic compounds which were to be formed in the primitive soup or soups. The great variety of starting-points that have been used for such experimental synthesis makes it probable that such compounds could have been formed, not only under the conditions that have been postulated, but under a great variety of other conditions as well. The experiments carried out by Miller and, after him, by a whole host of other chemists and biochemists in the United States, the Soviet Union and other countries, including Japan, show this clearly if crudely, and now a more detailed analysis has been carried out by organic chemists such as Oró, Calvin and Ponnamperuma. The whole resources of modern theoretical chemistry are being used to show that there are far more easy pathways for synthesis than had previously been thought of. The difficulty is going to be, as I have already pointed out, to find which of the available pathways was then actually used in building life on Earth.

Alternatives in the Second Stage

It is in the second hypothetical stage of biopoesis, of the polymerization of the simple molecules produced in the first stage, that other alternatives begin to appear. Of these the most important so far has been that of thermal synthesis and polymerization. A major theme of the Oparin-Haldane hypothesis has been the action of radiation, particularly ultra-violet radiation, to effect the early chemical synthesis in the cold. This is also the view which, with slight aberration and involvement of early synthesis, not on

Earth but on meteoritic material, has been expounded in the early chapters of this book. It is precisely here, however, that a radically different solution has been put forward by Professor S. Fox, of the University of Florida. He claims, on the basis of very extensive experimental evidence [46], that the syntheses, first of all of amino acids and later on of more complex *protein-oids*, can be achieved by normal thermal methods at relatively high temperatures, at between 160°C and 210°C, well above the boiling-point of water at present atmospheric pressure.

The thermal pathway to the synthesis of proteins is *a priori* an attractive one, although open to very obvious objections. There are still – and there must have been many more in the primitive Earth – sources of such thermal energy adjusted to these requirements, particularly in lavas, volcanic ashes and hot springs. The essential physico-chemical difficulty, of how to maintain a temperature of above the boiling-point of water without special pressure devices is surmounted, in Fox's experiments, by the use of certain quantities of melted amino acids, particularly aspartic and glutamic acids. In the laboratory, Dr Fox and his colleagues have prepared polymers containing all the twenty-odd amino acids in this way.

The Nature of 'Proteinoids'

He finds, further, that the products are prepared in the form of small spherical bodies, what he calls proteinoid microspheres, which he postulates would replace Oparin's coacervates as the origin of individual organisms. There can be no question here of doubting Dr Fox's results but only their relevance to the problem of the origin of life. Criticisms here are on two points: first, there is the high improbability of the formation of the necessary concentrations of amino acids, not to speak of the higher concentrations required for aspartic and glutamic acids, which are rather complex amino acids; and, secondly, there is the high improbability of the further development of the proteinoids, which are actually solid polymerization spherulites. Such spherulites are quite commonly produced by irregular or branched-chain polymerization, as in starch grains, which cannot effectively lead to a crystal, but forms an assembly of rigid to plastic spheres around nuclei. Any resemblance to organisms, such as the presence of double spheres indicating fission, is probably fortuitous. Moreover, Dr Fox has been concerned very largely with the mechanism of the primitive formation of proteins and has only later considered the formation of nucleic acids. It is true that he has also shown that a side reaction can, starting with aspartic acid, lead to ureidosuccinic acid, which is a key intermediate to the nucleic acid synthesis.

Generally speaking, this aspect of Dr Fox's researches seem to me to belong to the older experimental approaches to the origin of life which aimed at producing, like Oparin's coacervates, plausible imitations of primitive life *shapes* and at the same time at providing a mechanism for the formation of proteins from amino acids. This approach has been rendered rather 'off-side' by the demonstration of the template mechanism of nucleic-acid-protein formation. It is not obvious how the problem of the order of either nucleotides or amino acids in a given protein can be determined by a process depending on a chance mixture of amino acids produced by thermal synthesis. It must be admitted, however, that no other convincing mechanism for the evolution of this ordered structure has yet been postulated, although in general it would seem that a low-temperature selection is much more likely than a high-temperature one.

The Coacervate Hypothesis

In the account I have given in the earlier chapters, in the second stages of the origin of life I have made several references to Oparin's coacervate hypothesis, but the full Oparin picture would not seem to me to be one that can be uncritically accepted. In the theory as first put forward by Oparin in 1924 and increasingly since, he has considered the key feature of the latter stages of the development of life in the primitive ocean to be the formation of coacervates. It seemed to him to open the way of passing between an inorganic structure to one which might have some of the appearances of life and later evolve into it.

Coacervates, which were first described by Bungenberg de Jong in 1932 as composed of a mixture of a protein solution and one of gum arabic, have obvious attractions in any hypothesis about the origin of life. They are the nearest we can come to cells without introducing any biological – or at any rate any living biological – substance. But were they then necessarily a stage in the origin of life? I had abandoned this hypothesis myself as long ago as 1947 [12] for two reasons: firstly, because the method of formation of the coacervates implied the pre-existence of complicated polymer molecules, such as albumen and gum arabic, which themselves seemed to be necessarily products of life; and, secondly, because the coacervates did not seem to possess the necessary internal structure to carry out vital processes. The latter of these two objections is the more difficult to sustain, for the coacervates are pre-eminently bodies consisting of two differently charged colloidal miscelles, maintained in a state of equilibrium in the form of drops immiscible with the medium from which they were formed, one mostly of water containing a far more dilute solution of the same molecules which constituted the coacervate drops.

I, myself, had become familiar with coacervates through my work on the solutions of tobacco mosaic virus particles, and also with the forces which preserved this separation of layers and led to the formation and stability of the *tactoids* or orientated liquid crystal coacervates that such elongated molecules give rise to [34]. Tactoids differ from the normal isotropic coacervates by the length-to-diameter ratio of the particles of which they are composed. When this is large they tend to arrange themselves in parallel and to form doubly refracting fusiform liquid crystalline regions. The analysis of these tactoids shows that the separate particles are maintained at regular distances from each other by means of what are called long-range inter-particle forces, which are very sensitive to the hydrogenion and salt concentrations in the medium in which they are suspended. When the conditions of the medium favour higher concentrations, more than 30 per cent, the result is a gel; at lower concentrations an oriented sol. Both the gels and the sols in tactoids and coacervates are mostly composed of water and, consequently, they are able to accommodate large proportions of other molecules, both small molecular species such as salts and ions, and even large molecules such as those of proteins. This fact has enabled Oparin and his fellow workers [81] to show that coacervate drops can, when they contain enzymes introduced from the surrounding solution, carry out within themselves a number of enzyme reactions, and thus form a model for the biochemistry of cells as well as for their separate structure and water content.

These experiments are certainly interesting and, in their field, conclusive. They show that coacervates can be the seat of chemical reactions corresponding to metabolism in an active and not merely, as in the past, in a passive way and can thus imitate the behaviour of organisms in respect to such activities as growth. Nevertheless, in my opinion, they are open to the same criticism, of lack of relevance to the origin of life, as I have previously made in relation to thermal polymerization (pp. 124ff.). Consequently, I am not inclined to accept the coacervates as an intermediate stage in the origin of life, at least not at such an early stage as Oparin proposes. For me they come later than the evolution of the nucleic-acid-protein formation mechanisms and hence, in my view, occur first in the sub-vital areas. Nevertheless, I admit that these considerations are not by any means decisive ones and possibly the dispute on the relative order of the different processes in the biogenetic field may not be important at present and may be rendered obsolete by new discoveries and experiments. Effectively, the coacervate hypothesis does not take any further the explanation of the key phenomenon of replication: the modification of such replication by selection of molecules, a kind of natural selection which is replaced by the natural selection of organisms at later stages. What coacervates do show, however, is the extremely powerful effect of particles having large surfaces on chemical reactions.

It can be seen that a coacervate of some sort is likely to be formed once a variety of elongated protein and other polymer molecules are produced by whatever methods. These are not necessarily organic and, in fact, the presence of organic material in the original coacervates is a point which can be criticized. On the other hand, if the original coacervates were of organic origin, we are back at the situation which I, myself, postulated when I considered that the adsorption of the simple molecules from the sea occurred in the first place on mineral particles. Later these same particles were to act as bases and templates for the first stages of polymerization [23].

From a chemical point of view there is very little to choose between these alternatives, although logically if we are trying to discuss the *origin* of life, they are widely different. Indeed, Werner Kuhn [63] has shown that polyvinyl alcohol, PVA, in the form of a dilute gel, can react very much in the same way as Oparin's coacervates do, and probably for the same reason, namely, the existence of a wide network of polymer chains which can interact through hydrogen bonds and change their conditions with the change of pH and become what might be called an ionic motor which draws its energy from oxidation, much as living muscle does.

Nevertheless, even if they do not provide a clue as to the actual origin of life, Oparin's experiments have great value, showing the possibilities inherent in various colloidal systems. Such systems can contain both crystalline and amorphous elements. It is the former part that I consider as the first seat of polymerization of an ordered kind, but both may play their part.

Sub-vital areas: ooze and clay mineral adsorption

In the early stages of the origin of life, we may legitimately postulate that in the prebiotic stages the physical surfaces of the Earth will have been much as they are now. The phenomena of erosion, of river formation and seas will have occurred, and where they do there must necessarily be certain areas of shallow water, effectively estuaries. Estuaries on tidal water are necessarily exposed to continual flow in and out of the tide and, consequently, the mud in them is maintained continually in suspension except at two points of every tide, at high tide and low tide, in what is called the 'stand of tide'. This results in the precipitation of a small amount of the fine material in the form of what is called an *ooze*, a deposit which is up to 99 per cent water and the rest colloidal material, now mostly of organic nature mixed with a certain amount of mineral clay. As the layers of ooze are superimposed, they press on each other and dry out to some extent to make the characteristic mud bank. It is here that, whatever the oozes consist of, there will be found the most adsorbed organic molecules. And it was here, I postulated, that occurred the polymerization process and early life. The occurrence of surface polymerization was, indeed, one of the main ideas which I introduced [12] as a consequence of adsorption of small molecules on mineral surfaces. This has been realized experimentally by a number of workers, in particular, Akabori [3].

No great gap separates this from the conception of the primitive coacervates of Oparin, except that the sites are not particulate, but beds of indefinite extent. This vagueness about the origin of life is necessarily so now, but we hope it will not be necessary for long. Gradually, more evidence may accumulate and we may be able to get a more precise picture of what happened in these stages.

The idea of the origin of life as a surface reaction either on clay particles or coacervates has an alternative, that of Calvin, and to a certain extent of Oró, who argue that these transitions from monomers to polymers can best be effected through the action of specific molecules in dilute solution and not on surfaces. Either mechanism is at the present time about equally probable. The choice between them would require further experimentation. More particularly, it would require examination of whether the mechanism of chemical reagents is a plausible one, that is, whether the particular reagents are likely to have been in the primitive oceans in sufficient, necessarily small, concentration to achieve the condensations required for the synthesis of polymers. To decide whether the formation of life was a homogeneous reaction brought about by free molecules such as dicyanamides, or a heterogeneous one brought about by crystalline particles or pre-formed polymers still demands much study and experimentation.

Free energy sources

The advantage of the Oparin-Haldane hypothesis is not only or even mainly in the types of structures they proposed for early life, but rather in the process considered as a chemical process, as of the origins of the functions rather than of the structures of life. The evolution of life on any planet will depend not only on the basic molecules which will serve it in form, but also on its supply of free energy as Oparin and Haldane postulated in the concept of the primitive soup, and on the continual feeding of that stock by energy from outside by radiation, ultra-violet or visible. This problem will be treated again in Chapter 9. It is one of great generality, essentially a process of loss of entropy, a process, therefore, opposite to that which a system will naturally take up of itself, which is always one of increasing entropy or muddled-upness. Consequently, life must have had from the start either a source of free energy in itself or must have been able to take in free energy from outside.

This is postulated in the Oparin-Haldane hypothesis as it is in all those derived from it. They demand an early stage of the building up of free energy, starting from some primitive astronomical source either as radiation from the Sun or derived from local heat produced by radioactivity. This would tend to produce a state of chemical energy which would be intrinsically unstable and which would be followed by a second stage where the release of free energy in a continuous way would have to build up the structures and reactions which make life possible. Life in this sense would represent a region or regions going bad on the surface of an abiotic Earth. The Earth is only sterile as long as it remains without self-generated life.

In this picture, there would be a definite difference between the anabolic state, the building up of the chemicals in the primitive soup, and the catabolic state of running them down again and dissipating them as heat. If this were all the story, life would appear only to disappear again. Somewhere in between we must find a way of catching a fresh and continuous source of free energy. An alternative possibility, that life arose *pari passu* with the absorption of energy, so that it lived all the time on income and not on capital, has not been fully elaborated.

The Berkner-Marshall hypothesis (pp. 105ff.) in one respect alters the picture of the actual locus or loci of the origin of life on Earth. It is a suggestion that life may have evolved in shallow pools, not necessarily communicating with each other. The first stage, according to Fischer [43] may have occurred when photosynthetic many-celled organisms of an essentially plantlike nature contained enough animal cells to absorb most of the evolved oxygen, or for that matter sulphur, without allowing any contribution to the atmosphere. Only later, when more oxygen had been evolved and distributed in the atmosphere, would an equilibrium concentration of it be established all over the world, hence equalizing the condition of the different pools. I am not completely satisfied with such arguments, as I believe that the present-day plants are derived from animals and not vice versa, by the absorption of chloroplasts and other organelles, but this may have occurred at an even earlier stage. The earliest animals, essentially autotropic, having evolved from photosynthetic forms could have given rise later to modern eukaryotic animals and plants, the former subsequently losing their plastids and becoming entirely parasitic and mobile animals, the latter turning into sessile plants.

The Importance of the Nucleic Acids

The alterations brought about in recent years in Stage II of the original Oparin-Haldane theory are even more far-reaching. At the time of the original hypothesis, and for two decades later, it was generally believed by biochemists, owing very largely to their concern with enzymes, that the most important biologically active molecules were the proteins. Consciously or unconsciously they followed Engels in saying, 'Life is the mode of motion of albumens'. However, slowly at first and afterwards in a flood, it began to be realized that the nucleic acids were in many senses more fundamental than the proteins. This change went, on the one hand, with the conclusiveness of the association of the nucleic acids with the genetic material, as studied *in vivo* by Caspersson [38] with the ultra-violet microscope and, on the other, with an increasing knowledge of the chemistry of the nucleic acids and of their role as heteropolymers with the four nucleotides arranged in different order.

The growth of the knowledge of polymerization and polymer structure, mostly motivated by industrial uses, also contributed largely to this change of emphasis. With the progress of molecular biology, this all led up to the Watson-Crick hypothesis which gave a central place to the ordering of the nucleotides in the nucleic acids and the code by which they could be transferred to the building of proteins. It gradually became clear that a central place in the story of the origin of life would have to be given to this precise reproduction of molecular patterns brought about through the storage of such patterns in a self-producing order of nucleotides in the nucleic acids, particularly in the deoxyribonucleic acids, DNA.

The Development of the Nucleic-Acid-Amino-Acid Code

The key question in the origin of life is now seen to be the first development and subsequent modification of this code. The code itself is of no importance unless with it is taken the method of translating the code into something that can be used for further development of the other chemical reactions, particularly the formation of the ordered amino acids in the protein enzymes. This involves the evolution of the processes responsible for the finding of the separate amino acids and then for their correct ordering in proteins under the direction of nucleotides in the 'messenger' nucleic acids. This process may not have occurred all at once, but may have had intermediate and simpler stages. The essential point is that, to form any general hypothesis of the origin of life, there must be a mechanism for the translation or transfer on information contained in the nucleic acids to the proteins, involving also the mechanism of such translation carried by the ribosomes and polysomes.

The Identity of Molecules

The working into the picture of the stages of the origin of life of the vast and rapidly growing mass of knowledge accumulated in genetic studies and their biomolecular successors is obviously going to be a very difficult and complicated process and leaves much room for controversy. So far, it must be admitted that much thinking will have to be done before the two trains of thought represented by biomolecular mechanics and the history of the origin of life can be brought organically together. As to how this can be done, there have been numerous theories put forward in recent years, particularly those by Haldane in his last contribution to the subject at the Wakulla Springs Conference [52] in 1963. It was there that he tried to set out a blueprint for the primitive organisms containing a few nucleotides and a few amino acids forming nucleic acids and proto-proteins. Further contributions in the same symposium included the work of Buchanan, Lippman and C. Sagan, all of whom discussed this first formation of ordered polymers. What has to be accounted for is the genesis of identical molecules for the purposes of maintaining metabolism, structure formation and reproduction. But these molecules need not have had anything like the same complexity as they show now in living organisms.

The tendency now is to discuss these things as biomolecular studies, that is, in chemical rather than biological structural terms. More recently much work has been done in attempting to formalize the theory of the origin of life, conceived of essentially as a problem of chemical kinetics and thermodynamics. The most recent example of this is a memorandum of A. B. Zahlan [122] which discusses a theory of how life could arise as a result of random and purely chemical events, taking catalysis as the main agent and building up a scheme using information theory and topology and arriving at a set of systems with about six catalysts per system which could lead to the emergence of a sequence of chemical reactions involving replication, performed on metabolites supplied by the environment.

It is likely that many such schemes will be put forward, and, indeed, have been put forward in one form or another; but they seem to me all too formal and I feel that it will be necessary to go further and include information on actual observations of structure as well as of chemical reactions. In such chemical theories, the question of whether organisms preceded life or vice versa is left essentially open, though the view I have expressed here, that of life before organisms, is not generally acceptable. It is interesting to note that Dauvillier does in fact accept it [41]. The criteria for deciding for or against this view are not immediately apparent and it may be that in itself it is not an important question at this stage.

Alternatives in the Third Stage

In the third stage, that leading up to the evolution of the nucleated cell, matters are even less satisfactory, because here they may depend not only upon a deep knowledge of the present-day structures of such cells, organelles, but also on their methods of multiplication, growth and control. This is a study which is only just beginning but which will have to make use of all the new methods of comparative ultra-cytology employing the electron microscope and every refinement of biochemically controlled auto-radiography. These methods are now only in their infancy and will need to be extended over the whole range of the biological kingdoms, plants as well as animals, and particularly those of the admittedly primitive and anomalous prokaryotes such as the bacteria, before it is possible to draw conclusions from them bearing on the origin of life (p. 80).

The advance of biochemistry, the understanding of the inner structure of the cell, thanks to the electron microscope, and most of all to the rise of molecular biology, have revealed at the same time new aspects of life that need explanation. The very complexity of the structures revealed lead convincingly towards an origin in history and therefore have created a greater necessity to have a theory of its origin to explain the kind of structures and reactions that are actually observed to occur. It is already clear that the explanation of the reproduction or replication process of precisely identical molecules is an absolute necessity for any such theory. As they are examined by these new methods, the structures of living organisms are found to be composed of arrangements of identical parts, usually protein molecules, knit together in quasi-crystallinity. So, for instance, are the microtubules and the flagella and cilia presumably derived from them. These parts and the structures made from them furnish a method of classification and with it a clue, which never existed before, to the evolutionary inheritance in simple organisms. It is evident that we are at a stage in proto-biology that

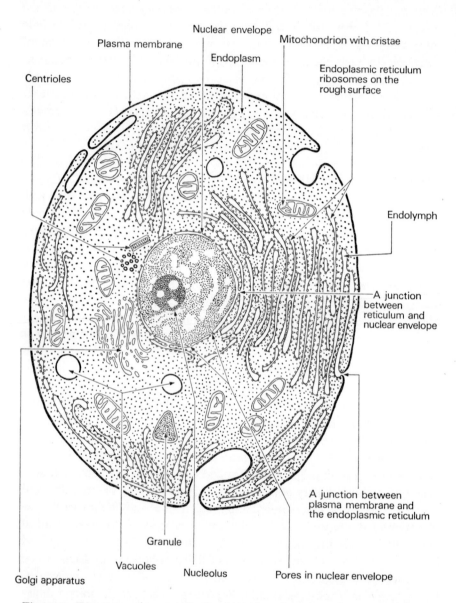

Centrioles

Plasma membrane

Nuclear envelope

Endoplasm

Mitochondrion with cristae

Endoplasmic reticulum ribosomes on the rough surface

Endolymph

A junction between reticulum and nuclear envelope

A junction between plasma membrane and the endoplasmic reticulum

Pores in nuclear envelope

Nucleolus

Granule

Vacuoles

Golgi apparatus

Figure 7. Diagrammatic generalized eukaryotic cell to show the relationships between its various components (*After Hurry* [57a]).

will require a complete recasting of old ideas, somewhat similar to that produced by the earlier invention of the optical microscope. Although plausible approaches to a theory of genesis of structure can be made – and I hope have been made in the early chapters of this book – we must admit that this basic question has not effectively and satisfactorily been answered.

Membranes

On the structural side, the chief gap is the lack of realization of the role played by the membranes in living systems. Our new picture of the cell is one of a highly complex organization of different entities, the endoplasmic reticulum and organelles such as mitochondria and ciliary bases, separated more and more by an elaborate set of divisions. These divisions are for the most part constituted by a set of membranes which certainly play a very active role in the life of the cell. The passage of ions through membranes, which in many cases is in the opposite direction to that in which they would naturally diffuse, the so-called selective pumping of ions from low concentration to high, is one of the functions of the membranes that we need to understand and explain and that will at the same time help to explain their origin.

It will also be absolutely necessary to explain the origin of organisms as separate entities. The evolution of the complex mechanism of separate and partially blocked-off systems within a cell, the larger gaps that exist between the cells and the environment, are all phenomena that must have a history of their own – or several histories. The formation of membranes and the inner architecture of cells must be taken into account in the future in all the comprehensive pictures of the origin of life.

The time basis of the origin of life, which has been discussed in Chapter 7, is also liable to different interpretations. In putting forward his specification for simplest organisms, Haldane propounded at the same time a way out of the difficulty of the highly improbable chance formation of life. As he pointed out elsewhere [51], the improbable is not the impossible; it is only something that happens not very often, but it becomes impossible if the time in which it is more likely to happen is longer than the time it is given, and 4,500 million years, which is all we have in which to evolve life, is a serious limitation to any chance of its origin. The more we know about life, the more complicated its processes seem: therefore, at first sight, the less likely it is to occur.

Against this, there is another consideration. Life, in the last few thousand million years, has become an extremely stable system. Biochemical evolution, except for the bacteria, has virtually ceased. Morphological evolution has become so slow that it was possible, up to a hundred years ago, for serious biologists to deny that it ever occurred at all. Cats and dogs had remained, they believed, ever since the creation, cats and dogs. This follows from the extreme stability of the mechanisms which nearly always returned the system of species to one of its relatively few stable modes. This cannot always have been the case. Organismal evolution is now absolutely and relatively slower than it has been in any other period in the history of this planet. When it was faster, there was all the more chance for events to happen that were intrinsically improbable. It is on these grounds that Haldane stated [52] that he saw no reason for a long period of chemical evolution preceding organic evolution.

The situation must be reconsidered now in the light of the Berkner-Marshall hypothesis. If evolutionary explosions are functions of metabolic activity, in turn determined by $O-CO_2$ concentrations in the atmosphere, then the rate of evolution would show marked peaks at certain periods. It is suggested, for instance, this occurred in the carboniferous period and also at the end of the secondary period when the giant reptiles appeared. However, this is still very uncertain ground.

To examine and probe these considerations requires clearly much deeper studies than any that have been undertaken hitherto. It will require the product of armies of workers with new and ever more specialized instruments. There are, however, strong indications that these armies will be forthcoming and that the processes of fundamental biology will prove in the next few decades as interesting and as well financed as those of nuclear physics have been in the last few. They are certainly likely to be more rewarding in practice in curing disease and in improving conditions of life than was the perfecting of the atomic bomb in destroying it.

Summary: The Genesis of Order

I have tried to show in Chapter 6 how the question of the development of order of the first polymers, the nucleic acids and the proteins, has become one of the key questions of biopoesis, if not *the* key question. It can be seen to take place according to two possible schemes: either (1), as Ponnamperuma [98] has put forward, the irregular sequences are first formed and then selected according to the regularity of any of their parts; or (2), the complicated sequences are built out of associations of simpler ones with small variations. I have, as indicated earlier (p. 65), considered the last point of view as the most probable, but the others should certainly be kept in mind.

The various views cited towards the end of this chapter are set out there not because they are necessarily able to be proved true or untrue, but because it is judged that they have a current relevance to the future of the enquiry on the origin of life. I have chosen among them already and have selected the path which appeals most to me for present understanding and future work. I may be, and probably am, wrong, but in logical necessity I cannot tell in which direction: if I could I would have changed my formulations. At any moment a new observation may be made or a new theoretical deduction may be arrived at which puts the weight more on any of these theories or on some quite new one, rather than on my own choices. They should for that reason, if not for any other, be kept alive and in mind. They may be needed.

Determinism and Teleology in Biopoesis

It can be seen that the modern view of biopoesis includes elements both of deterministic character and of the older teleological character. The former is a logical consequence of the nucleic-acid-protein enzyme mechanism, the concept of prescription; the latter is the operation of natural selection in evolution.

The controversy between the two philosophically opposed views can now be seen to be more apparent than real. They can co-exist in a scheme that is self-consistent as a whole. It is true that the mechanism applied to higher organisms is incredibly complex and the only question that may remain is whether there would have been time for it in the 4.5 aeons since the origin of life on Earth. Even such a basic mechanism as photosynthesis, which of necessity must have come near the beginning, involves mechanisms in the chloroplasts themselves requiring the formation of dozens of specific enzymes.

Chapter 9

Outstanding Difficulties in Accounts of the Origin of Life

THIS chapter is concerned with the difficulties and objections that may be raised or have been raised to any or all of the theories of the origin of life. These objections may range from those that might arise at a given stage to any theory, to general objections to any attempts to account for the spontaneous origin of life. Among the latter can be found the general objection about the formation of life by chance events, which now takes the form of the first living molecule coming about by accident through a chance concurrence of atoms – this is the old Democritan picture in a new style and far less convincing than the original.

Chance in the Origin of Life

Most of the difficulties that face any explanation of spontaneous generation of life in its earlier stages depend not so much on the problems themselves as on the methods by which they are stated and dealt with, on the refutation by *a priori* arguments based on the improbability, or even the impossibility of the genesis of life without external interference. Such arguments really apply not so much to the genesis of life itself, but rather to the nature of the particular hypothesis that is made to explain it. To some extent, therefore, the criticism of these hypotheses is useful, if wrongly directed, because it should serve to narrow down the possibilities of the genesis of life or of any stage of it. Such arguments, for instance, as that some particular stage happened by chance are always laid open to a straightforward statistical calculation of what that chance is, and it is usually very low.

The success of any such criticism, however, may only indicate that the original hypothesis has been badly constructed. The probabilities are made to be multiplied and not added, and if the stages are so chosen that the probabilities inside each stage and from one stage to another are all very nearly the one, the total probability of the development should also be great. Where we find a particularly low probability for something that we know actually happens, is where we need to look to see a flaw in the argument. Haldane finds, for instance, that a happening of a particular sequence in a nucleotide chain requires the simultaneous occurrence of 10^{17} trials, for which there is neither space nor time enough in the whole history of the Earth. This implicitly assumes that the outcome of each trial is equally improbable, whereas it may well happen that the energy of the state corresponding to any particular trial is so much lower than the rest that much fewer trials than indicated by pure chance would be necessary to establish it as successful. This argument is equivalent to saying that in the origin of life nature is always playing with loaded dice – sometimes very heavily loaded.

For instance, the concept of the polymer chain as a series of twisted loops, or at least containing twisted loops, referred to above (pp. 74f.), produces a heavier bias in favour of some types of sequences and reduces, correspondingly, the number of trials needed to determine which is the one that is likely to be chosen. In any case, whether this hypothesis is true or not, it must be recognized that to enter into an argument on the operations of chance in protein or nucleic-acid sequences is likely to be a very uncertain logical procedure; for the fact is that we know the order of only a single sequence of nucleotides in one natural nucleic acid.

When a sufficiently large series of natural sequences has been worked out, the next step would be, clearly, to determine whether there are any notable recurrences in them – to find, so to speak, the rhyme pattern. These rhyme patterns, if they fit into any order, would reduce enormously the range of possibilities. In any case, all arguments based on chance, apart from their insufficient logical basis, are intrinsically pointless, though they are often advanced in an apparent attempt to prove that life cannot have originated by itself at all.

Alternatives to Chance: Special Creation

For instance, Mora claims: 'that the real objection to the proof that self-ordering is impossible, is to support an alternative', and this alternative, deprived of the 'escape clauses' which Mora himself repudiates, such as life having come from some other part of the Universe, is equivalent in the last resort to asserting the operation of metaphysical, spiritual entities. In some cases this is expressed quite naïvely: it turns to the argument of creation by design by a creator or demiurge (literally, worker for the people). But, as this is still not very fashionable among active scientists, an equivalent half-way house is postulated in the form of a life force, the nature of which is left indefinite and is defined only by its product, life, which is characterised by its inner 'urge' to maintain itself and spread into any possible environment [68].

Now, with both these alternatives – self-ordering or transcendent design – in the field, it is always open to the sceptic to refuse to choose between them. However, in practice, the sceptic can only concentrate on the materialist alternative because this is the only one which gives anything to argue about or experiment with. Much of the arguments ranged against the materialist alternative are against the probability hypothesis of life originating by itself. On the other side, the defender of the spiritual view is always able to proceed from the more familiar to the less familiar. We have been for ages conditioned to the idea that a God could create man in his own image, as a sculptor produced a statue from lifeless matter. This is the old idea of Aristotelian matter and form, a straight technomorphic analogy made acceptable by the wondrous perfection of the artists of early civilizations in their lifelike imitations of living beings. This has made the idea of a creator God intellectually acceptable for millennia. Even more technomorphic is the modeller God, who makes man from clay and animates him by the 'breath of Life' as in Genesis 2, 7:

And the Lord God formed man of the dust of the ground, and breathed into his nostrils the breath of life; and man became a living soul.

Nowadays, people may find this somewhat difficult to believe literally, but still easy to imagine. As long as man was conceived of as directly earth born, or sky born, as in the various Greek or other legends, this provided no essential difficulty, but it is at least two hundred years since this kind of thinking was admissible to scientifically trained minds. Its last appearance was in the legendary *Golem* of Rabbi Löwe of the Court of Rudolf II in seventeenth-century Prague [120].

The concept of evolution propounded by Darwin seemed to put an end to these spiritual imaginations, but it did not take long for the religious-minded to assimilate it as well. All that was necessary was the act of creation of the first organism and a directing hand controlling without interfering with its subsequent evolution, such as Newton conceived, 'Divine intervention to adjust in detail the perturbations of the originally created planetary system', a kind of bowling-alley god who cheated, but not much, as the bowls rolled toward their targets.

Already, however, such hypotheses seemed not only to be less plausible, but also too scientific to capture the whole-hearted magic of the old tradition. It is difficult to imagine a god of any kind occupying himself creating, by some spiritual micro-chemistry, a molecule of deoxyribonucleic acid which enabled the primitive ancestral organism to grow and multiply. The whole hypothesis has now come to its natural end in absurdity.

The last ditch from a structural view is, in fact, never reached, wherever it may stand at any given time. Thus Descartes invoked the pineal gland as the seat of the human eternal soul for no better a reason than that no other use could be found for it at the time. In his essay on *The Passions of the Soul* he writes: 'the part of the body in which the soul exercises its functions immediately is in nowise the heart, nor the whole of the brain, but merely the most inward of all its parts, to wit, a certain very small gland which is situated in the middle of its substance'. His reason for this is that, unlike all other parts of the brain, this gland is single and not double, and hence 'there is no other place in the body where they (our sense impressions) can be thus united unless they are so in this gland.' The gland is now known to be the endocrine control organ, but as long as we can count on finding some part of our picture of the world that cannot be understood, a way can always be found for divine interventions.

Criticisms of Spiritual Explanations of Life

At the time of the Reverend Dr Paley, in his *Evidences for Christianity*, the argument for divine creation and maintenance of the world was more frankly stated, in opposition to Dr Erasmus Darwin's materialist views. Nevertheless, the Senate of Cambridge University, with unconscious irony, set Paley or Logic as subjects for the 'Little Go' Entrance Examination for more than a hundred years. Now that we are embarking on a serious scientific discussion of the question of the origin of life, it is time that these aspects of the question were brought into the open and we were furnished with a more precise, complete and self-consistent account of the spiritual or divine origin of life than any that have been produced as an alternative to the mechanistic one. Such an argument, which may need a propounding of questions capable of answers, and free from logical escape clauses or revelations, should provide us with a clearer path to further scientific advance, even if it does not reach the end.

The arguments about the operation of chance are absolutely general ones and however they are concluded they do not help us in understanding the origin of life. Their only use is to clear away certain explanations that are not explanations. This goes some way to supplying the explanations by default, but it is absolutely necessary, further, to look into the details of all proposed schemes for the origin of life to see where they can be effectively criticized and put out of court. It ought at least to be possible now to check all other explanations of the origin of life to see that they also contain nothing that can be disproved. This may not leave a very large residue, but that residue will be very much more valuable than a number of hypothetical explanations that are intrinsically implausible; in particular they should contain no escape clauses that would apply to any explanation, such as the infinity of space and time in which chance can operate.

To examine such special cases, it is necessary to look at the whole question in the framework of the stages of the origin of life which are, in one sense, far more beyond dispute than the particulars of any stage. Now that it is becoming admissible to assume that life may have arisen by whatever process it did, by natural means or, at any rate, by means in principle knowable by us, we need not be concerned with having to prove that the account of every stage is correct – we cannot do so, in any case. But we should be quite willing to admit ignorance in preference to any set of explanations that cannot be logically proved or tested experimentally. There should be no 'saving the appearances', however useful this process has been in the early stages of the history of science.

Difficulties, some major, needs must remain. Some of these are set out in the thirty-two questions which are appended (Appendix 4), together with the provisional answers to some of them and some indications of how they might be answered. The first set of difficulties touches the very arrangement of the origin of life into stages as indicated in the divisions of the book in Chapters 4, 5 and 6, and the attempt to correlate them in time set out in Chapter 7. It remains to be shown whether these stages are really consecutive stages or are overlapping to such an extent that they really represent modes rather than periods of time. This touches the fundamental problem as to whether the chemical evolution of life actually preceded or was concurrent with the evolution of organisms. There is undoubtedly *some* overlap because, clearly, chemical evolution did not stop when organic or organismal evolution started; it is still going on in a minor way, as witness the biochemical differences of the different species alive today. However, besides these general difficulties, there are specific difficulties applicable to the three principal stages I have outlined: first, that from the formation of simple organic molecules from their cosmic precursors; secondly, the polymerization of such molecules and the evolution of the self-replicative molecular systems, which is now represented by the nucleic-acid-protein process of replication; and, thirdly, the steps between that and the origins of the first organisms and of the first cells.

Stage I

There is no difficulty in principle in forming most of the molecules which we recognize as the basic molecules of life from their inorganic precursors. This has been done now by a very large number of workers in many countries (p. 45). What is interesting, is that not only is it possible to do so, but it also seems that different methods tend to give rise to the same molecules and these molecules are just the ones that occur most often in life, including proteins, the fundamental nitrogen bases of the nucleic acids, and sugars, with a special reference to ribose. The only section of the common types of biological molecules that are not fully represented in the synthetic experiments are those of the fats; in fact, we cannot say yet whether we have any plausible account of the formation of the lipoid sheets which play such a vital part in the later stages of the origin of life.

However, it is clearly not enough to explain the formation of these primitive molecules: one has to explain them in terms of conditions in which they occur and in the likelihood of such conditions existing on a primitive Earth or even on a primitive asteroid. We must check to see if the methods are the same as those we have assumed gave rise to the organic compounds on meteorites. What is still needed is a physical-chemical explanation of the origin of these molecules that suggests the presence of suitable sources and sinks for free energy.

Energy Transfer and the Need for a Fluid Medium

It is here that we have to face a fundamental choice between, on the one hand, conditions that will enable energy to be stored in one place and dissipated in another, which implies a liquid system, and, on the other, a concentration of active molecules so great that there is time for the transfer of this energy to its appropriate recipient before its dissipation in simple heat motion. To meet these conditions would seem to exclude a completely dry locus for the origin of life and make it intrinsically a phenomenon of the hydrosphere, thus excluding from further evolution the carbonaceous materials on asteroids and meteorites. This is a reason why we need not consider seriously the apparent life-forms claimed to exist in the latter (Appendix 2). If they were to prove to be real life-forms, they would point to an origin on some large planet, such as the Earth, which is heavy enough and warm enough to maintain a hydrosphere and then we must face the problem of transport. Life is essentially a product of water, a proposition that would be fully approved by the makers of the creation myths of 10,000 years ago.

Chirality

The molecular character that is most definitely an indicative characteristic of life is that of *chirality*, right or left-handedness, manifesting itself physically in optical rotation. We can observe such optical rotation only in substances made by living creatures, but it must be confessed that the problem of the origin of optical rotation remains from the time of Pasteur the key unsolved problem of detailed biogenesis. To account for it absolutely is extraordinarily difficult, because at our level of knowledge we cannot find any intrinsic difference between right- and left-handed structures. However, as we know it, life is a linked set of reactions and, therefore, their component molecules must depend on fitting their chirality, right- or left-handedness, together. A body of the wrong chirality will not fit and will take a different or no place at all in metabolism. Therefore, we can see at once that if life starts and works, it has to work on a chiral basis as, indeed, the artificial isotactic polymers of Ziegler and Natta do. One could conceive an animate world consisting of two parts, right- and left-handed, but the organisms from these two parts could not react – could not even mate together or eat each other. If such an ambidextrous world existed, it has long since gone out of existence; it may have been a necessary stage, but only at a very primitive stage of life.

It must be admitted that the explanation of chirality still remains one of the most difficult parts of the structural aspects of life to explain. It is quite understandable why Pasteur, as a chemist, made it the basis of his whole theory of biology. We may never be able to explain it because it may be a consequence of one singular event of which the decision between a right- or left-handed molecular structure was determined by chance, and the chirality of all the rest of molecular structures were henceforth thereby determined. If this is the case, we might expect right or left chiralities on the molecular level to occur equally frequently in the different life clones and other life-bearing planets. The alternative assumption, that there is some minute free-energy difference between right- and left-handed forms, possibly of nuclear origin, as the law of non-conservation of parity indicates, would, on the contrary, lead to identical chiralities wherever life was found in the Universe. This question of chirality, though admittedly unanswered, is certainly one of those that can be left over for further observation and experiment: the fact that we cannot solve it now is not sufficient reason for abandoning the search for physical-chemical theories for the origin of life. It may well be that this is a pseudo-difficulty which will turn out to have a quite simple and rather trivial explanation, even though we do not grasp it yet.

There is one other major difficulty which comes between Stage I and Stage II, namely, to decide the mechanism for the formation of the intermediate and larger molecules of organic nature on the Earth. This implies either some effective chemical mechanism for bringing the small reactive molecules together to build larger ones or a physical mechanism for concentration which will make further combinations more likely. I have here chosen the latter of these and proposed concentration by surface adsorption on common minerals of marine clays. However, chemical theories attributing the combination to the presence of soluble reagents with a certain cosmic abundance, mainly cyanogen derivatives, have been put forward by distinguished chemists such as Professors Calvin and Oró who have suggested that not only monomers but polymers can be produced in this way from dilute aqueous solution at low temperatures. I would say at present there is not enough evidence to decide in favour of one or the other of these alternatives and they are not necessarily mutually exclusive; some macromolecules may have come by the adsorption pathway and others by the action of soluble reagents. There remains a third pathway, discussed in Chapter 8, of high-temperature synthesis of amino acids and nitrogen bases, associated with the work of Professor Fox, which I consider, for reasons given there, to be a somewhat improbable method of concentration, but one that would have to be kept in mind. A similar difficulty arises in the case of the coacervate hypothesis, also discussed in Chapter 8, which, although providing an experimentally very probable basis for biochemical reactions, still lacks a plausible explanation of its abiotic origin.

Stage II

It is in the second stage that the major difficulties begin. It must be admitted, particularly in the light of the telling criticisms of Mora [69], that no one has put forward a plausible account of the self-generation of molecular replicative mechanism. There is a fundamental difficulty in providing for the origin of the order of the monomers in biological polymers. It is here that the essentially mathematical and philosophical problems of the mutual dependence on chance and natural selection first arise. It seems to me that these two working together can account for the phenomenon, but this is only my opinion and I can offer no proof. What we have, however, are very intriguing and suggestive hints. We may not know how the play starts but we have clearer and clearer views of the original cast: the organic bases, the phosphates and the amino acids, all of which can be plausibly accounted for from non-biological origins. What we lack still, as mentioned earlier, is a plausible model for an origin of the fats.

Sources of Free Energy

There remains another gap in the second stage of the physical-chemical processes of the origin of life (pp. 70f.), that concerning the distribution of energy in primitive life processes. We know there must have existed both exergonic and endergonic molecular reactions, that is, those requiring energy and those giving it off. What we do not know is how such endergonic reactions are linked with the exergonic in different molecules, because this is what actually happens in existing life. It is by the coupling of these that the physical-chemical aspects of life are maintained. This, again, is a question that can be settled by experiment. We may not know how nature organizes this coupling, but if we manage to find some way of doing it, it will show that it can be done.

The Origin of Replication

The major difficulty in Stage II, however, is the crucial one of the origin of a molecular replication system. I have stated earlier that I consider such replication to be a necessary precursor of the existence of any separate organisms and, therefore, have put forward the rather unpopular view that life existed before organisms; but it is conceivable that this is not the case and that some kind of organism that had no molecular replicative system did actually exist and gave rise to a mechanism of protein and nucleic acid replication production in the course of its existence. I still find this an unacceptable alternative, because without definite molecular reproduction it is very difficult to see what an organism means: if it is merely a piece cut out of an undetermined extension of metabolically active material, it has no *raison d'être* of its own.

At some stage the chemical processes occurring in the primitive seas must have become self-contained. This may be considered to be the actual date of the beginning of life, though it need not have been the same date in all places. The highest probability, it seems to me, is in favour of a primitive form of life starting in one specific place, or a very few such places, and gradually spreading in concentric circles from there. For such regular spread, the absence of violent mass-transporting currents is implied. These proto-organisms need not have been autonomous at the beginning. They existed and could exist only in a general chemically active medium. At a later stage various different centres of activity of different kinds might be picked up and incorporated as, for instance, the proto-chloroplasts responsible for photosynthesis, thus producing a permanently self-containing system dependent only on a continuous input of visible radiation.

At about the same stage other organelles of the type of the mitochondria responsible for oxidation might have been incorporated. Cellular life would then have a poly-genetic origin, would be a kind of necessary hybrid. This does not apply to all life but applies more particularly to the more developed parts of it, the eukaryotids, nucleated organisms with mitosis which are responsible for all the higher forms of life. Looked at in a different way, we might take this point in time, when life ceased to be the using up of previously stored energy and became a continuous process, as the point at which it really began.

None of this, strictly speaking, implies separate organisms, yet it clearly leads up to them. To have an organism implies a boundary and also implies something which differentiates one organism from another, even if they are of the same species. Now, whichever way this question is answered, the fundamental problem is that of finding how the replicating molecular system originated. This involves the solution of two problems which must be taken one after the other. How did such a system first occur and how did it modify itself subsequently? In tackling such problems the sceptics have made it more difficult for themselves by considering mainly the way these are solved in existing life, which is highly sophisticated and complicated, and then proceeding to argue that the solutions of such problems are quite inconceivable and involve fundamental breaches in scientific method.

Now the difficulty, really, is to explain not the sophisticated system of today but any unsophisticated system that might have preceded it, in the way I have tried to outline in Chapter 6. Such argumentation necessarily involves postulation of proto-systems, proto-enzymes, proto-coenzymes and proto-nucleic acids. This in itself is objected to on the grounds that, following Occam's Razor, we have no right to multiply systems without reason. Here I think we have a reason, but the reason only allows us to postulate a system, it does not tell us precisely what system to postulate. Here, again, we must admit that we have to diverge considerably from what has been accepted as scientific method in the past.

Is Biopoesis a Part of Science?

The assertions made are not going to be provable, at least not yet, not until we can make a living system. But does this necessarily, as the sceptics assert, remove all such thinking from the field of science? I think rather that some extension of that field is required, made necessary in trying to explain an origin for any system. We have to find the criteria for reasonable guessing and hope the picture will be filled in. Dr Mora [69] scorns such procedures:

Of course, we may resort to some unprovable argument, just to make us feel better, to have an illusion that we are going to be able to see the solution of the problem. One of these assumptions is that when all the biochemical details are known, maybe everything will make sense and the mosaic will show the picture. However, this type of thinking encourages us to avoid exactly those problems of complexity and interrelatedness that are so characteristic of the living.

Nevertheless, in a negative way this procedure may be justifiable; at any rate it has plenty of precedents in the history of science. It may be that, having accumulated all the biochemical information we can, we still do not see the picture. In that case we have not necessarily wasted our time, we have found out something about biochemistry; in any case we can be quite certain that if we do not accumulate and assimilate the biochemical evidence, we will not see the picture, and in that sense too it has been worth while looking.

But there is more to it than that. The analysis of biochemical processes, combined with the experiments that have been carried out already – and those particularly reported in connection with Stage I, with the formation of the essential biochemical molecules – provide us with a number of hints. Now these hints, even if they do not count as positive evidence, cannot be neglected in any good and comprehensive scientific method. The fact that the essential elements of biochemical synthesis are a limited set of molecules which are produced preferentially by completely abiological and unintentional chemical experiments is in itself a *prima facie* case for their playing a decisive role in the origin of life. We cannot prove that life actually originated in this way, but we can say that there is a strong suspicion that it did: it is a biological case of circumstantial evidence. Such circumstantial evidence is provided by the preferential formation of the key purine, adenine, and by the existence of high-energy phosphorus-containing nucleotides functioning as coenzymes, particularly the predominant adenosine triphosphate (ATP). It is also pointed to by the multiple and detailed similarities to be found between the enzyme proteins, particularly by those containing *tetrapyrrole* groups, with or without transition elements, which are the basis of the cytochromes occurring in every cell and of the oxygen-carrying haemoglobin and the photosynthetic protein chlorophyll. It is not too naïvely hopeful to think that soon a picture will appear in the mosaic; in fact, bits of the picture are appearing already and we have to build on what we know to reach the rest of it.

Another hint, and a very strong one, is the recurrence of reduplications of runs of monomers in polymers. This is the kind of thing we also notice very much in the formation of language and later on in the building of poetry out of the same language: the repetition, not just of an element, but of a whole series of elements in exactly the same order or in the same order with little modification. Another example from human affairs is the evolution of the Chinese ideographic script from a very small number of primitive hieroglyphs combined in a number of different ways.

It should be evident from the discussion so far, that the kind of problem we face in setting up an account of the origin of life or, strictly, of any spontaneous origin, is a function of how much we know about it – and we know very well now what we do not know. For instance, if we knew the order of the nucleotides in any complete amino-acid order which it codes, we should begin to know something. But we should also need to put behind that a knowledge of all the earlier stages of that order, of the simpler nucleotide sequences that preceded it and this I am sure will come out of pursuing the studies of nucleotide and protein sequences in a series of other organisms.

However, this would not excuse us from doing nothing about it until all the sequences are worked out. We must work provisionally on what we know, hoping that when we know a bit more it will become clearer. Nevertheless, it must be admitted that this is not itself a scientific judgement; the economy of pursuing a scientific argument, especially one of such complexity, is that there must be an optimum strategy for discovering things. It may be wrong to rush forward and argue about solutions which we cannot at the time justify, but it may be equally reprehensible to wait and thus hold up the whole process of scientific discovery in advance. There may be a very good intermediate way of proceeding, a strategy of science which will come out of the generalizing 'science of science', but until such a science is systematically studied and evolves general rules, we do well to follow the old scheme of advancing wherever we can and hoping that the other supporting units will come up. This may not be ideal, but it may be the nearest we can get to the genesis of order in an essentially disordered world.

The origin of order has been much discussed in recent years. W.H. Thorpe [111], following largely the work of Elsasser and Polanyi, maintains that biological laws do not at any point contradict those of physics but are such that they can in no sense be deduced from those laws: 'laws governing living systems are, *in essence*, different from those governing non-living systems'. He also suggests that it is conceivable that evolution by natural selection automatically provides purpose or directedness making meaningless the question, 'What is it for?'

He quotes Waddington as saying, 'there is nothing philosophically mysterious about this. But still it would be frivolous to consider it unimpressive.' It is clear that this fundamental argument will not be settled for a long time, reflecting as it does essentially differences in temperament and education between mechanistic and metaphysical biologists.

Molecular Selectivity

Another major difficulty which also occurs in Stage II is that of molecular selectivity. Horowitz [56] put forward the extremely suggestive idea that natural selection applied to molecules in the era of biochemical evolution, just as natural selection applied to organisms in the era of organic evolution. A modification occurring in an enzyme molecule through mutation, he argued, might enable it to catalyse reactions which let the whole organism do without a component that was in short supply. It would consequently be favoured and the original one would disappear, much as mutations were favoured that enabled an organism to live under unfavourable circumstances so as to take the place of an earlier one which could not do so.

Mora [69] has criticised this point of view severely on the ground that it implies the pre-existence of exact reproduction to permit the necessary mutation, and it therefore cannot be used to explain the origin of replicative systems themselves. This argument has some force, but I do not think that it is completely logical. I can see the possibility of reproducibility and mutation coming together *pari passu* in the earlier stages of evolution of biochemical substances.

Molecular Evolution

In this view, reproduction and selection must have grown up together. We know that in existing life the later forms are involved with the earlier right down to the proto-molecules which are already highly complex and sophisticated. The haemoglobin, for instance, of the higher animals is derived with its four tetrapyrrol groups as clear marks of having been evolved from the simpler, single group tetrapyrrols which occur, for instance, in myoglobin. Indeed, Pauling has traced the ancestry of the haemoglobins right to the invertebrates [87]. If the biochemical unit molecules become more complicated with time, traced back they must have been once much less complicated. The question is, how much less complicated can it be to work at all?

This is a question discussed by Haldane [52] in his specification for a simple organism at the Wakulla Springs Conference:

Suppose, then, that we have reduced the amount of RNA needed to specify a protein to the minimum – what protein would be needed? If our culture medium included amino acids, ribose, the four bases, and a source of high-energy phosphate, the following reactions would have to be carried out:

First, formation of nucleotides.

Secondly, coupling of nucleotides to form chains.

Thirdly, combination of amino acids with ATP or some related substance.

Fourthly, coupling of these amino acids to form a peptide chain.

In existing organisms, these reactions are catalyzed by different enzymes. Even in the simplest organisms, it is desirable that an enzyme should not only be efficient but specific, that is to say, should catalyze a limited series of reactions. Otherwise, the control of metabolism would be impossible. I want to suggest that the initial organism may have consisted of one so-called 'gene' of RNA specifying just one enzyme, a very generalized phosphokinase, which could catalyze all the above reactions.

This still remains rather complicated, but all its elements are of the type of small organic molecules which we know experimentally are formed from the simple cosmic gases, and their putting together itself may not be such a complicated business.

In arguments showing that life cannot be produced by chance, much play is made in drawing on the thermo-dynamic argument that life is a system of very low entropy or, let us say, of high order. But, as these critics point out, the highest order is to be found in crystals and if life was produced of itself, it would be in its lowest energy state and be crystalline and, therefore, as we know, not life at all. The normal crystal is a three-dimensional lattice with regular repetitions in all dimensions and, therefore, occupying densely a certain volume and by that not susceptible to change.

Generalized Crystallography

It should be apparent that life could never have been of this sort because the essential feature of reproducibility implies a different kind of order altogether. For a molecule to reproduce itself, a new molecule which is growing bit by bit on the old one must, as it were, feel or know what the old one was like. This it can only do in a very limited way on the surface or growing edge of a crystal face and this limits such growth to mere repetition and to the consequent production of a uniform, regular and hence inert, three-dimensional structure. For similar reasons it cannot do it with a two-dimensional regular structure – the template mechanism does not work. Logically, the only kind of order that is acceptable is a one-dimensional order, a thread molecule.

The general type of a regular one-dimensional order is a helix and Rich [101] has found that such helices as occur in the ribose nucleic acids reproduce themselves even *in vitro* by adding on individual links to the chains.

Much of the argument on the impossibility of the chance formation of life hangs on this very little recognized nature of generalized crystallography (Appendix 3).

Some purely geometrical considerations may go quite far to explain some of the main features of the results of regular chain formation. Every helical system tends, if longer than a certain length, to twist and coil with itself, forming the loops we are so familiar with in the cords of telephone receivers

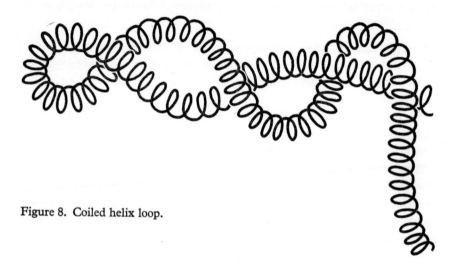

Figure 8. Coiled helix loop.

(figure 8). If the ends of the loops are cut, this arrangement transforms into one of the matching of two different chains, in other words, applied to nucleic acid, into a primitive form of sexual reproduction, one which comes very close to the requirements of making life itself. It is the production of standardized lengths of polypeptide or polynucleotide chain that makes possible the higher level of crystallization that is observed first of all in the oligomolecular proteins like haemoglobin, where a small number of protein molecules of the same or different character meet together to make a larger molecule and, on a larger scale still, the haemocyanins (plate 15). Ultimately this would lead to the whole hierarchy of larger systems, either of the helical tubular nature such as those of the microtubules, or of the spherical kind such as those of the spherical viruses. Other such arrangements and their possibilities for forming even more complicated structures were present in the stage of molecular reproduction which may have preceded that of complete organisms.

Stage III

It is in the third stage that we meet with the greatest difficulties in explaining the origin of life because in this case it is rather a matter of lack of knowledge than lack of imagination. For nearly 130 years the discovery of Schleiden and Schwann, that organisms consist of cells, has been the central doctrine of biology. Consequently, the notion that the cell is the simplest element of living things has sunk very deep. Especially at first, a cell was conceived of very much as a monad, something which performed in certain observable ways, but inside which we could not see very much as to structure. The whole of this attitude is now completely changed due to modern advances in the resolving power of microscopes, particularly the electron microscope and, further, through the basic discovery of Müller that the chromosomes in the cell were the places where the hereditary units postulated from breeding experiments, the genes, had their place. Cytology, indeed, has been a subject in its own right for some fifty years, but the cytology of the optical microscope was really karyology, that is, the study of the nucleus and particularly of the processes of cell division which revealed the chromosomes as isolatable entities.

Multiple Origins of Cells

For a long time, therefore, the passage between the complex molecule and the cell seemed a simple one, the less that could be seen of the cell the easier it was to imagine that it could be very easily formed. Now we are faced with a different and, indeed, almost opposite difficulty. We know too much about the cell and at the same time not enough: too much because we are lost in the complexities we observe there – the multiplicity of organelles and their mutual relations; and not enough, because we do not even know how most of the organelles are generated and how much the intrinsic factors of their growth and multiplication are independent or are controlled by the general nuclear genetic control.

It is by now fairly plain that the cells of existing organisms are themselves extremely sophisticated and elaborate organizations with a long history behind them. What is not plain is exactly what preceded them. One of the major problems that still remains unsolved is how far the cell is a unity or a multiplicity, how far it is a social or colonial kind of organism or how far it is a single organism which has broken up in different organs. It is difficult to reconstitute the simpler ancestral cells. We cannot always use, and in fact may never be able to use, the analogies from the simpler organisms we find today. A long-established comparative method can still, however, be used.

153

The division already alluded to (p. 80) between the two varieties of single cells, the prokaryotes, with separate places for genetic material, and the eukaryotes, with a definite nucleus, the latter forming the cells of all existing animals and plants other than bacteria and a few algae, are other steps in this progress. The indications are that the latter are derived from the former and that the eukaryotes are really composite organisms that have preserved their original parts as organelles.

The simplest free-living organisms we know are the mycoplasmas, already mentioned (p. 89), which contain some of the elements we now find in cells, but very much reduced in size and complexity. The separate parts of the mycoplasmas, which are only some 500 Å in diameter, appear as spheres, possibly organelles, and there seems to be no trace of elaborately folded membranes.

That reduction in size and complexity may be a sign of a primitive nature but, on the other hand, may be a consequence of degeneration due to a parasitic habit. However, these are not strict alternatives; the reduction of a parasitic habit may actually follow the same lines as once occurred in a primitive organism. In the same way, the apparently simplest living things of all, the viruses which were at one time taken to be examples of extremely primitive organisms, now appear as parts of more sophisticated organisms or organelles that have been adapted to the intracellular parasitic habit. This may throw considerable light upon the development not so much of cells but of their organelles. For instance, we find in both the same mechanism of self-assembly of small protein molecules to make very complicated structures.

Bacteriophages

Among these, the most complicated structure is the one which is treated as the simplest example of life in Haldane's original paper of 1929 on the origin of life. At the time of its discovery, d'Herelle's bacteriophage was an almost negative concept, a clear spot on a bacterial plaque inferring a unit living thing. Now it is known as one of the most complex of pre-cellular organizations, containing at least six different quite complicated protein molecules as well as a DNA centre which, as double-stranded DNA, is able to mate and have its genetics traced. Nevertheless, the bacteriophage is not a complete organism because it is quite incapable of generating its own materials for growing and it is obligatory parasitic on bacteria. It is in many ways similar to a multitude of different organelles which have their own separate genetic systems.

It is now becoming evident that even in the development of the bacterio-phages there is a combination of control from the genetic core of the bac-teriophage DNA to that of the cell itself. One of the most characteristic features of life is the extent of control of the different parts so that they can behave in a related way both in the short term and the long term developing systems. Control, indeed, implies the system of signalling and reception of the different parts of the cell, and this is clearly a matter which has an evolution of its own which we are only just beginning to discover.

It should be clear that it is at this point in the genesis of the cell that we must really wait until more of its complex structure is unravelled. All the time we can be learning more about the relations of nuclear and cytoplastic direction of inheritance in whole or in part. At the same time we can develop still further the new auxiliary methods which can be added to those of electron microscopy as, for instance, the diffraction study of electron micro-scope photographs of stained virus which can convey more than the photographs themselves on the structures of viruses [61]. Other electron-microscope techniques that need to be developed are the auto-radiography of sections showing the distribution of particular tracer molecules such as thymine, a good indicator of DNA. By such means the concept of bio-chemistry, which was at one time a matter of studying living tissues on what might be called a butcher or cook scale, can be reduced to a micro-topo-chemistry, in which the fate of each molecule can be traced into the particular part of the cell where it operates, and cells appear as multiple factories with a complex economy of their own. This is so whether they are isolated cells of single-celled organisms of a tissue culture or cells operating in the body of a higher animal or plant.

It is only when such studies have proceeded much further than they have so far that we can begin to study the arguments about the latter stages of the origin of life, namely, the control of reactions, which is often taken as a characteristic of life and even given a mystical importance. Much of histori-cally later biology, though it was the first to be studied, was taken up with the question of control in an organism of many cells, and even inside each organelle in each cell, such as the chloroplasts in which photosynthesis takes place. We are now very much in the same position, in regard to the perfor-mance inside the cell, as the scientists of the seventeenth century when the first microscope revealed the nature of the tissues of the complex organism.

It is in this latest site – we dare not say last refuge – of vitalism that it would be wise to hold our hand and not dogmatize in the absence of evi-dence, which it is only a matter of time before we have. The fact is that we do not know the answers to most of these questions: it is open to us to say either that we shall never know or we will soon know, but the proof of the pudding will be in the eating. All that is certain is that we will never know unless we look.

Summary

This concludes the section of the book that is concerned with pointing out the particular problems that are still the key obstacles to the acceptance of any theory of self-genesis of life. These can be summarized as:
1. The occurrence of sustained metabolism;
2. The origin of chirality;
3. The occurrence of homo- and hetero-polymerization;
4. The replication of order in hetero-polymers;
5. The primacy of indefinitely extended life over the earlier formation of organisms;
6. The first genesis of membranes;
7. The heterogeneous origin of the cell from different organelles and the evolution of their mutual control.

These are not the only but the principal problems to be solved. A more complete list is given in Appendix 4. They would not have been listed as problems if we had the solutions: the most I can indicate here is where to look for the solutions and to express the hope that they will be found. One thing, however, should be clear – the search will go on.

The Future Development of Studies of the Origin of Life

As has been frequently mentioned in this book and, indeed, as is obvious from the following of ideas in it, the study of the origin of life has started seriously only within the last two decades. However, the essential clues were given as far back as the 'twenties with the Oparin-Haldane hypothesis and now, with the increased interest in the subject, we may confidently expect further rapid advances. There is still much unfinished business to be done. Much of it will come from the outer, non-biological side, including much more detailed study of meteorites; and one thing we may expect also in the near future are studies of cosmic dusts that are caught in flight by rockets or satellites, or picked up off the surface of the Moon, an operation which will probably take place well before any attempts to land men there.

It is, however, on the genetic, biochemical and molecular biological side that we may expect the greatest advances. The hypothesis of a genetic code embodied in DNA has still to be proved in detail, and it is highly probable that it will turn out to be far more complex than we have thought so far. We may expect more information from more carefully carried out synthesis of the Miller type and better correlation with the probable conditions existing on the primitive Earth. It was clearly essential at the outset to establish the fact that complex organic compounds could be produced in this way. It will now be necessary, following the work of Oró, to give a complete quantum-chemical analysis of the reactions that give rise to them, particularly in relation to the relative amounts of the different nitrogen bases and sugars that are produced. The role of phosphates has also to be examined much more carefully and correlated with what we know about the occurrence of phosphates in the rocks and oceans. Most workers so far have used metaphosphates, particularly ethylmetaphosphate, as a starting-point, but this seems rather an intrinsically improbable compound and some other more likely one must be looked for. The possibilities of the commonest phosphate mineral, apatite, should be more thoroughly explored; it may have unexpected enzymic properties.

Finally, in respect to the evolution of the cell itself, much more careful studies are necessary, with tracers, ultra-radiography and electron microscope, to elucidate the intra-cellular mechanisms and their genesis. Comparative ultra-cytology is a subject which is only in its infancy. Now most of these studies will take place in any case in the service of medicine and in the search for mineral resources, particularly oil. For the basic geological question as to the abiogenic origin of at least some mineral oils has still to be settled, and it is likely that it will be as a by-product of the search for deeper and deeper oil deposits.

All these, however, are types of studies which are already being carried out. Undoubtedly, though we cannot specify them, many radically new types of studies will also contribute to the same understanding. The essential point here is that the findings of the different sciences should be correlated and consciously brought together to form a clearer and clearer picture of the origin of life. Sooner or later, and the sooner the better, this correlation will have to take a modern form of information storage and retrieval. It is appropriate that for such a new field of study and one which evokes the discovery of new methods to deal with it, recourse be sought by the most complete and novel method of securing the continuous availability of knowledge. But this in itself can only be a beginning. The search for the origin of life must be undertaken in a planned way as a kind of 'combined operation'.

Already the absence of this planning and conscious staff-work is seen in the wild proliferation of papers and ideas on the origin of life, with a bibliography of extreme length and confusion. There have been several congresses already, beginning with that in Moscow in 1957, which had been occupied in discussing the origin of life and at which many important and interesting papers had been presented. What we need now is the establishment of a small group, perhaps of twenty or thirty people of sufficient influence and representative character to plan further work on studies on the origin of life and to ensure that the plans are carried out. This planning, of course, must not be exclusive. It should still be perfectly free for anyone coming new to the subject to put forward his own ideas, and the forum for examining these must be found. But certain researches require to be pursued specially for this object and not only incidentally in the pursuit of some other. At the least such an organization should be able to furnish a complete and up-to-date account of progress in all matters affecting the field of the origin of life.

The theories or speculations on the origin of life, unlike those in pure physics, will need to have at hand or on call masses of apparently irrelevant and unconnected observations. We may therefore expect with some confidence that, as more of these accumulate and their explanations are pushed further, a greater and greater knowledge of the origin of life, and consequently of its essential nature, will be forthcoming. So far we have only had the statement of the problem and some tentative solutions. These solutions may be confirmed or put in question and, certainly, new problems will arise, but in the solution of these the understanding of the world in which we live will be very largely increased. What this has meant already in the general fields of science and philosophy is discussed in the next chapter.

Chapter 10

The Influence on Contemporary Thought of the Discussions on the Origin of Life

We have been told so often and on such tremendous authority as to seem to put it beyond question, that the essence of things must remain forever hidden from us; that we must stand forever outside nature, like children with their noses pressed against the glass, able to look in, but unable to enter. This concept of our origins encourages another view of the matter. We are not looking into the universe from outside. We are looking at it from inside. Its history is our history; its stuff, our stuff. From that realization we can take some assurance that what we see is real.

G.WALD [118]

THE growing acceptance of rational accounts of the origin of life as a regular part of scientific thought is a symptom and a portent at the same time of the growth of modern science and of its all-inclusive character. This is irrespective of the particular forms which these accounts take. The forms, as we have seen, have greatly changed in the last few years and are going to change further, but the essential fact here is that the *idea* of a rational and explicable account of the origin of life of any form at all is bound to have a profound effect on life and thought. Inevitably, it recalls the controversies of a hundred years ago about the origin of species. But, whereas Darwin brought together only the sciences of biology and geology in tracing the origin of animals and plants – including man – from some hypothetical primitive organism, the new synthesis goes much further and involves chemistry and astronomy as well: in fact, the whole range of modern science. As such it is a characteristic product of the new trend in the development of science – the convergent generalizing trend that is replacing the divergent and specializing trend of the nineteenth century with its various subjects separated by thought-proof partitions. It is, however, unlikely for some time to come to have anything like the popular impact of *The Origin of Species*, for the matters that occupied Darwin were essentially familiar to his readers. He dealt with the forms and lives of animals and plants and found a credible explanation of their likenesses and differences.

Man's Views of the World

Discussions on the origin of life itself must move in far less familiar territory for some time to come. Until notions such as relativity and the quantum chemical theory become commonplaces of education, most of the chapters of the origin of life must remain abstruse and unfamiliar. Yet their impact on the whole framework of human thought is indeed already, in its early stages, of decisive import. Basically, man's social view of the world he lives in has not changed for the 8,000-odd years of civilization. Yet points of view and theories certainly have changed.

For the irrational, mythical, god- and devil-ruled world of early civilization, the Greeks substituted an orderly world ruled by law and fate. But the substitution from the wills of gods to the almost equally arbitrary rule of necessity changed little. The complete and all-inclusive Christian cosmology from creation to the final destruction of the world was at first a return to the earlier views, though it was reconciled to the Greek philosophy in the great Thomist *Summa*, which effected a synthesis of Aristotelian, Mohammedan and Christian views. In principle, this should have sufficed: it did not matter what picture there was of the world if everyone agreed on it; but such universal agreement could never in fact be reached, there were too many heretics and it was impossible always to suppress them. Nevertheless, in the Middle Ages, most educated people all over the world accepted for a while a single world picture whose influence spread as far as India and China. With the Renaissance, the point of view changed again, away from an Earth-and-Man-centred Universe to one still ruled by law, but by a universal law spread over wide extremities of space. Nevertheless, everything on Earth was destined to remain constant in spite of its violent but accepted variations – the seasons, storms and disorders of the elements – and the world of nature was a familiar world. It required looking at, putting in order, cataloguing, using reasonable categories – that was all there was in the programme of natural history.

Darwin, a hundred years ago, began to change all this again: time and history entered nature; as in the social world of machines and democracy, there was progress and evolution. The notion of the necessity of science as a means of changing nature for man's benefit – itself quite an old idea – began to achieve the reality of accepted fact.

Life in the Universe

With the twentieth century, the place of current, terrestrial life in the Universe is beginning to appear. The advances of biochemistry and of molecular biology now make it almost but not quite certain that life on this Earth now is a single phenomenon. Not only, as Darwin proposed, are all organisms genetically related but, also, the very molecules out of which they are built are based on the patterns of the original small abiogenic molecules that were found in the primitive soup or even – and this seems most likely – on those of polymers that these molecules gave rise to in the second stage where the critical process of molecular replication first appeared.

These arguments strictly apply only to the kind of life that we are actually aware of, the particular life we call terrestrial. We may yet find on other planets, schemes of life which are different, but probably only in the detail of their chemical reactions, not in the essentials of the types of process or in the chemical elements that are involved in them. The precise mechanism of photosynthesis, for instance, may be different on Mars from what it is on Earth. (Now these views have been controverted, but I think it is not a point worth arguing, for the matter will be indubitably settled when we are able to examine actual examples of these extra-terrestrial lives – a task already in hand at vast expense.)

A Plurality of Lifes

My own assumption, for the present, is that we may consider life on each planet to be separated from life on other planets by almost impassable gulfs. This is a gulf of an entirely different order from that which separates organized beings from those on other islands or continents on Earth. It might, however, be taken to be reasonably analogous to, as it were, a clone, a group of related organisms covering the whole planet and forming its biosphere. On different planets, therefore, there might be several such clones developed at different absolute times but possibly in parallel as far as stages are concerned (Chapter 8).

The unity of every clone of living matter is reinforced by referring to a great variety of individual species of organisms, now for the most part grouped together in metazoic and metaphytic organisms, many-celled animals and plants. This may appear to us a necessary consequence of life, because we know it in the example we have here on Earth. It is not beyond the imagination, however, to have several stages of such comings together, such as we have seen already on Earth with the development of society, particularly with the single human society which seems to be taking over the

M

responsibility, so to speak, for the life of all other species. They are allowed to exist as some are so useful to man. However, the unity of human society is of a lower order of unity, even if of a higher order of complexity, than that of the individual animal or plant.

The unity of the individual larger animals, though not in the same way as the larger plants, is maintained by the evolution of internal communication systems. Those common to plants and animals take the form of transport of specific chemicals or hormones. These are responsible for the so-called vegetative properties of animals and the growth of plants. Such chemical communication systems, however, are not sufficiently fast for any animals higher than the sponges, which are really colonies of single cells.

Vegetative and Animal Life: Communication

Where movement has to occur, sensation must accompany it to direct it, as is already observable in jelly-fish. This, in a sense, is the basis for the individuality of an organism, although it is not absolute except in the highest organisms, and not even in all the vertebrates where, even in man, some of the nerve system can rebuild itself by regeneration. The presence of a nervous system, however, makes the death of an animal almost inevitable, for once this system is destroyed or damaged beyond repair the animal becomes virtually a vegetable and has to be sustained by outside help.

Nevertheless, if the individual higher animal is doomed to death by its very complexity, the social animals – and man in particular – achieve a practical immortality through their means of communicating with each other and thus of creating a lasting tradition. The tradition itself may be actually built in genetically, as in the social insects, who work by instinct, or as in the evolution of bird song; while in human societies it may be continually modified and modifiable and generate various means for maintaining itself, in particular the mechanisms of speech and writing.

The Unquestioning Acceptance of Life as Natural

Despite the enormous changes brought about by the advance of science in man's understanding of his place in the Universe, man's attitude to nature and his mode of living in it have changed far less. The basic problems of life and death were not answered and, in fact, there was no serious attempt to answer them because they were not seen as problems at all – they were natural. Birth and death, eating and sleeping, even perhaps thinking, were completely taken for granted; they were just parts of the human condition to which all must bow and find the best accommodation they could.

Men must endure
Their going hence, even as their coming hither;
Ripeness is all.

Edgar speaks for Shakespeare.

But now that the old essential biochemical and historical framework for life, as it has been known and experienced and even partly understood for centuries, is no longer with us, we find that these assumptions are potentially threatened, not only for man but for all of nature. If science has not shown us a way of good living for all, it has opened up the prospect of universal death, not only for the whole of the human species but for all live things on Earth. To avoid this fate we must take thought; but we must do so also to avoid other consequences, wished for or not, of the understanding that science gives to the human race. We have, for instance, to prevent the deaths of hundreds of millions of children all over the world which, nevertheless, are now becoming inevitable, because economically and politically the governing classes in wealthy countries cannot face the necessity of putting them in the way of providing adequate means of life for themselves. This means much more ample supplies than those which the traditional but hopelessly inefficient methods of agriculture and industry over most of the world are able to provide.

In fact, we will have to give up taking things for granted, even the apparently simple things. We have to learn to understand nature and not merely observe it and endure what it imposes on us. Stupidity, from being an amiable individual defect, has become a social crime. These are some of the confused and multiple motives for the investigations which have come together to form our present elementary and limited understanding of the origins of life in the Universe.

The Need to Study the Origin of Life

The major practical reason for studying the origin of life is that we cannot understand current life without this study and, if we cannot understand it, we cannot control it. We need to study the origin of life in order to make sense of life itself, to see its possibilities and its limitations and, hence, see how to promote the one and overcome the other. In a broader sense, the study of its origins is a further attempt to get meaning out of life. Many forms of meaning have been given to life from earliest times, but they have progressively been found more and more fallacious and, hence, ultimately untenable. Right up to the Middle Ages and beyond, the purpose of life in the universal scheme was supposed to be known – it was an article of faith.

Different men in different civilizations had given different answers to this, but they resembled each other sufficiently to be considered variants of one answer. The easiest answer of all was that life had a meaning in terms of a plan of a provident all-wise and all-powerful god. God's will must be done and, if it was difficult to understand precisely what was God's will, different answers about it were permissible. But only one of these answers could be right. It was not given to many to know which it was, only to true believers.

This central core of belief has been gradually eroded since the scientific revolution in the seventeenth century. Yet, even in the minds of those who have, usually unwittingly, destroyed this or that bastion of accepted faith, it has persisted. Paradoxically, the more it is attacked, the more firmly do human minds cling to it. Hence the resistance to further investigations that would seem finally to put an end to such an interpretation of the Universe. Although the resistance to new ideas is not as fierce as it was in the days of Copernicus or even of Darwin, it still exists. Yet what has been found out already about possible origins of life is enough to shake accepted bases of belief more fundamentally than any of the discoveries of the past. Schematically, at least, the entire structure of the Universe, in all its interactions in space and time, are beginning to come clear to us, and after this discovery nothing can be the same.

Myths of the origin and fate of man have been demanded and provided since the dawn of history, but nothing that is still satisfying at the same time to the head and the heart has been provided. Faith has been called in on one side to remedy the defects of observation and reason, *fides praestat supplementum sensuum defectui*. On the other side, what has passed for a purely scientific picture of the Universe, has now come to appear as particularly senseless, dry and unsatisfying. The echoes of Pascal's cry 'le silence de ces vastes espaces m'effraie' are still ringing. Now, at last, the whole story is beginning to make sense, and doing so not just in the sense of the 'consolations of philosophy' but in practical ways of ending man's troubles and increasing his capacities.

The New Meanings of Life

Much of this new understanding and new perspective is due to the breakthrough in the understanding of life which occurred in the middle of this century. What we are discovering is far more complex and far-reaching than that of the behaviour of light and fundamental particles which were made at its beginning. Thirty years ago, N. W. Pirie wrote his iconoclastic essay 'The meaninglessness of the terms "life" and "living"' [91]. Though he himself may feel the same today, most scientists are more willing to look into the questions which he had declared impossible to answer – and some even claim to have answered them. The answer they are finding is effectively a compromise. Life is not an assembly of mechanical or chemical interactions, but is found to have a quality of its own, and those who dislike the very notion of quality and reject it from the world of science, now find satisfaction that the qualities of life are explainable both in structural and evolutionary terms.

The work of the biochemists and later of the molecular biologists has shown how the appearances of life are biological and scientific consequences of the determination of intimate structures down to molecular and atomic level. They are substances and structures which are specifically suited to their functions. These molecules, however complicated, are very limited in number compared with that of all the molecules that could be made from the same atoms arranged in different ways. They are apparently selected for the purpose. We are beginning to know how life works, but until we have the complementary knowledge of how it came to be like it is, some can still fall back on wishful thinking and imagine it as part of some great design, made and carried out by some divine artificer. Instead of this, the new knowledge of how the molecular mechanisms of the main elements of reproduction took form in the first place, is completing the work of molecular biologists in realizing how the functions have been carried out in natural systems throughout the whole of cosmic history.

The Code of the Cryptogram of Life is Beginning to Break

Now, the molecular biologists, biochemists, biophysicists and geneticists have contributed, as I hope I have shown, to building up such a hypothetical historical picture of origins of life from cosmic dust and gas, through the self-reproduction of molecules to the formation of organisms. Whatever the appearance of the picture in detail and whatever logical difficulties it presents, it is still an enormous advance in human understanding to be able to present a picture at all. Life is beginning to cease to be a mystery and becoming practically a cryptogram, a puzzle, a code that can be broken, a working model that sooner or later can be made.

While removing most of the mysteries of life, it has not reduced in the minds of the scientific biologists of today any of the appreciation of its complexity and its beauty. Indeed, these are likely to be increased by the addition of new knowledge and the vision of new things hitherto kept in the dark. Inevitably, the gulf between the organic and the inorganic now seems to be wider than ever appeared before, but it is no longer seen as a difference of principle or nature, rather is it seen as a difference in complexity and time. Every cell and still more every organism is as complex as the most complex machine built by man and as old as any rock found on earth. This is far from crude materialism as it is from mystical vitalism. The key to it is seen to be the persistence of precise reproduction for millions of years, modified by slight and infrequent imprecisions, the mutations, which give us the varieties of life, including its successes and its failures, and ultimately build up, with the operation of natural selection, the full scheme of organic evolution.

History, Faith and Piety

The kind of knowledge of the Universe which we are now approaching is one in which history plays a central role and is particularly destructive to some of the basic attitudes which have persisted all through human social history, particularly those of faith and piety: faith, in the sense of the actual virtue of believing things for which there is no evidence:

> Now faith is the substance of things hoped for, the evidence of things not seen.
> Hebrews 11, 1

(Admittedly pure wishful thinking.)

Piety, in the sense of doing things just because they were done before. It is not just that these attitudes will be or will have to be violently combated (that would be a very difficult task considering the amount of vested interests and institutions they are linked with) but, rather, that in the world of belief the old faiths will become essentially unintelligible if not ridiculous and many of the activities they inspire will be seen to be trivial if not dangerous, such as interference with population control.

We see now that in an evolutionary world a living organism or some interpretable relic of it, such as a skeleton or shell, is naturally more than the material of which it is composed, because it carries with it, by implication, evidence of a complicated ancestry dating right back to the beginning of life. The great discovery of molecular biology is that the notion of reproduction, limited through all these centuries to the reproduction by organisms themselves, now extends to the most microscopical parts of the structure of organisms and to their most minute actions. Every motion of every animal, for instance, from the smallest to the largest, relies on the reaction of one single type of molecule, a tripartite unit, adenosine triphosphate (ATP), in which a nitrogenous base, adenine, is linked to a sugar to make adenosine and, in turn, to three metaphosphate radicals. Its existence implies also the existence of a number of enzymes, each different and each precisely built up of some twenty amino acids that are placed in the correct order, without which they would function either badly or not at all, by specifically ordered nucleic-acid polymers which, in turn, come from an almost precisely reproducible basic stock of ordered nucleotides. The same precision is demonstrable on the wing of a bird or on the scales of an insect. The animate world is transitory in every structure as in every action, but fixed by inbuilt molecular patterns which are thousands of millions of years old.

In other words, all the patterns of life are not planned, as we plan a machine or a work of art, on the basis of an idea or a model; but *prescribed* along various operational prescriptions which do not involve knowledge of the final product. This is the form which modern molecular biology has given to the 'final causes' of Aristotelian biology.

The Molecular Immanence of Life

What the studies of the origin of life are adding to this picture is just beginning to be worked out. The comparative knowledge of the structures of the sequence of amino acids in protein molecules has been traced, for instance, in the haemoglobins all the way from man to fish: we need to develop the newly recognized discipline of chemical paleo-genetics (p. 147). Ultimately, we should be able to trace the structures of enzymes and coenzymes right back to their first predecessors, the self-producing molecules ultimately derived from abiotic combinations of the atoms in the Sun and combined together by the action of its radiations. This corresponds philosophically to an *immanent* theory of the construction of objects and beings, their precise nature depending, in the last resort, on the qualities and properties of the atoms themselves and this, in turn, through the quantum chemical theory, on the properties of pure numbers.

Sir Walter Raleigh had posed the question: 'Why blood is red and why the grass is green are mysteries that none can reach unto.' This is precisely where modern quantum theory is reaching. The redness of the blood, for instance, is written into the molecule of haemin; this is to be found not only in the blood of vertebrates, but also in the larvae of some flies, the blood-worms in stagnant pools, and in the nitrogen-fixing nodules in the roots of peas. In all these cases the colour is effectively due to the quantum states of the complex, partially filled electronic shells of ferric iron as modified by the porphin groups in which it is placed. Electron shells have existed as such ever since the first iron atoms were built inside a primitive supernova, and are potentially determined in mathematical quantum theory.

A Definition of Life

All these considerations lead us to what may now be accepted as a provisional, though I hope improved, definition of life:

> *Life is a partial, continuous, progressive, multiform and conditionally interactive, self-realization of the potentialities of atomic electron states.*

This immanent definition of life requires more detailed explanation of the terms used. It covers only a *partial* realization of some of the potentialities of atomic states, for only a very few of the potentialities are, in fact, used in terrestrial life. More might be if the evolution of life went on longer, less if it were cut short, most may never be realized. The term *continuous* implies the basic continuity at least of terrestrial life, every organism proceeding from another organism, for the most part with little change. The term *progressive* implies that the continuity of life is being broken all the time at rather wide intervals by the appearance of new forms of species which, by natural selection, represent a progress on the forms that were there before. This use of the term 'progressive' does not, of course, imply any kind of moral judgement. What it does imply is that the new forms are derived from the old and usually occupy places in the general scheme of life which were before unoccupied. 'Progressive' in this sense includes every form of predation and parasitism. However, its real significance is in the appearance of new methods of internal and external *communication* with greater adaptation to and conquest of the environment. The term *multiform* implies the simultaneous existence at any time of a very large range of species modified only by the appearance of new and the extinction of old. I have called *conditionally inter-active* that which occurs in ecology. The old and new forms between them make up sets of definite ecologies so that each form exists in the environment produced by itself and by other forms. The term *self-realization* implies the working out of each form or individual as determined by its genetic composition in relation to the environment in which it finds itself. This, indeed, may be a 'self-producing' environment, as in social animals and, most particularly, in human society. The final phrase, the *potentialities* of electronic and atomic states, taken in conjunction with the first word, *partial*, points to the dependence of life ultimately on the atoms from which the basic molecules of living organisms were formed. These, in turn, depend on the frequency of occurrence and the distribution of the nuclei of these atoms on the parent Sun or planet Earth. Though there are exceptions for trace atoms like vanadium, the main structure of life is based on the commonest of the cosmic elements which make up the greater number of molecules in living substances. And this applies, too, to the basic molecules, especially when favoured singularities lead to their stability as, for instance, in the molecule of adenine [97].

The Chemical Evolution of Life

This part of the definition effectively implies the chemical evolution of life. The condition for using any particular electronic state is ruled by the history of that particular molecule and of all its predecessors in molecular evolution. That is why most of the potentialities never get used at all.

The central idea of the immanence of life was first brought out in 1913 in L. J. Henderson's book, *The Fitness of the Environment* [54]. There he discussed why the properties of certain molecules such as those of water and carbon dioxide made them eminently suitable for the occurence of the metabolism of life. He seems to have thought of this as *evidence* for the pre-existence of a master plan of nature, but all the instances he cites could be taken in the modern sense contrariwise, as evidence that life had to make do with what it had, for if it had failed to do so it would not be there at all. Most creative vitalist and teleological views of life have implications that take them out of science and out of good sense altogether. In order to conceive and to execute a plan as a human being would do, or a god made in his image, both the material and the mode of work on it must be known beforehand, with no material or mental model of how this knowing and making can have occurred. It is postulated by the vitalists that the assumption of one bit of nonsense effectually implies all the other nonsense that may have been thought of. Hypothesis has to be piled on hypothesis, each with less support and more improbability. When the Marquise du Deffand was asked, in the eighteenth century, how she explained the miracle by which Saint Denis, after his execution, walked six miles carrying his head in his hand, she wrote to d'Alembert: 'The distance doesn't matter; it is only the first step that counts'.

However, vitalist explanations are often put forward honestly, without the realization that they imply theological constructs which are becoming more and more difficult to sustain. The life force is a non-material force by definition. It must therefore work by some kind of spiritual intuition. This is often taken to imply the action and knowledge of supernatural beings. Even without invoking a god, it is included in the *archaei* of Theophrastus Paracelsus, spiritual chemical agents of digestion which turned out in the end to be no more complex than enzymes, but to imply life very definitely. Sooner or later both metaphysical and theistic explanations of life will be seen to be useless and essentially absurd.

The Primacy of Numbers

The definition of life just discussed may well seem to be a return to the first Pythagorean-Platonic idea of the primacy of numbers; hypothetically it may be possible for a perfect mathematician to deduce the forms and functions of living things from the properties of the numbers themselves, and even perhaps a machine might carry out this process. But long before this, our gropings are helped and, in fact, made possible at all, by the examination of the structures and behaviours of actual objects, including living organisms. Even this will not be quick or easy. So far it has taken groups of intelligent and well-equipped crystallographers and molecular biologists twenty-five years to elucidate, in part, the structure of *one* biologically active molecule – the enzyme ribonuclease. And with nucleic acids it will be an even more difficult process; it has taken some forty man-years to elucidate the structure of one small nucleic acid molecule which codes for the amino acid alanine. Yet millions of these molecules are constructed with precisely the same form and exist in every cell of every organism – plant or animal. A partial working out of the practical problems of molecular structure of life must for a long time precede any theoretical analysis of what they may be.

The Meaning of Life and Living

We are now in a position to specify more accurately the meaning of the terms 'life' and 'living' than anyone could have been at the time Pirie wrote his celebrated essay (pp.161 f.). That does not mean yet that we can be precise. Some of the ambiguity of the position depends on what we consider to be the criterion for life. This cannot be an intrinsic limitation; it is essentially arbitrary and conventional. Here we must draw a line somewhere between the stages in the hypothetical scheme given here for the origin of life, that is, somewhere between the primitive soup with its molecules of fairly simple organic compounds, such as nitrogenous bases, already pointing in the direction of life, and the first self-sufficient cell. It would seem logical to draw this line at the end of the second stage, that is, with the emergence of the nucleic-acid-directed protein molecule synthesis; in other words, with the emergence of the precise replication of molecules. Some might like to put it further back with the first polymerization of nucleotides and amino acids: others, further forward with the eobionts or the coacervates of Oparin; others, still, with the first appearance of photosynthesis with visible light. Such differences are, for the moment, not of great importance. The point at which we define something as alive, or describe some object as living, can be fixed quite arbitrarily in the first place in a sequence of development. I choose to consider something as alive now if it contains a self-reproducing molecular system such as that of the nucleic acids and protein production mechanism in an active form or, preferably, activated by some non-living or living stimulus. The latter part of the preceding definition of life is put in to include among the living, the viruses, which contain in their nucleic acid part the directive mechanism. The synthesis of their protein will require all the other elements of that synthesis, including the energy, to be provided by the host which is parasitized by them.

The Unliving and the Dead

Here we must distinguish between non-living forms, those which are simply inorganic, abiotic, in origin and do not owe anything of their form to the action of the living organism, and the dead, which are parts of the formerly living things without the activity or the possible activity of the nucleic-acid-protein cycle, the molecular reproductive cycle. By such a definition both wood and coal are dead and so would be limestone insofar as it is made out of actual former living shellfish, but not limestone derived from inorganic volcanic calcareous deposits.

It would seem that this immanent definition might be taken to imply a completely deterministic picture of life, but on examination this will be found to be very far from the case. I think, however, it touches very deeply the whole question of scientific law and scientific development. The so-called laws of science were discovered one by one in the course of the examination of all aspects of nature, not only of the numerical aspects. We have, for instance, the exact sciences, the biological sciences and the social sciences, with their own laws which apply only to their own fields. The new, unitary picture of science does not recognize these distinctions or, rather, recognizes them not as reflecting the different parts of nature but as the different stages of man's appreciation of the understanding of nature. These stages also may have an objective reality – I am referring to concrete existences in organisms of nerve mechanisms or thoughts which have no relevance until the necessary structures and functions have evolved.

Explanations in terms of creator gods or life forces are soon seen to be essentially tautological expressions of ignorance. In this sense laws can always be taken as comprehensible and even describable, but on further examination it appears that the terms of the descriptions are simple analogies and tell nothing new.

The Defects of Mechanistic Materialism

The basic defect of mechanistic explanations in biology is that they effectively ignore the time factor. They treat the objects studied, whether they be cells, organisms or societies, as different entities, each to be explained by its own appropriate laws: but these laws put together do not amount to a system. That can only appear from the emergence of the law from previous law or, rather, from a system which obeyed a previous law as made clear by an evolutionary theory. It does not matter whether this theory is complete or absolutely correct in detail. Such intuitions as that of Engels: 'Life is the mode of motion of albumens', still holds, even though we are getting to know far more about proteins, and their genesis from the nucleic-acid-protein cycle, with its ever more elaborate details. But the law at any stage must apply to the structure which gives it reality and, thus, can only come into existence with those structures. The biological law has no meaning without the system which gave it birth. The laws of animal motion, again, fail to materialize for organisms which have no spontaneous motion of their own. The laws of biochemistry, the properties of antigens and antibodies, imply the existence of a metabolizing entity ultimately cellular. The laws of heredity imply the existence of the modification of DNA and RNA structures.

All through the story we have to consider the process of self-generation from an earlier stage, going back to the initial self-generation of the first organic molecules from the cosmic particles. It is not a one-way development – there are back reactions. The presence of life itself modifies the environment, and sometimes in a completely drastic way such as that of altering the atmosphere by blocking the ultra-violet light of the Sun through the production of ozone from plant-liberated oxygen. Much of the later stages of life are predominantly governed by this biologically created environment, more so now than at any time, when human societies have come into it with their conscious interference, effected more and more through science. Under the guidance of Marxist dialectic, these ideas have become more and more apparent, but Marxist thought is not necessary to understand them and certainly not necessary at all to justify them. They are justified by their correspondence to observation and to use.

172

Problems of Life and Death

Many of the problems that have concerned mankind ever since his social emergence and long antecedent to civilization, are implicitly problems about the origin of life. Such problems as the elementary ones of life and death itself, and the more sophisticated ones about supernatural and divine governance of the Universe, are now expressed in the form of: 'Has the Universe a purpose?' or 'Are mind and matter related?' or 'What are mind and matter conceived of absolutely in themselves?' Whatever the abstraction or sophistication given to them, they can now be seen to contain an implicit term, the nature of life. To formulate such questions we necessarily take life for granted and imply, in the first place, the presence of a thinking being, then a thinking human being and then a hypothetical divine thinking being. We have so long been accustomed to thinking in these terms that we never seem to be making any assumptions at all but simply restate commonsense, accepted opinions. Looked at more closely, the picture of perception and action has always referred to a perceiving and acting *subject*, not necessarily a man but at least an animal. Natural philosophy has been built round similar concepts such as that of knowledge and will, with the implications of a neuronic system centred on a single brain.

We shall be coming to regard the whole of past philosophy as well as the whole of past science, particularly biological science, as representing the best effort that can be made with the knowledge available at various times to interpret macroscopic phenomena, whether physical or social, in terms of entities implied in the phenomena themselves, and going no further because it is impossible to go further without more knowledge. But it is precisely that knowledge which is now accumulating in step with the increased resolving power of instruments and the developments in chemical and physical theory. *The region of the mysterious is rapidly shrinking.* Enough is known, at any rate, to know that the old explanations cannot possibly be true. The field of ultimate relevance has been changed and if it is changed again – as it certainly will be – it will never revert to its former state. The unitary picture of life as a process, beginning in the distant period of cosmic evolution and unfinished at present anywhere, is a new background or theatre on which all philosophy must be based.

It is not my purpose here to enter into the discussion of these deep problems (Chapter 9), but only to point out that when they are discussed in the future, the relevant portion of this physical and chemical background of life must be taken into account. Any solution that does not do so is implicitly condemned as inadequate and even circular. More cannot be got out of the argument than was put into it.

Rewriting All Science

All this means a vast rewriting of the bases of science and human thought. Perhaps it is premature to speak of it now, partly because such efforts normally require a generation or more of thinking and discussion, but also because we are at present in the critical stage of discovery of the actual facts of the origin of the mechanism of life, even if the basic intuition of coded molecular reproduction which underlies, not only organismal reproduction but even normal metabolism, is in question. That question is not, however, a critical one: it is concerned with the continual refinement of pictures already guessed at on inadequate evidence. We are in one of the periods described by Kuhn in his book, *The structure of scientific revolutions* [62] as a change of paradigm, and certainly in the greatest yet in the history of science.

In such changes, the most active minds are concerned with the discovery of the facts that justify the change and only later with the erecting of an orderly scheme for an alternative view. Yet there always have been some who have seen the implications before the full picture in its scientific form emerges. Thus, Giordano Bruno saw the implications of Copernicus's abandonment of the Earth-centred Universe with its closed spheres, and the opening up of a possible plurality of worlds and what that meant to a revealed scheme of salvation strictly limited in time and space. Indeed, he had died for this belief even before Galileo had made the scheme scientifically respectable. So, in the present transformation, giving an enlarged picture of the origin of life, it is difficult to speculate on its implications before it is by any means complete.

Generation and Corruption

With our new definitions in mind, we can re-examine the old discussions about life as set out by Aristotle. Aristotle's concept of generation can now be seen to refer to the normal reproduction of an organism, sexually or asexually, from an ovum or an egg derived from one or two parental cells. This generation is now seen as a complete process but as one composed of many stages. In the first stages, what we call embryonic, the new organism is more or less in contact with its maternal organism, but only for nutritional or protective purposes. It is autonomous as far as its growth and differentation is concerned and, at some stage or another, rather indefinite; it may acquire the internal organization that separates it out as an individual and enables it to evolve its own organismal activities and the direction of its own nucleic-acid mechanisms.

Slight variations in the order of the nucleotides in this may lead to changes from the parental type; it may be advantageous, in which case it is more likely to establish itself as a new variety or a new species, or not, in which case it will die out. The extent of life of the organism as a whole depends to what extent it is individualized: highly in the case of motile animals, less so in the case of colonial animals like corals, and hardly at all in many vegetable species.

Corruption, as the antithesis of generation, is also seen to be a complex process. In one sense it is universal and continuous. In practically all organisms, certain cells are regularly separated off and actually die. Red blood cells have an average life of some six months. The total death of a complex organism, however, means an irrecoverable suspension of the overall collective metabolism of the organism; in high organisms, the cessation of the heart or breath.

Some ambiguity arises from the word 'irrecoverable', for this depends on the efficacy and immediacy of the methods of recuperation used, which may be continuously improved. Despite these, clinical death, as it is called, applies strictly only to the organism and not to its component organs or cells; they survive for a longer or shorter period deprived of their regular supply of blood and nutriment. But merely cellular survival would be deemed by Aristotelians – and correctly deemed – as the corruption of the organisms as a whole, and its surviving cells, being no longer capable of co-ordinate action, fall a prey to their own internal enzymes and to the invasion from outside of bacteria and other organisms.

It is these phenomena that serve in Aristotle's thinking to renew the whole fabric of the Earth and to start new chains of generation and life. While he was not correct in his assumption that life arises directly from the products of corruption, it is certainly ecologically true that it arises indirectly from them. How then, in consequence, are we to regard the fatalities of birth and death ? Birth, or, rather, conception leading to the growing up of a new organism, is nearly always a net gain for life in the Universe, representing at its lowest level a vast addition of information and the possibility of more information from the elements or simple compounds of which the new being is built.

Massacre of the Innocents

For most organisms, it is a necessary part of the ecology of life that most young are doomed to an early death; only one in a hundred, a thousand or a million actually survive to adult life. In fact, at least in the sea, it is the young that furnish much of the food for the adults. Involuntary in-fanticide is the necessary fate of most of the young of many species. This has been, over the whole of evolutionary history, one of the bases of the ecology of both sea and land. Much of the plankton, the zooplankton particu-larly, is composed of the eggs and embryos of adult, larger marine animals. Many predators on land live largely on the young of herbivores who are easily captured and killed. This overabundance of generation also occurs, in a different sense, in the plant world, where seeds and fruits are effectively produced in overwhelming numbers so that in the general slaughter or decay at least one survives.

A series of recent discoveries has shown that the survival of human civilization in the face of natural disaster and human predatoriness has been due to agriculture, and to this day human beings live very largely on their field plants, carefully collected and bred, on their roots, leaves and, most of all, on their seeds. But we may say that though man does not live by bread alone, it is on seed grains, the size and yield of which has been vastly in-creased by selection, that the whole human race still exists. Without wheat, maize or rice, human beings would have a hard time of it.

In the various stages of organic evolution many ways out of this general massacre of the innocents have been found: by restricting the number of young born and ensuring that each one would be better cared for by bring-ing the young forth alive from the bodies of their mothers or by careful preservation of large eggs. In such ways the massive death of millions of young are prevented and, in the higher animals, the fatherly care by parents of their children – in the birds, for instance – not only allows for more of the family to survive but also provides a link through which the cultural patterns of life can be passed on.

The Origin of Societies

The same ecological considerations are now seen to apply to the human race. Now that we have found a way of saving the lives of children, we have to find food for them. That, after the abolition of nuclear weapons and other scientific means of mass murder, is the most vital problem in the world today. But we should not be hypnotized here by analogies from the rest of the animal kingdom. As soon as we face these problems fairly, we will find a solution. It is only in the very long run and then under ideal circumstances that we will have to equate the production of human beings to the means we may have at the time for feeding them and looking after them; but this is certainly not now when we know through science all the means of pro-viding the food yet do not do so. It remains for a growing population to make what they can out of a traditional and very inefficient agriculture burdened by all the new stresses of war preparations and capitalist exploitation.

Human Death

The problem of individual death is also taking on a different aspect. The living motor of most higher organisms has been evolved to last a fairly long time, but to succumb in the end, as in a motor-car, to failures in essential parts that are, in the state of nature and for all higher organisms, irreparable and lead inevitably to death. A rabbit becomes slower in his movements and is inevitably, sooner or later, caught by the fox. An elephant wears out his teeth, can no longer feed in the jungle and inevitably dies. For the individual man, however, though death has the same inevitability, on account of the social nature of mankind it is much more deeply realized, however long it is postponed. Just because of his social nature, man is the only animal that really appreciates the dangers and horrors of death.

Yet it has now far less ecological excuse. The medical profession has at last succeeded in realizing some of its permanent dream of prolonging life. Its success has been slight compared with its successes in conquering infective diseases and saving the lives of children. As a social being, man can pass on much of his experience by his example, his words, or his writings. These, however, are very meagre and poor substitutes for continued life until we succeed in discovering any way of transferring human memories from one person to another. For the moment we must accept death, though we need not face it with the pious but necessary resignation of past ages. This is well expressed in the Book of Job:

For there is hope of a tree, if it be cut down,
that it will sprout again, and that the tender branch thereof
    will not cease.
Though the root thereof wax old in the earth, and the stock thereof
die in the ground; yet through the scent of water it will bud,
    and bring forth boughs like a plant.
But man dieth, and wasteth away:
Yea, man gives up the ghost and where is he?
As the waters fail from the sea, and the flood decayeth and drieth up:
So man lieth down, and riseth not:
Till the heavens be no more, they shall not awake, nor be raised out of their sleep.

                                                                14, 7–12

Death has been and always remains a personal and social tragedy, but inevitable and necessary as it has been in the early history of organic evolution, it is abundantly clear that it no longer fulfils a useful role in human societies. Until now, however, while recognizing it as inevitable and as an evil, nothing practical could be done about it except to delay it a little. Animals and primitive human beings died, but they did not know death; once death was known, every kind of psychological device was found to enable men to bear or evade the knowledge of death. The first of these was burial. With more prescience than good etymology, Vico even derived the word 'human' from 'inhumare', to bury. This practice of burial is often taken as the clearest indication of the human status of what would otherwise be taken to be an ape society.

Around the idea of death has grown the whole of the death-denying religions, from the austere Buddhist view that death is the natural consequence of the desire to live, then to the variety of glorious afterworlds devised first for an aristocracy and latterly spread to all human beings. Now, as we have grown to know the facts about death and its relation to the increasing fragility of more complex organisms, we see that death is by no means inevitable in principle but only inevitable in practice and we are stirred up all the more to find ways of postponing and evading it. For the moment we must accept it, not as some kind of mysterious fate, but as the consequence of inheriting bodies of which death has been the normal termination.

Curiously enough, in animal evolution natural selection has had little to do with the postponement of natural death, or death from old age, that is, not due to violence or accident, or to disease. As such deaths usually occur after the end of the reproductive cycle, no genetic mechanisms exist to provide any elimination of the tendency to die young. Any mutation in the direction of longevity consequently cannot be passed on directly, though indirectly it may be linked with some other quality of like toughness, which occurs at other, younger ages, and hence be spread through the population.

We are now in a better position to appreciate the origin of death in organic systems and, indeed, to appreciate its ecological use and function there. Such conclusions, however, do not apply to the human race. With the organization of society it has developed its own particular communication systems that extend far beyond the realm of individual life experience or inherited instincts. We must now recognize death, not as a mystical fate imposed by the retribution of a jealous god, but essentially as an inherited resultant of biochemical facts and processes. How far it can be avoided altogether by surgical measures of organ transplantation or by blocking the regular cross-linked polymerization of fibrous proteins of tissues which make them hard and brittle, we cannot yet know. We do know, at least, that the bounds set for us at present are not immutable. One can already find ways of putting off death and we are certain to find more, but we are still in the position of Thor among the giants, grappling with that old Troll Death, yet doing no more than bringing her to her knees. We have more hope to succeed than he had because we join a greater strength than Thor's with a greater wisdom than that of Odin.

Immortal Life

The last word about death has still to be spoken; the important thing is not the death of the individual man or species, but the effective immortality of life itself, that is, the effective indefinite reproducibility of genetic carrying nucleic-acid molecules. What I am attempting to say is *Life does not die*, but more accurately we have to admit that *Life has not died* – and that potential calamity is still with us. We still have to find how to combine the potential immortality of the simple bacterium with the complex and differentiated life history of the highest animals.

At one further remove we must pass from the animals to the societies which some of them, and particularly man, have formed. Now a society has a principle of continuity and hence of immortality which does not apply to the individual animal because immaterial factors, consisting of set or variable patterns of behaviour, are built into a society and give it continuity from one generation to another. It does not matter whether this occurs by genetic transmission as in the case of the instincts of birds or insects, for instance, or as produced by parental conditioning as in the case of the higher mammals and some other species. Of course, a particular animal society can be so disrupted that it dies out, though, in general, the culture not only persists but also transforms in the process. At this stage the only culture we know that does this fully is that of human societies, though others may have done so in the past and may still in the future. At present, *man's is the only self-conditioning society*.

Here we are entering another realm of existence, what Teilhard de Chardin has called the noösphere [108]. Although this term is somewhat vague and erroneously equated with the more directly physical lithosphere, hydrosphere and biosphere of the Earth, it is convenient to use because it enables man's mental, social activities to be seen in the general framework of the evolution of life. This illustrates, too, the general principle of evolutionary acceleration, significant changes occurring in the noösphere several orders of magnitude more rapidly than in the biosphere. The time of noösphere changes can now be reckoned in decades instead of aeons.

This acceleration is still continuing and the enormous changes marked in the last few years of our range of knowledge, covering such discoveries as the mechanisms of inheritance and of the nature of life, mostly achieved in the last ten years, as well as the more remote but fundamental discoveries of the atom, high-energy particles and the recession of enormously ener-getic nebulae, also bear witness to it. We may be approaching within a few years another key point in cosmic development in which the human or socio-logical noösphere is replaced, bit by bit, by the workings of its material emanations in the form of scientific apparatus and computers. Already the occupation of science has become the indispensable basis of modern econ-omy including industry, agriculture and medicine, and it is likely that it will be much more so in the near future. This is occurring at a time when the world is suffering from the greatest degree of disharmony between its various regions and cultures than it has ever experienced. The great new powers of science are being used for the pursuit of old and trivial ends. Our language is still essentially paleolithic; our religions are of Iron Age date; our econ-omy was built out of the first industrial revolution and examples from all these stages are among us. The pursuit of old ends by modern means is al-ready going far to destroy civilization and threatens the complete destruc-tion of humanity.

However, once the potentialities of an evolving universe are fully, or even partially, grasped by the whole of mankind instead of by a small privileged élite, this awareness will act as a countervailing force and tend ultimately to level up the whole of humanity to the highest potentialities.

These are only a few of the ways in which the new knowledge and the new speculations on the origin of life are begining to affect modern scientific and popular thought. The implications, as can be seen here, are both wide and deep and have a direct bearing on many of the present-day problems of human societies. Such studies, even if apparently purely speculative and impractical in character, are not, however, likely to die out because they have struck root in one of the most active human enterprises. Whether we like it or not, the exploration of space is becoming one of the major and best-supported enterprises in the scientific and industrial countries in the world today. Yet we may hope that it may become more a matter of science and less of national prestige and warfare, and that other studies will take some of its place.

The preliminary optical observation of the Moon and Mars at close range is only whetting the appetite of man to land there. Already studies are being made to anticipate the organic forms or organisms likely to be found, not so much on the Moon as on the other planets. The United States Space Agency has an Exobiological Section containing hundreds of scientists of different disciplines and has for its immediate object the prevention of contamination of planets by organisms from the Earth, which might possibly prevent altogether any knowledge of life in other parts of the solar system. Some of the researches touched on in this book have been done by those working in this exobiological laboratory. To paraphrase Kepler's aphorism: 'God has provided every animal with the means by which it can live'; for astronomers he has provided astrology; for biopoets (students of the origin of life) he has provided exobiology – and when that source runs dry, the subject will have established itself so firmly as a necessary background to modern biochemistry and medicine that there is no likelihood that its study will be cut off at the root.

In fact, new developments in exobiology, coupled with their applications already being prepared in equipment for landings on the Moon and planets, raise the whole question of the nature of life and its origin to practical questions which must be dealt with now and researches into them are already under way in numerous laboratories. In order to recognize life outside the Earth, working tests for life have been devised and tried out and the conceptions already inferred from the start of the speculation on the origin of life have to be worked into criteria for molecular, biochemical and organismal stages, for which apparatus is already being designed in anticipation of finding other forms of life than those which exist on the Earth. It is to be hoped that these researches will not be so hurried that, not only do they fail in their objective, but irretrievably damage the environment on other planets by introducing to them or taking from them, elements which will destroy these other forms of life or, for that matter, our own. This would seem elementary common sense, but the tragedy of the destruction of the environment carried out by scientific man on the Earth in the unintentional or intentional slaughter of wild life, from butterflies to whales, does not give rise to any feeling of security in this matter. All this shows that the arrival on the scientific scene of the study of the origin of life is a timely and even an overdue phenomenon.

In quite a different sense the studies of the origin of life have a practical bearing on its maintenance on Earth. It is a trivial observation to say that if life originated by itself, the processes by which it did so, though very slow, must have been very simple in the first place, and therefore they are capable of being imitated by modern scientists, imitated and perhaps improved on. The main chemical operation, that of enzyme-furthered reactions is now beginning to be understood with the recent discovery of the structure and much of the action of one enzyme – lysozyme. It appears that the enzyme action is essentially due to the structure of the protein part of the enzyme, which has actual physical cavities that fit the substrate molecules holding them in place, while the chemical action is carried out with the help of a coenzyme. Unlike the chance reactions which are usual in chemistry by the action of heat, enzymic reactions are really solid and not gaseous or liquid-state reactions. They are topochemical. The complicated protein which was needed to produce them in the first place in living systems is not strictly necessary. Already without knowing it they have been substituted in chemical industry by organometallic complexes such as the Zeigler catalysts for making the polyethylene and polypropylene plastics of commerce. More recently still, Volpin and Shur [116] have shown that this can be done in the most difficult but important chemical reaction of all, the low-temperature production of ammonia from atmospheric nitrogen. From this, in the measure that it is better understood, will come a new chemistry which has learnt the lesson from the chemistry of living systems, but attacks the problem more rationally and more simply and economically as well. The origin of life therefore has now acquired a practical as well as a theoretical importance in science.

Within a few years or decades the picture of the origin of life will become part of the normal accepted knowledge of most educated people. And with the general extension of knowledge, particularly scientific knowledge which is advancing so rapidly, doubling approximately every ten years, we may expect educated people in this sense to be far more numerous than they are now, and to be found all over the world and not only in some historically selected and privileged parts of it. The study of the origin of life is sure to prove a greater solvent of old ideas and attitudes than any branch of science has been in the past, for it tends to complete the picture of man in relation to the Universe, a picture no longer limited to this Earth or to historical time, but reaching out to the bounds of the Universe and to the origin and fate of stellar systems.

Long before we have established contact with other intelligent beings elsewhere among the galaxies, we shall have seen not only where we stand but something of the long path we have travelled. The great liberation of the human mind, of the realization first stressed by Vico and then put into practice by Marx and his followers that *man makes himself*, will now be enlarged with the essential philosophical content of the new knowledge of the origin of life and the realization of its self-creative character. We are now beginning to glimpse at some of the stages and details of that process in the far past. This will help us to appreciate our position in the present and the future on Earth now and soon in the Universe at large. That future depends on us now, on our understanding, on our knowledge and our wisdom.

Postscript

Postscript to 'The Origin of Life'

SINCE finishing the text of the main part of this book, research in many fields relevant to the origin of life has continued and, indeed, has accelerated. Some of the recent findings affect the conclusions arrived at, mostly in the way of amplifying them but not in any way flatly refuting them. This postscript contains some of the main points where the new information is really relevant to the thesis of the book.

I have divided it into four sections which correspond to the stages of the evolution of life discussed in the book itself:

1. New data on the origin of life on Earth and other planets;
2. New data on the early occurrence of organized aggregates;
3. New ideas on the origin and development of vital biochemical processes;
4. The time element in organic forms.

1. New Data on the Origin of Life on Earth and Other Planets

The exploration of the surface of the Moon and the planets has become the main object of space exploration, so far with unmanned vehicles. The results serve only to confirm earlier pictures of the Moon and also, somewhat surprisingly, Mars, as essentially bodies formed by an accretion of pre-planetary meteoritic material and, subsequently, of vulcanism. Ranger and Surveyor studies of the Moon have shown, both at intermediate range and close range, pictures of its surface. It appears not to be covered by a layer of dust of any thickness but, instead, by fused and possibly vesicular rock-like volcanic slag, pitted with small craters, produced either by meteorites or ejecta from other volcanoes on the Moon. This, however, only marks the beginning of a long study and will require a different and very much improved apparatus to collect and possibly bring back material from the Moon. So far, no direct or indirect trace of life has been observed.

The studies of Mars show a surface arrangement markedly and surprisingly similar to that of the Moon, with a large number of intersecting craters and no terrestrial-type mountains. The atmospheric effects so far visible are derived from earth-based observations and have not made themselves felt in the close-range photographs. On Mars likewise, no trace of life has been observed. It would only be fair to say that in any one single passage of an unmanned vehicle sending back photographs to Earth this can hardly be expected. It would take a long time for any climatic changes to be observed.

Much further study has been made on meteorites but the question of their organismal origin is still very much an open one, with the balance of opinion against anything of a biogenic nature. The main body of the most probable meteorites show this. The carbonaceous meteorites have been studied in detail by a number of observers, particularly by Fredriksson [34a]. He describes the main part of the Orgueil meteorite as being composed essentially of clay minerals, serpentines or chlorites containing a number of secondary minerals as well as bituminous crusts of low temperature stability.

Fredriksson, however, does not pay any attention to the presence of olivine crystals and olivine glass globules, which are abundant in Type I meteorites, indicating their probable formation from heated gases cooled very quickly. Nevertheless, one must agree with his conclusion, on the basis of flying-spot analysis of minerals, mostly from the Orgeuil meteorite, that all of these can never have been formed by any equilibrium process. The different types of minerals have been mechanically mixed at some time subsequent to the formation of the parent body but before its breaking up. This evidence is amplified by the observation in another meteorite, the Sharp's meteorite [71a], of inclusions which belong to Type I carbonaceous chondrites, showing that these inclusions had been formed previously to the formation of the chondrite and, therefore, both stones must have come from the same place. If this should prove to be generally true, it much simplifies the problem of meteorite origins.

My own conclusion from all this (p. 273) is that the meteorites, especially the carbonaceous meteorites, are first formed from aggregations of silicate and carbonaceous materials which built up parent bodies of small dimension – of the order of 100 km or less diameter – and appeared about 4.5 aeons ago, and these were the seat of subsequent astrovulcanism. As part of these explosive eruptions, blocks of different composition in the lapilli or blocks of sintered clay minerals were ejected which, after subsequent alterations in an atmosphere predominantly an oxidizing one, ultimately reached the Earth after a relatively short time of flight of less than an aeon.

In no case does this provide evidence for the existence of life on the parent bodies of the meteorites and their study, therefore, throws no light on the origin of life as such, but it may be important for the genesis of the materials such as the hydrocarbons from which life subsequently evolved (p. 52).

The question of the origin of the hydrocarbons has been studied in the new subject of paleobiochemistry, particularly by P. H. Abelson [2] and his school, and by M. Calvin [36]. It would appear that hydrocarbons are the safest markers in early organic chemistry. Most oils are of biological origin, but some may be also abiotic in origin. Some of the former have inclusions of parts of the chlorophyll molecule, particularly phytane (C_{20}) and pristane (C_{19}). Both are isoprene derivatives and are found in rocks of age 3×10^9, i.e. as old as any micro-fossils.

2. New Data on the Early Occurrence of Organized Aggregates

The absolute dates of the first traces of life, referred to in Chapter 7, are now known to be too recent. The earliest living forms for which there seems to be some definite evidence are now generally considered to be the Fig Tree cherts of South Africa, as studied by Bargehoorn [7a]. His earlier study of the Gunflint fossils has shown mono-cellular, even multicellular, algae, whereas the Fig Tree fossils seem to be of a lower order and consist of single-celled bacteria and they may or may not have been photosynthetic. They are dated at 3.1 aeons. Other studies have shown the reef algae, presumably plant fossils, *Conophyton* from the Sahara [48a], but these consist of massive formations and have been much altered, and it is impossible to find out much of their vascular structure, if it existed at all.

All the observations point to the great antiquity of life and add to the difficulties which have to be faced in proposing that the origin of life itself took place in the aeon or aeon-and-a-half since the Earth's crust was formed (p. 104). The time scale of the evolution of organisms in relation to the evolution of the Earth's atmosphere, as discussed in Chapter 7, may have to be shortened. There would seem to be no room for a long period of the order of more than one aeon of the anoxic atmosphere demanded by the Berkner-Marshall hypothesis (p. 105ff).

The history of planetary atmospheres has been discussed, particularly by Rubey [102a]. He concludes that on certain planets, such as Mars, an atmosphere similar to that of the Earth is most unlikely, for Mars is too light to retain even oxygen or water, which would boil there at 10°C. A reducing atmosphere is also most unlikely as H_2 would escape easily. Consequently abiogenic synthesis is unlikely to occur. This does not apply to the Earth. Volatile substances have probably been retained on Earth from the earliest period.

Many workers, particularly Matthews and Moser [66a], have varied the original Miller experiments by reacting ammonia and methane not in the presence of water but dry. In this way α-amino acids are produced, not readily hydrolysed as in the original experiments in an aqueous medium. The intermediate substance is aminocyanomethylene, $H_2N—C=C=N$. This polymerizes spontaneously, giving rise to a number of peptides forming a yellow or brown liquid. This method has been suggested as an alternative way of forming organic polymers on a primitive Earth. I consider this process unlikely in practice because of the evidence for the presence of water. But it has the advantage of forming organic bases such as adenine. The authors, however, maintain that:

Four aeons or so ago this over-all polymerization sequence proceeded efficiently and selectively in the atmosphere of Earth and led to the formation of a protein-dominated layer that concentrated in the oceans of the then sterile planet. Today it is likely that such processes still are occurring on Jupiter and on the myriad other planets possessing atmospheres of methane and ammonia, cosmic molecular precursors of hydrogen cyanide and life.

3. New Ideas on the Origin and Development of Vital Bio-chemical Processes

These arise essentially from a deeper understanding of the biochemical principles involved. It now appears that the process of polymerization of a linear character occurring, in the first place, without enzymes or nucleic acid templates must be postulated. Subsequent changes that involve the coiling up of such polymers from more complicated membranes and soluble protein molecules can now be seen to have occurred without any further involvements of vital agencies and to be essentially a kind of irregular or generalized crystallization.

The importance of the principle of self-assembly is involved here and finds its geometrical place from among the standardized forms of particles containing only a few protein molecules, the complex particles and sheets which we can now think of as extended polypeptides in the first place. The importance of membranes seems to have been first expressed in the bacteria in terms of muco-proteins containing sugar molecules, only later covered with phospholipids such as form the unit membrane of the higher, eukaryote, cell forms. It would appear that the amount of membrane in the prokaryote forms is very limited and mostly concerned with the cell wall, which also has a part to play in the multiplication of such cells. This is a form which characterizes the bacteria of today and their prokaryotic precursors, the mycoplasmas. However this may be, the early forms of life show the extreme persistence of particular structures, especially in the organelles. One of these, the flagella, in the typical $9+2$ fibre form are difficult to explain. It has been observed, however, that among the primitive worms a more complicated range of structures, of which the $9+2$ may be a degenerate form, contain as many as thirty-six sub-fibres in an outer ring [111a].

4. The Time Element in Organic Forms

One of the great discoveries of the last few years has been that, following the work of Monod and Jacob, of the factors influencing the activity of the genetic mechanism. In understanding this mechanism, the first stage is that of the association of one gene with one specific protein, especially with an enzyme. It now appears that of equal, if not of greater, importance have been the factors responsible for the turning on and turning off the activity of a particular gene. It would appear that the genetic mechanism, particularly in the eukaryotes, but reaching right down to the viruses, is heavily over-determined.

The complete chromosome, which is, for practical purposes, the whole living part of a virus, contains genes the great majority of which never come into action at all but are activated externally by changes in the environment. These changes may be activated in the first place biochemically, as by antibiotics, and in the second place by genetic determinants originating in other parts of the organism. These operons, as they are called, act as repressors of gene action and/or derepressors, which negate the action of the repressor and consequently allow the gene to act.

This may turn out to be the basic mechanism that determines differentiation in embryology, in the first place, and somatic evolution, in the second. It is essentially the opposite and complementary role to gene action itself and it is a play back between the environment and the organism, adding the factor of sensitivity to changes in environment, which is in contrast to the purely mechanically conceived action of the gene itself.

This work is obviously only in the very first stages and its further elaboration may make altogether simpler the account of the origin of the more common forms of life. In particular, it throws light on the evolution of multicellular organisms (p. 92f). Essentially, it does this by multiplying the possibilities of the structural plasticity of the organisms by stressing the importance of the environment in determining, by the prescriptive methods already discussed, which of the factors, old or new, will be called into action, and when.

The total effect of the addition of new ideas to the theory of the origin of life is now largely conditional on the duration of the evolution of the code for the production of proteins. This is now a much more serious problem than it was and it has to be fitted into a shorter time. There does not seem to be any reason at present, but there may be later, to abandon the idea of a Stage II, in which the simple molecules formed in the primitive ocean, or in bits of it isolated in differentially oxidized pools, formed the more complicated structures and evolved without building separate organisms into a system which found a regular way of generating proteins and nucleic acids. The most striking fact nowadays is the universality of the genetic code, which is one of the bases of the unity of life. The problem of the evolution of the code is now one of the main problems of biophysics and, as we solve it, we ought to be able to form a better picture of the circumstances under which it would have taken place.

One outstanding fact has now been verified: that the code for proteins and nucleic-acids is nearly uniform over the whole of the existing species of life. The implication is that it must have been established at a very early stage in the genesis of life, probably at what I have called Stage I or, at most, the early part of Stage II, before the formation of actual organisms. In other words, the existence of the code is one of the most important evidences for the genesis of life on Earth. If we ever find life on another planet, it will be most important to ascertain whether a similar code or an identical code exists there.

There must be a clear separation between the ideas of an uncatalysed equilibrium formation from atoms or radicals of molecules such as adenine, and serial formation of the heteropolymers, whether of protein or nucleic acids, through a code-like mechanism. Two major principles seem to be emerging: the first is the formation of linear polymers in series of, unlike monomers, a certain order, and the second is the three-dimensional arrangement of any system of such polymers subsequent to their formation in a minimum energy condition. We should be able to distinguish clearly between what may be called ordered synthesis or biosynthesis, depending on the code, and the subsequent *completion* of the macromolecule in *three dimensions*, not requiring any intervention other than the laws of chemistry, particularly those of conformation and packing.

This self-completing macromolecule has a peculiar status in the general theory of forms of matter. It can constitute a minimum in the free-energy space, but no very deep minimum such as occurs in the primary valency molecules that are dealt with mostly in organic chemistry. However, as a real minimum, it will require an activation energy to alter it so as to occupy another minimum energy state. Therefore, if the temperature is not too high, it represents a stable structure in itself capable of going into solution and undergoing further changes of aggregation such as regular crystallization. Changes subsequent to the completion of the molecule are of two kinds: one regular – the formation of true crystals, which has been achieved in either of two ways, the first being normal crystallization, in which the units are the conformational equilibrium forms of individual proto-molecules in indefinite large numbers; and the other – the formation of primitive limited crystals such as the haemocyanins and chlorocruorins, already mentioned (p. 83), or of fibres like those involved in the structures of the microtubules (p. 82f). The other kind of change involves the further possibilities of combining with other molecules and even with polymers in the muco-proteins of the primitive cell membranes of bacteria. This is the basis of the celebrated globular-fibrous transformation and its synthesis like proteins, as specifically studied in insulin [63a].

I have already discussed in Chapter 4 the role of the proto-enzymes and proto-coenzymes in these processes. With these two principles operating, the genesis of life is reduced to its barest chemical formulation. The difficulties stand out much more clearly and they can be pin-pointed as difficulties of a logical or chemical order. In all cases the new knowledge is helpful, particularly in the chemical field, where the nature of chemical kinetics is becoming more and more clearly topochemical, that is, consisting of interactions only between atoms in close contact, of the order of one or two Ångströms apart. Indeed, the new revelations of the mode of action of enzymes make this clear. In the case of lysozyme, this is indicated very definitely because here we have the action of the enzyme carried out by means of parts of the molecule which fit round, as it were, and hold a substrate group in a close link; the enzyme action is explained by the actual levels of energy in the adjacent parts which require to have both the right quantities of free energy and the right position of the atoms, and this involves fixed relative positions of enzyme and substrate atoms. These requirements would seem to imply that the enzyme function comes before the enzyme structure itself, that the enzymes are formed, as it were, by folding protein chains around the pre-existing substrate.

The origin of life belongs clearly to that part of chemistry dealing with structures with known atomic positions, in other words, with fixed low-energy positions, and the changes of energy have to flow through a molecule the atoms of which are not free to move or susceptible to statistical considerations such as temperature, but with precise calculations depending on actual positions, fixed in respect of both the molecule of the enzyme and of the substrate. In other words, we can say that *the molecular biology of biogenesis consists of successive stages of topochemical reactions.*

We have to consider, first of all, external conditions which are originally cosmo-geological in nature, including the nature of the atmosphere and hydrosphere at any given time in the evolution of life. Secondly, we have to consider the evolution of the basic elements of auto-synthesis which between them built the code and, ultimately, the organisms themselves. While this simplifies the problem, it also makes it much more difficult to solve: much too much had to be done in too short a time. The question is whether an aeon is long enough to allow this double process of auto-synthesis to take place. The apparent shortage of time for biogenesis on a primitive Earth, arising from the discovery of the age of the Fig Tree fossils, may not be as serious as it seems because the lower limit is also not fixed on Earth. The figure given for the age of the St Paul's rocks is 3.5 aeons. But 3.5 aeons, however, is not necessarily the date of the *earliest* rocks: it may be much earlier than the St Paul's rocks, a figure of 4.5 aeons is quite possible. This would give an aeon-and-a-half or two aeons for the evolution of the chemical side of life which is more or less what we estimate was needed in the earliest Stage I. In any case, as we have previously stated, the rate of change at this stage may have been much quicker than at both the earlier or the later stages for different reasons. For at the later stages the forms of life became more stabilized and more liable to destruction.

This view also ties in with the concepts of generalized crystallography even more closely than with those of biosynthesis. The new idea here is that *generalized crystallography is the key to molecular biology.* We can now divide all structures, organic and inorganic, into two categories, the ordered and the disordered. In the ordered category, when each atom is fixed, it is in the minimum free-energy condition; in the disordered category, on the other hand, there is only a statistically low-energy system, it may be a liquid or a strictly amorphous solid such as a glass or a denatured protein. We still have to find suitable words to characterize such an object as a protein molecule, a standardized and very low-energy structure. Liquori [64a] has suggested the name 'crystal molecule' which I find very suitable. Such crystal molecules can function in solution as enzymes, can be crystallized artificially or can occur in nature in a crystalline or fibrous form. The fibrous form is equally essential to understand from the point of view of biosynthesis because it determines the nature of the structures that all the organisms, when they are formed, have to adopt.

These structures are in the first place responsible for the stabilization of the inner environment which fixes the conditions for further synthesis.

The problem remains, but it is essentially a metaphysical problem, as to how did the first organism know how to make itself. We can say now that what can be known can be made, but that is not the same thing as saying that everything can be made whether it is known or not.

The question of adaptation, which was a great problem for biogenics in the nineteenth century, must be even more strongly put nowadays, because now we have to explain the adaptation of molecules to their functions, involving the kind of knowledge which is more complicated than that of organismal forms. So far, all we have had to answer this question are hints of methods, such as the origins of adenine triphosphate, ATP, the key nucleotide for oxidation purposes. Life, indeed, seems to have been formed by the interaction of external generalized factors such as oxygen or antibiotics interacting with internal structural properties determined by what molecules have been made already in the structures. The kind of difficulties already touched on in the criticisms by Dr Mora (p. 136) are adumbrated and might be dealt with here, perhaps not most effectively.

There has been altogether too much slurring over of the present difficulties in the study of the origin of life, which makes many biologists, biochemists and biophysicists treat the whole thing as not science, properly speaking. By and large, now, we have a much more coherent and understandable picture in which the difficulties seem to be standing out much more clearly than they did before and they are problems that will have to be gradually tackled. I have added some further problems to those listed in Chapter 9 (p. 156). Very many of the answers may, in fact, have already been given without knowing it in the above discussion. Many others will appear explicitly once this is analysed. But the final proof remains to be found, and that it is *by actually making what we are talking about*. This should not be an insuperable task; the fact that a protein, insulin, has been made artificially is a milestone in this investigation. In 1965, Chinese teams in Peking and Shanghai showed that they could do by human traditional techniques, that is, by methods of analysis and *description*, proceeding to synthesis, what nature has done automatically by the unconscious methods of *prescription* (p. 69f).

The very grave difficulties that have faced any attempt to give a chemical account of the origin of life are themselves, paradoxically, a proof of the ease of the problem and the possible consequences to humanity of solving it. There is a fundamental difference between the deliberate construction of chemical forms in the laboratory and those self-made in life itself. The very fact that the molecules of insulin have been made artificially should show that the problem is not an insuperable one and it will be more easy to solve the more we know about it.

In this sense the main problem of the clue to the chemical origin of life is actually being solved by this synthesis and others like it. In itself it justifies the pursuit of the study of biogenesis. **If life once made itself, it must not be too difficult to make it again.**

So far, I have only considered the effect of new knowledge on the genesis of life at the chemical stage, in Stage II, the origin of the code and of the reproduction of proteins and nucleic acids. Both of these arise also in the later stages in the evolution of the organisms which overlap the general question of organic evolution as set out by Darwin. The Darwinian mechanisms of natural selection must, in my opinion, operate even at a molecular level, certainly in the formation of structures and tissues, for example, the organelles such as cilia and mitochondria, and also of nerve cells and ganglia. The whole process of karyo-kinesis is an example, nearly the last example, of the decisive operations of molecular chemistry in the history of evolution.

The final example of biochemical direction in life is rather one of reaction to external changes, whether brought about by mechanical damage as in the healing of wounds, or by the effect of bacterial toxins, immunology, the co-ordination of antigens and antibiotics. The remaining part of the higher branches of evolution concern other kinds of internal communication motivated by nerves, sense organs and their connections, and moderated inter-communications in social animals in the building of the noöspheres of Teilhard de Chardin. This explanation, which covers the whole of biology, is coherent and provable or capable of disproof.

The development of nerves had two functions: one immediate, in ordering the transformation of muscle protein and in reacting to external stimuli, in sensory nerves; the other, in keeping a record of these actions, the processes of memory, which are now also beginning to be considered as essentially of a molecular-biological character. The specific memories are considered to be recorded as memory protein molecules, produced by specific nucleic-acids, themselves formed under the influence of sense data, though this subject is still in a state of rapid growth and acute controversy.

It now appears that the genetic factors are not really necessary for the control of nerves. Certain diseases of animals and man, particularly the disease of sheep called scrapie, can be transmitted by organisms even smaller than viruses and containing no nucleic acids. This may be the pointer to a new and deeper analysis of the simplest possible organisms.

The question of replication may have to be referred to a separate nucleic-acid mechanism which belongs to the infected organism rather than to the infecting particle. If not, this may require revision of much of my thesis.

An attempt to bring together the whole process of biogenesis is given in outline in the following Summary and in the Addendum. They are intelligible only in the light of the preceding discussion.

Summary, mostly of Stage II

IN MY present argument, which is strictly provisional, a picture of the whole process of biogenesis can be summarized in the following thesis:

The genesis of PATTERNS from a number of different standardized ATOMS, self-generated in stars or nebulae.

1. Different equilibrium molecules occur spontaneously.
2. These are of low free-energy – STABILITY.
3. Similar ones can clump together – SEGREGATION, abiotically.
4. Some are copied precisely – REPLICATION – in Stage I, – 4 aeons.
5. Some are varied – MUTATIONS, EVOLUTION, – 4 to – 3 aeons.
6. Some variations are rewarded – natural selection of molecules – SELECTION.

Addendum

There is no such thing as the origin of life. Life is originating all the time – it is a continual process of interaction between successively self-generating entities which contain elements both of necessity and of history. Beginning at the beginning, it is a by-product of cosmic self-generation, of creating energy sources in the building of stars and planets. It is marked by the energy of atoms produced by nuclear reactions pouring out in the Universe, and all but an infinitesimal proportion is wasted. The universe system is apparently as incredibly inefficient in generating information and significance. The material basis is built in definite stages through the intrinsic properties of atoms which make, spontaneously, on the Earth's surface and hydrosphere, molecules, polymers and ordered polymers. They are formed successively into energy traps, transmitters and methods of coded reproduction in precise detail of molecules, in such a way that they can continue to renew themselves and increase in complexity.

While preserving in this way the essential patterns, they also by the same process modify these patterns and lead to continual evolution. Thus organisms can be formed which have the property of building new, specific environments for further interactions. The elements of an organism are topochemical changes such as enzyme action and enzyme sequential coming into action. This is made possible by membranes in isolating parts of the system in the self-blocked-out organelles and cells in the first place, and in all cell-groups or organs which characterise the organism of the metabiota (metazoa and metaphyta) with its internal communication systems, first of a chemical and then of an electrical basis. Meanwhile, another section of these, the plants, evolve successively energy traps in the chloroplasts, which ensure energy production in a continuous externally-derived light field, and later by its metabolism keeps the whole system, plants and animals, working. The animal portion, which runs down its energy, is able to evolve motion and sensation, the combination of the two giving rise to an ecology with appropriate food chains. From this come methods of communication between organisms and with them soon the reproduction of organisms and the appearance of societies of which man is temporarily the final product on Earth. The character of life is the opposite of mineral existence – like a stone: 'I will not be moved.' In contrast, life will move itself while preserving its essential nature.

July 1966

In the last year, the structures of several more protein enzymes, including ribonuclease, chymotrypsin and papain, have been worked out by X-rays. The general picture is as follows: they are examples of limited order heteropolymers. The actual arrangement of these linear polymers may be considered to be of two stages of 3-dimensional organization by the so-called self-assembly process. The stages are: (1) the core, which may or may not be completely rigid, held together by covalent bonds; (2) the tail or tails, which are linear polymers forming part of the whole polymer, but whose 3-dimensional arrangement is determined by weaker forces, mainly van der Waals', for the non-polar parts, and hydrogen bonds and possibly ionic forces for the polar parts.

The feature which gives rise to crystallinity of compounds of this degree of complexity is the precise starting and stopping of the primary chain. The crystallization of identical molecules is really the function of a repeat process. This is the basis for all biological functions; the individual protein molecule may, in turn, be treated as a crystal molecule, that is, a molecule with definite positions of its atoms, but lacking any repeat or nuclear symmetry operations. The word crystal must be understood in the Pickwickian sense of general crystallography.

May 1967

Appendix 1

The Origin of Life*

A. I. Oparin

Grau, teurer Freund, ist alle Theorie,
Und grün des Lebens goldener Baum.

GOETHE

The Theory of Spontaneous Generation

EVER since he took the first steps towards a conscious life, Man has tried to solve the problems of cosmogony. The most complicated and also the most interesting of these is that of the origin of life. At different times and at different stages of culture different answers have been given. The religious teachings of all ages and peoples have usually attributed the appearance of life to some creative act by a deity. The first students of nature were very naïve in their answers to this question. Even to a man of such outstanding intelligence as Aristotle in ancient times, the idea that animals, including worms, insects and even fish, could develop from mud presented no special difficulty. On the contrary, this philosopher maintained that any dry body becoming moist or, on the other hand, any wet body becoming dry, would give rise to animals.

The authority of Aristotle had an exceptionally strong influence on the outlook of men of learning in the Middle Ages. In their minds the ideas of this philosopher became interwoven with the doctrines of the fathers of the Church, often giving rise to suppositions which, to our eyes, appear stupid or even ridiculous. In the Middle Ages it was held that although the preparation of a living person, or of something like one in the form of a 'homunculus', in a retort by the mixing and distillation of various chemical substances was extremely difficult and impious, nevertheless it was undoubtedly something which could be done. The production of animals from non-living materials seemed to the scientists of those times to be so simple and ordinary that the well-known alchemist and doctor, van Helmont, actually gave a receipt according to which it was possible to prepare mice artificially by placing damp grain and dirty rags in a covered vessel.

There are a number of writings from the sixteenth and seventeenth centuries describing the transformation of water, stones and other inanimate objects

*This is a translation by Ann Synge of A. I. Oparin, (1924) *Proiskhozhdenie zhizny.* Moscow. Izd. Moskovskiĭ Rabochiĭ.

into reptiles, birds and beasts. Grindel von Ach even gives a picture of frogs formed from May dew, while Aldrovandi gives drawings which show how birds and insects arise from the twigs and fruit of trees.

The idea that the maggots in rotting meat, fleas in dung and intestinal worms are generated spontaneously from decaying materials was generally accepted as an unalterable truth which was in full accord with Holy Writ. Also, in the writings of those times, we often meet with numerous texts by means of which the authors hope to convince their readers that the theory of spontaneous generation has the full support of the Bible.

However, the further science developed and the more the study of nature came to involve the use of accurate observations and experiments rather than just argument and philosophizing alone, the narrower became the region in which the learned men believed that spontaneous generation could occur.

As early as the middle of the seventeenth century Redi demonstrated by simple experiments that there was no basis for the opinion that spontaneous generation of maggots takes place in rotting meat. He covered the meat with a thin gauze and thus made it inaccessible to those flies from whose eggs the maggots would develop. Under these conditions the meat putrefied but no maggots whatsoever appeared. It was as simple as that to refute the idea of spontaneous generation of insects.

Thus, so far as living things visible to the naked eye were concerned, the theory of spontaneous generation had no support. However, at the end of the seventeenth century Kircher and van Leeuwenhoek discovered a world of tiny creatures, invisible to the naked eye, and only discernible with the microscope. These 'tiny living beasties' (as van Leeuwenhoek called the bacteria and infusoria which he had discovered) were to be found wherever decay was taking place; in decoctions and infusions of plants which had been allowed to stand for a long time, in decaying meat and broth, in sour milk, in dung and in the fur on teeth. 'There are more of them (microbes)', wrote van Leeuwenhoek, 'than there are people in the United Provinces.' It was only necessary for a substance which sours quickly and decays easily to stand for some time in a warm place for microscopic living creatures which had not been there before to develop in it immediately. Where did these creatures come from? Had they really arisen from germs which had happened to fall on the decaying material? How many of these germs there would then have to be everywhere. The idea inevitably arose that it was indeed in the rotting decoctions and infusions that the spontaneous generation of living microbes from non-living material took place. This view received strong support in the middle of the eighteenth century from the work of the Scottish clergyman Needham. He used meat broth or decoctions of vegetable material which he placed in completely closed vessels and boiled for a short while. By doing this Needham reckoned that he must have destroyed all the germs which were present and new ones could not get in from outside because the vessels were completely covered. Nevertheless, after a short while microbes appeared in the liquids. From this demonstration Needham drew the conclusion that he was witnessing the phenomenon of spontaneous generation.

However, there was another learned man who opposed this view. He was the Italian, Spallanzani. He repeated Needham's experiments and became convinced that more prolonged heating of the vessels containing the organic liquids sterilized them completely. A bitter quarrel raged between the proponents of the two opposite viewpoints. Spallanzani showed that, in Needham's experiments, the liquids had not been heated enough and that the germs of living things were still present in them. Needham retorted that it was not he who heated his liquids too little, on the contrary, Spallanzani heated his too much and by such rough treatment destroyed the 'generative power' of the organic infusions which was very tricky and unstable.

Thus, each of the contestants stuck to his opinion and the question of the spontaneous generation of microbes in putrefying liquids was not solved one way or the other for a whole century. During this time quite a large number of attempts were made to prove or disprove by experiment the occurrence of spontaneous generation, but none of them gave a definite result. The question became more and more embroiled and it was not until the middle of the nineteenth century that it was finally solved by the studies of a French scientist of genius – Pasteur.

Pasteur first showed the extremely wide distribution of microbes. In a series of experiments he showed that everywhere, but especially near human habitations, the air contains tiny germs. They are so light that they float freely in the air, only falling to the ground very slowly. On the slightest breeze they fly up again and are carried around us invisibly. The air of large towns is positively swarming with these crumbs of life. A single cubic metre of the air in Paris in summer contains up to 10,000 viable germs. If they encounter favourable conditions they grow, develop and begin to multiply at an extraordinary speed causing the decomposition of liquids which putrefy easily. Thus, it is not the putrescent liquids which give rise to the microbes but the microbes falling from the air which cause the putrefaction of the liquids.

Pasteur explained the mysterious appearance of micro-organisms in the experiments of earlier authors as being due to incomplete sterilization of the medium or insufficient protection of the liquids against the access of the germs. If the containing retort is carefully boiled and then shielded from germs which might enter it with the air, then, in a hundred per cent of cases, there will be no putrefaction of the liquid and no formation of microbes.

Pasteur used a great variety of devices for sterilizing the air entering his retorts. He sometimes heated it in red-hot tubes of metal or glass; sometimes the neck of the flask was plugged with cotton wool in which all the minute particles carried in the air were trapped; or finally, sometimes the air was passed through a fine glass tube shaped like the letter S, in which case all the germs were trapped mechanically on the damp surfaces of the curves of the tube. Whenever the precautions were sufficiently reliable the appearance of microbes in the liquid was not observed. Maybe, however, the prolonged heating had changed the medium chemically and made it unsuitable for supporting life. Pasteur easily refuted this suggestion. He dropped into the sterilized liquid the cotton-wool plug through which air had passed into the retort and which therefore contained germs. The liquid quickly putrefied. The boiled liquid was, thus, a perfectly suitable soil for the development of bacteria. The only reason why this development did not occur was the absence of seed in the form of germs. As soon as the germs fell in the liquid they began to grow at once and gave a good harvest.

Finally, Pasteur succeeded in showing that it is possible to keep such easily putrefied liquids as blood and wine for long periods even without any heating. It was only necessary to remove them from the animal (where they do not contain bacteria) aseptically, that is, taking precautions against bacteria falling into them from outside.

Thus, Pasteur's experiments showed beyond doubt that the spontaneous generation of microbes in organic infusions does not occur. All living organisms develop from germs, that is to say, they owe their origins to other living things. But how did the first living things arise? How did life originate on the Earth? In what follows theories will be examined which attempt to solve this problem.

The Theory of Panspermia

Pasteur is rightly considered as the father of the science of the simplest organisms, i.e. microbiology. His work gave the impetus to extensive studies of a world of minute creatures, invisible to the naked eye but inhabiting the earth, water and air. The investigations undertaken were not now, as formerly, directed merely towards describing the form of the micro-organisms; bacteria, yeasts, infusoria, amoebae, etc., were studied from the point of view of the conditions necessary for their life, their nutrition, respiration and multiplication; from the point of view of the changes which they bring about in their environment and finally from the point of view of their internal structure in its finest details. The further these studies proceeded the clearer it became that the simplest organisms were by no means so simply constructed as had once been thought.

The body of any organism, whether it be plant, mollusc, worm, fish, bird, beast or man is made up of very small droplets which are only visible under the microscope. It is built up from these droplets or cells as a house is built of bricks. The various organs of different animals and plants are composed of cells of different sorts. In becoming adapted to the work carried out by a particular organ the cells of which it is composed are changed in one way or another but, essentially and in principle, all the cells of all organisms are alike. Micro-organisms differ only in that their whole bodies consist of a single cell. This similarity in principle between all organisms confirms the idea, now generally accepted in scientific circles, that all living things on the Earth are connected with one another; they form, so to speak, a family of blood relations. The more complicated organisms arose from simpler ones which gradually changed and grew more efficient. Thus, it is only necessary to explain how some very simple organism could have been formed in order to be able to understand the origin of all plants and animals.

However, as has already been said, even the simplest creatures, consisting of only one cell, are extremely complicated structures. Their main component, called protoplasm, is a semi-liquid, ductile, gelatinous substance, permeated with water but not water soluble. Protoplasm is made up of a large number of extremely complicated chemical substances (mainly proteins and their derivatives) which are never found except in organisms. These substances are not simply mixed but are in a special state which has not yet received much study. Owing to this the protoplasm has an extremely fine structure which is poorly differentiated even under the microscope, but is extraordinarily complicated. The idea that such a complicated structure with a completely determinate fine organization could arise spontaneously in the course of a few hours in structureless solutions such as broths or infusions is as wild as the idea that frogs could be formed from the May dew or mice from corn.

The extreme complexity of the structure of even the simplest organisms struck some scientists so forcibly that they were sure that an impassable abyss existed between the living and the dead. The transition from dead to living or organized seemed impossible, either in the present or in the past. 'The impossibility of spontaneous generation at any time whatever', writes the well-known English physicist W. Thomson, 'must be considered as firmly established as the law of universal gravitation.'

How then did life appear on the Earth ? There was a time when, according to the views now generally accepted among scientists, the Earth was a white-hot ball. Astronomy, geology, mineralogy and other exact sciences provide evidence for this and it is beyond doubt. This means that conditions on the Earth are such that it was unthinkable, not to say impossible, for life to exist on it. Only after the Earth had lost a considerable amount of its heat by dissipating it in the cold of interplanetary space, and the cooling had gone so far that the water vapour had formed the first hot seas, did the existence of organisms like those we now see become possible. In order to explain this contradiction a theory was evolved which bore the rather complicated name of 'panspermia'.

H. E. Richter was the originator of this theory. Starting from the hypothesis that everywhere in space there are small particles of solid material (cosmozoa) which have been cast off by celestial bodies, the author suggested that along with these particles and possibly attached to them, there were the germs of micro-organisms. Thus these germs could be carried from one celestial body which was inhabited by organisms to another which was not yet inhabited. If on this body the conditions of temperature and moisture were suitable for life, then the germs would begin to grow and develop and would be the original parents of all the organic creatures on the planet concerned.

This theory attracted many supporters in the world of science, among them such outstanding minds as those of Helmholtz and W. Thomson. Its proponents were mainly concerned to demonstrate scientifically the possibility of such a transfer of germs from one heavenly body to another with conservation of their viability. In fact, when all was said and done, the main question was whether or not spores could complete such a long and dangerous journey as a flight from one planet to another without being destroyed and while retaining the ability to grow and develop into a new organism. Let us examine closely what dangers the germ would meet on the way.

In the first place there is the cold of interplanetary space, about $-220°C$. Having been cast off from its home planet the germ would be doomed to spend long years, centuries or even millennia at such an appalling temperature before some lucky change would give it the possibility of arriving in a new world. The question inevitably arises as to whether the germ could survive such an ordeal. To solve this problem experiments were made on the resistance to cold of present-day spores. Experiments along these lines showed that spores tolerate cold excellently. They remain viable even after having been kept at $-200°C$ for six months. Of course, six months is not 1,000 years but, all the same, this experiment gives us reason to suppose that at least some spores could stand the severe cold of interplanetary space.

A far more severe danger to germs is presented by their complete lack of protection from light rays. Their path between the planets is penetrated by the rays of the Sun which are destructive to most microbes. Some bacteria are destroyed by the action of direct sunshine after only a few hours while others are more stable, but all, without exception, are unfavourably affected by very strong irradiation. This unfavourable effect is, however, considerably mitigated when there is no oxygen in the atmosphere, and we know that there is no air in space so we have some reason to suppose that germs of life could survive even this ordeal.

But let us assume that a lucky chance has given our germ the opportunity of falling into the gravitational field of some planet on which the conditions of temperature and moisture are favourable for the development of life. It remains only for the wanderer to submit to the gravitational force and to fall on its new land. But here, at once, just as it is reaching its destination in space, a terrible danger awaits it. Before this germ had been in air-free space, but before it can arrive at the surface of the planet it must pass through a fairly thick layer of air which surrounds its planet on every side.

The phenomenon of 'falling stars' (or meteorites) must be well known to everyone. Scientists now explain this phenomenon as follows: there are, floating in interplanetary space, lumps of material of greater or lesser size, fragments of planets or comets which have flown into our solar system from distant parts of the Universe. When they pass close to the Earth they are attracted to it, but before they can fall on it they have to pass through the atmosphere. Owing to the friction of the air the quickly falling meteorite becomes heated to white heat and becomes visible against the dark vault of the sky. Only a few of these meteorites reach the Earth in the form of red-hot stones from the sky. Most of them get burnt up by the intense heat long before they reach its surface.

A similar fate must befall the germs. However, various considerations indicate that destruction of this sort need not necessarily occur. There is reason to suppose that at least some of the germs reaching the atmosphere of any planet would reach its surface in a viable state.

Futhermore, there is no need to dwell on colossal, astronomical periods of time during which the Earth could have been sown with germs of life from other worlds. These periods are reckoned in millions of years. If, during this period, even one of the thousands of millions of germs could have reached the surface of the Earth satisfactorily and found there conditions suitable for its development, then this would be enough for the formation of the whole organic world. All the same, in the present state of scientific knowledge, this possibility, though conceivable, seems not to be very probable.* In any case we have no facts which would directly contradict it.

However, the theory of panspermia is only the answer to the problem of the origin of earthly life, and not in any way to that of the origin of life in general.

Carus Sterne writes: 'If this hypothesis merely pushes the beginning of life backwards to the time of the first appearance in the world of celestial space, then, from the philosophical point of view it is a completely useless labour because whatever could have happened in the first world was also possible in the second and third and would be the act of creation or spontaneous generation.'

'There are two possibilities,' said Helmholtz, 'organic life either began (came into being) at some time or else it has always existed.' If we accept the former view, then the theory of panspermia loses all logical point, for, if life could originate at some point in the Universe, there is no reason to suppose that it could not originate on the Earth as well. The partisans of the theory under discussion therefore accept the theory of the eternity of life. They recognize that 'life can only change its form, it can never be created from dead material'. Thus they put an end once and for all to any further study of the problem of the origin of life. They try to set up an impassable barrier between the living and the dead and to impose a limit on the efforts of the human mind and on the boundless generalizations to which exact science leads it.

But do we have any logical right to accept the fundamental difference between the living and the dead? Are there any facts in the world around us which convince us that life has existed for ever and that it has so little in common with dead matter that it could never, under any circumstances have been formed or derived from it? Can we recognize organisms as formations which are entirely and essentially different from all the rest of the world?

We shall try to give an answer to these questions in the next chapter.

The World of the Living and the World of the Dead

The first and most eye-catching difference between organisms and the rest of the (mineral) world is their chemical composition. The bodies of animals, plants and microbes are composed of very complicated, so-called organic

*Even such an out-and-out defender of the theory under discussion as Helmholtz says in this connection, 'I cannot deny it if anyone thinks that this hypothesis is not very probable or even in the highest degree improbable.' And he adds further that he is forced to take up the point of view of the theory of panspermia because of the complete impossibility of explaining the origin of life scientifically in any other way.

substances. With very few and insignificant exceptions we do not find these substances anywhere in the mineral world. Their main peculiarity consists in the fact that at high temperatures in the presence of air they burn while in the absence of air they carbonize. This shows that they contain carbon. This element is present in all organisms without exception. It forms the basis of all those substances of which protoplasm is made up. At the same time, however, it is no stranger to the mineral world.

The diamond is certainly more or less well known to everyone. It is a precious stone which, in the cut form, is much used as an adornment under the name of brilliant.

As early as 1690 the English scientific genius Newton put forward the idea that the diamond, the hardest and brightest body on the Earth, must contain combustible material. This suggestion was quickly confirmed. A diamond was submitted to trial by fire at the focal point of a burning mirror. It did not survive the test but became covered with cracks, glowed and burnt away before everyone's eyes. Later and more accurate experiments showed beyond doubt that the shining diamond is the blood-brother of the unattractive graphite, the substance from which pencils are made. Both consist entirely of carbon. They have no component other than this element.

However, carbon is met with in the mineral world, not only in the pure state, but also in combination with other elements. Chalk, marble, soda, potash and other compounds all contain carbon. In general, one of the most valuable properties of carbon is its tendency to form the most varied compounds with other elements. In the substances which make up the bodies of organisms the carbon is always found combined with hydrogen, oxygen, nitrogen, sulphur and phosphorus and often with several other elements. All these elements are widely distributed in the non-living world. In combination with oxygen, hydrogen forms water; the air around us consists of a mixture of oxygen and nitrogen; sulphur and phosphorus are found in many of the minerals which make up rock formations. Thus we see that all the elements which enter into organic compounds are also found in abundance in the mineral world. Even this alone gives reason to doubt the existence of any essential difference between the world of the living and that of the dead.

It may be, however, that this difference concerns not so much the elementary compositions as the actual compounds made up from the elements.

It has been considered that the substances of the organic and inorganic (mineral) world are so unlike one another that the former could not be obtained from the latter by artificial means under any circumstances. Some chemists of that time even maintained that it was impossible to obtain organic bodies simply because these substances could only be formed within the living organism by the action of a special 'vital force'. However, as early as 1828 the chemist Wöhler succeeded in preparing an organic substance artificially and so to cast doubt on the importance of the famous 'vital force'.

Since then the study of organic compounds has been advancing with rapid strides, and the further it has gone the clearer has become the falsity of the idea that there is a fundamental difference between these substances and inorganic bodies. Starting from the simplest inorganic substances, chemists can now prepare artificially almost all the substances which are encountered in organisms. Although some of these substances have not yet been obtained there is no doubt that they can be obtained in the near future. The structure of these substances has been studied in extreme detail. No special means of combination of the individual elements has been found in them. They obey the same physico-chemical laws with the same constancy as inorganic compounds.

The essential similarity between organic and inorganic substances has now become so obvious that not a single serious natural scientist would deny it and the protagonists of the view that there is a fundamental difference between the living and the dead have already stopped. They assert that organic compounds whether prepared artificially or isolated from organisms are just as dead as minerals. Life may be recognized only in bodies which have particular special characteristics. These characteristics are peculiar to living things and are not seen in the world of the dead.

What are these characteristics? In the first place there is the definite structure or organization. Then there is the ability of organisms to metabolize to reproduce others like themselves and also their response to stimulation.

Let us go over each of these characteristics and see whether it is really present only in the living organism or whether it is not, in some form or another, also found in the mineral world.

The most important and essential characteristic of organisms is, as is demonstrated by their very name, their organization, their particular form or structure. The bodies of all living things, beginning with the smallest bacteria and algae and ending with man, are constructed according to a definite plan in which the greatest importance attaches, not to the external visible organization but to the fine structure of the protoplasm of the cells which make up the organism. This structure is the same in general for all members of the animal and vegetable kingdoms. Unfortunately it has still not been studied very much. Various investigators have seen different structural formations in the semi-liquid protoplasm in the form of fibres, networks and alveoli. However, as these formations are so extremely small it is very hard to see them, even with the best microscopes now available. All the same it is certain that protoplasm has a definite structure and is not a homogeneous lump of slime. This structure holds the secret of life. Destroy it and there will remain in your hands a lifeless mixture of organic compounds.

Some scientists believe that this structure itself, this organization, could not have been formed spontaneously from structureless and, according to them, lifeless substances. Following the ancient Greek philosopher Empedocles, they repeat, in one form or another, the idea that the organization is closely bound up with the spirit which both constructs the body and is destroyed or flies away when the particular form is annihilated. However, if we adopt this position we must agree with another philosopher, Thales, in ascribing a spirit to a magnet since this extremely simple spirit which expresses itself in the attraction which iron holds for the magnet, depends on the structure of the magnet, that is to say on the arrangement of the particles in it. This structure has only to be disturbed, as when a magnetic stone is ground up in a mortar, and it will lose its spirit just like an organism which has been cut into pieces.

The world of the dead or mineral world is certainly not lacking in definite forms, it is not structureless. It is a property of most chemical substances that they try to take up particular forms, that is to form crystals. We now know that the finest particles of the substance forming the crystals are not just arranged anyhow in them, but are arranged according to a definite plan depending on the chemical composition and the conditions under which the crystals are formed by separation from a solution or from the molten state. It is here that a transition takes place from the hitherto formless, structureless substance to the organized body. In a solution the smallest particles of the substance are in disorder; the same is true even when a substance is melted. However, when a crystal separates out, the particles arrange themselves relative to one another in a strict order, like soldiers forming straight ranks on the command 'Attention!' The form of the crystal and the whole range of its other properties depend upon this arrangement. If the crystal is destroyed by disturbing the arrangement of the particles all these properties disappear.

There is thus no doubt that even the simplest crystals have a definite arrangement. At first glance this arrangement seems to be extremely simple. However, we shall immediately put this idea aside if we remember those marvellous 'ice flowers' which appear on the panes of our windows on a frosty day. In their delicacy, complexity, beauty and variety these 'ice flowers' may even look like tropical vegetation while all the time being nothing at all but water, the simplest compound we know. In small droplets of it the particles were scattered in disorder but they were cooled, the wind blew, the temperature fell below zero and these particles, complying with the eternal laws of nature, which are the same for both the living and the dead, arranged themselves in a definite order and, on the simple window pane, they produce pictures of fabulous gardens, glistening in the sunshine with all the colours of the rainbow.

If we leave the simplest compounds aside and go on to look at those forms which produce more complicated substances an even more varied and involved picture will be presented to our gaze which, in its complexity, is in no way inferior to the most detailed picture of the structures of organisms. However, before we enter on this review we must make a small excursion which, though perhaps rather tedious, is necessary for our further discussion into the realms of the comparatively young science of colloid chemistry which has already acquired great importance.

As early as 1861, the English scientist, Graham, divided all the chemical bodies known at that time into two main classes, crystalloids and colloids. To the first class belonged such substances as various salts, sugar, organic acids and so forth. The substances in this group formed crystals easily and, when dissolved, gave clear and completely transparent solutions. If such a solution is poured into a bag made of vegetable parchment or the bladder of an animal and the bag is placed in pure water, the dissolved substance will pass through the walls of the bag and be washed out of it by the water.

Colloids present a completely contrary picture. They very seldom crystallize and then only with great difficulty. Their solutions are usually cloudy and they cannot pass through vegetable or animal membranes. Graham assigned such substances as starch, proteins, gums and mucus to this group.

It turned out later that such an assignment of all substances between two groups was not altogether correct since the same chemical compound could turn up both as a colloid and as a crystalloid according to the conditions of the solution. Thus 'colloidness' was not a property of a particular substance but of its particular state.

There was, however, a considerable element of truth in the classification made by Graham since substances which have very large and complicated particles very often and easily give rise to colloidal solutions. The study of the colloidal state is therefore of special importance since the vast majority, if not all, of the substances of which protoplasm is made up have very large and complicated particles and therefore must give colloidal solutions.

As we have already said, colloidal substances do not give crystals, but still they are fairly easily precipitated as clots or lumps of mucus or jelly. We may take as our example of such formations the protein of eggs which is precipitated on boiling and the gelatin which sets on cooling (well known to everyone as a jelly). The separating out of such coagulates or precipitates from previously uniform solutions sometimes takes place amazingly easily for apparently insignificant reasons.

The coagulates or gels obtained by precipitating colloids are, at first sight, quite structureless. If we examine a lump of jelly under the microscope, even at a high magnification, it appears to us quite uniform. However, scientists have now invented very effective instruments with which they have succeeded in revealing the complicated structure of coagulates. Here it is not a question of straight lines and planes such as we meet in crystals, for here we have a whole network, a whole skein of fine threads which are interlaced, separating from one another and coming together again in a definite, complicated order. Sometimes these threads are very fine, on the other hand, sometimes they are thickened, fusing with one another to form small enclosed bubbles or alveoli.

The structure of coagulates is strikingly reminiscent of that of protoplasm. Unfortunately this structure has not yet been sufficiently well studied for us to be able to say anything conclusive about this resemblance. However, there can be no doubt that we are dealing here with phenomena of the same order. There is no essential difference between the structure of coagula and that of protoplasm.

It may be, however, that the difference between living and dead does not lie in the organization which, as we have seen, is present in both worlds, but in the other features which we mentioned, the ability of living organisms to metabolize to reproduce themselves and to respond to stimuli.

The shapes of crystals are unalterable, they are formed once and for all, while an organism may be compared with a waterfall which keeps its general shape constant although its composition is changing all the time and new particles of water are continually passing through it. The composition of the living body changes in just the same way. The organism takes in different substances from its environment; after a number of chemical changes it assimilates these substances, transforming what had been foreign compounds into parts of its own body. The organism grows and develops at the expense of these substances. However, just as a factory requires a certain amount of fuel to carry on its work, so, if the organism is to carry on its unceasing activities it should consume, that is to say break down, at least part of the material which it has assimilated, and this is what actually happens. In the process of respiration or fermentation the organism breaks down substances which it has already taken in and the products of their degradation or decomposition are given off into the environment. Thus life consists of continual absorption, construction and destruction.

However, if we make a detailed analysis and simply contemplate the phenomenon of metabolism which has been described, we shall not find, even here, anything specifically characteristic of the living world. In fact, the phenomenon of feeding, the assimilation of substances from the environment, is, of course, found in its simplest form even in crystals. Thus, a crystal of common salt, which is well known to everyone, will, if it is immersed in a supersaturated solution of the same substance, increase its size and grow by absorbing individual particles of substance from its environment (the solution) and making them part of its body. Even here, in this simple phenomenon, we have before us all the characteristic features of the phenomenon of nutrition. There is even more similarity between this phenomenon and the processes which occur in colloidal coagula. A lump of such material has the ability to extract from solution and absorb the most varied substances such as dyes. These latter do not just remain on the surface of the lump but penetrate deeply into it, some of them simply adhering to the tangled threads which constitute the lump while others enter into chemical reactions with these threads and combine firmly with them, forming component parts of the whole lump.

Study of the process of feeding of living protoplasm shows that this process too takes place in exactly the same way as has just been described. Solutions of different chemical substances penetrate into the protoplasm as a result of the action of comparatively simple and thoroughly studied physical forces, just the same forces which operate in colloidal coagula. Having entered into the protoplasm, one substance will quickly pass out of it while others will enter into a chemical reaction with it, combine with it and become parts of it. And here, all in all, we have a simple chemical reaction and not anything mysterious such as could only be accomplished by a 'vital force'.

Thus, when various chemicals are absorbed by lifeless coagula we are dealing with processes which take place in a way which is completely analogous with the first stage of metabolism, that is to say, feeding.

The following example shows that, even in the world of the dead, we can find processes which are essentially just the same as metabolism as a whole. If we take a small piece of so-called spongy platinum (platinum is one of the 'noble' metals which can be obtained by special methods not as sheets or solid lumps, but as a very delicate sponge with very fine holes and delicate walls) and throw it into a solution of hydrogen peroxide in water* then

*Hydrogen peroxide is a chemical compound which, like water, is composed of hydrogen and oxygen only but there is twice as much oxygen in it as in water. This compound is fairly

bubbles of oxygen will immediately begin to form on the surface of the lump. They are formed by the breakdown of the hydrogen peroxide and the process goes on quite rapidly and only stops when all the hydrogen peroxide has been broken down to oxygen and water. If we then remove, dry and weigh our piece of platinum we shall find its weight has remained just as it was before. The same piece may again be thrown into a new amount of hydrogen peroxide and will again decompose it quickly while itself remaining unaffected. Thus, a comparatively small piece of spongy platinum can decompose an unlimited quantity of hydrogen peroxide.

Chemists have been interested in the mechanism of this process for a long time, and as a result of many investigations we now know for certain that the decomposition of hydrogen peroxide by platinum takes place in the following way. First the peroxide is adsorbed on the platinum. As the peroxide cannot penetrate into the metal this adsorption only takes place on its surface. That is why it is important to use spongy platinum for this experiment as it has a very large surface at which the metal is in contact with the liquid. The particles of peroxide do not simply adhere to the surface of the platinum but form a chemical compound with it, namely the hydrate of platinum peroxide. Thus the piece of metal, like the living organism, extracts particles of hydrogen peroxide from the water and assimilates them into its body. However, it does not end at that. After a short time the hydrate of platinum peroxide on the surface of the metal breaks down to platinum, water and oxygen, the last being given off in the form of bubbles of gas. The reduced platinum can combine with a new portion of hydrogen peroxide and again break it down, the products of the decomposition being oxygen and water. The process is repeated until there is no hydrogen peroxide left in the solution surrounding the metal.

In the example given we have the simplest but still complete prototype of metabolism. It contains all the important elements of this process. The absorption of substances from the surrounding medium, their assimilation and breakdown and the giving off of the products of their decomposition. Just the same process takes place in any living organism, for example in any bacteria cultivated in a solution of nutritive substances. The bacteria absorb the substances from the solution, assimilate them and then break them down, giving off to the outside the products of their decomposition. Thus, a simple piece of metal behaves in just the same way as a living organism.

In this connection it must be pointed out that both phenomena (the metabolism of organisms and the decomposition of hydrogen peroxide by

stable and can usually stand for a very long time without breaking down. When it breaks down for any reason it gives rise to oxygen and water.

platinum) are not only similar, in their external form, but the actual mechanism of the process is similar in both cases. In all organisms, without exception, metabolism is brought about by means of so-called enzymes. This name is given to substances, the chemical nature of which is still only poorly understood, but which can comparatively easily be isolated from any animal or plant in solution in water or as a powder which is easily dissolved in water. All enzymes now known have the power to act on substances forming part of the living body in a very remarkable way. They alter these substances in one way or another (either by breaking them down or by causing them to combine with one another) while themselves remaining completely intact. A detailed study of this phenomenon has shown that enzymes act on the different organic compounds of the living body in just the same way as does platinum on a solution of hydrogen peroxide. In fact metabolism, in its most important aspects, does not consist of anything but a long series of successive enzymic processes following one another and related to one another like the links of an unbroken chain.

At present one of the most extensive sections of physiology, the science which studies the functioning of living organisms, is devoted exclusively to the problem of metabolism. The further the study of this complicated process goes on, the more closely and accurately we get to know the essential features of the processes which are carried out in the living cell, the more strongly we become convinced that there is nothing peculiar or mysterious about them, nothing that cannot be explained in terms of the general laws of physics and chemistry.

Thus, even the ability to metabolize cannot be taken as a special characteristic peculiar to living organisms.

We still have two 'peculiarities of life' left to discuss, namely, the capacity for self-reproduction and response to stimuli.

In what does the capacity of organisms for self-reproduction consist? In the simplest case it amounts to this: the elementary organism, the cell, divides itself into two halves each of which then grows into a new daughter cell in which the structure of the mother cell is reproduced down to the finest detail. This property, however, does not belong only to organisms, but to all bodies possessing a definite structure, without exception. Let us take the simplest case as our example. If we take a crystal of any substance such as alum, break it into two halves and place them in a supersaturated solution of the same substance what will happen will be that the halves of the crystal which had been placed in the solutions will quite quickly replace their missing faces, angles and edges at the expense of particles which had previously been floating freely in the solution. Before growing larger they take a form which reproduces in the finest details that of their mother, the original crystal.

The question may, however, arise that in the example which we have given we forcibly broke the crystal whereas the division of the cell apparently takes place spontaneously. Is that not the fundamental difference between the two phenomena ? The fact is, however, that it only seems to us that the division of cells takes place spontaneously, it really takes place under the influence of definite physical forces (capillary attraction, surface tension) which, though they certainly have not yet received much study, still are of just the same kind, in principle, as all the other physical forces.

An even more interesting phenomenon is that of the 'seeding' of super-saturated solutions. It occurs as follows. In some cases it is possible to concentrate a solution of a particular substance very strongly without that substance separating out in the solid form. However, if the most minute crystal or grain of the substance in question is dropped into the solution crystals will immediately begin to separate out of the solution, sometimes in such quantities that the whole mass becomes crystalline.

This shows that a crystal can cause the formation of bodies like itself which would otherwise not have been formed. If the particles which are scattered at random throughout the solution are to arrange themselves according to a definite plan to give a definite organization or form, that form must already be present.

Here we have the occurrence of the most amazing phenomena which may serve as a key to the understanding of other extremely complicated phenomena of the same order. 'Let us take the example of sulphur,' as Carus Sterne says, 'this is known to be a simple substance yet it depends on the temperature at which it changes from the liquid to the solid state which of two very different forms it will take, octahedral or prismatic*. If we place two such crystals on fine platinum wires in a supersaturated solution of sulphur in benzine then, in the neighbourhood of the prismatic crystal new prisms will be formed while octahedra will be formed near the octahedral crystal. When the two armies of crystals approach one another, the latter form is victorious at the first clash. Here is an example of the struggle for existence in the realm of crystals! '

Let us now go on to take a look at the last of the peculiarities of living things which we mentioned, that is, at responsiveness to stimuli. In all living

*On crystallizing, different substances take on regular geometrical shapes. The crystals are characterized by these forms. Some substances may crystallize in different forms under different conditions. In particular, sulphur can give crystals in the form of octahedra (two four-sided pyramids joined together by their bases) or hexagonal prisms.

things without exception we meet with a property which in its most general form may be described as follows. In an organism external and internal stimuli will cause something of the nature of a discharge and will induce the performance by it of some definite action (e.g. movement, etc.) which will carry out in a particular way according to its structure and the means at its disposal. It is a very characteristic feature of responsiveness that there should be a quantitative disparity between the energy, that is to say the forces, required to excite or bring about the response, and the work which is the response of the organism to the stimulus in question. Thus, for example, a relatively slight touch can be enough to induce the organism to move from one place to another or to carry out some other work requiring the expenditure of much force. The organism draws from within itself the forces (energy) required for this work.

Some scientists believe that responsiveness is a specially characteristic feature of organisms. However, if we take this view we shall have to regard a railway locomotive with the steam up as a living thing. In fact it is only necessary to apply a slight stimulus by shifting a lever and the locomotive will start to move, carrying out a very considerable amount of work at the expense of the fuel which is burnt in its boiler. This work is many times greater than that expended in moving the lever and is carried out in complete accordance with the structure of the locomotive.

Responsiveness is to be found, not only in organisms, but also in any physical body which has any noteworthy store of hidden (potential) energy. Comparatively insignificant causes may lead to the discharge of this energy which will lead to the carrying out of some particular work. A landslide caused by a comparatively slight movement of the air, the explosion of a powder magazine caused by a spark which happened to fall in it – these are very simple cases of the phenomenon of responsiveness.

With this we will finish our short review of the main feature of living organisms. We have seen that not one of these can be held to be inherent only in living things. But if this is so we have no reason to think of life as being something which is completely different in principle from the rest of the world. If life had always existed and had not arisen by generation bodily from the rest of the world, if it had not separated itself or, crystallized out at some time from this world, then it would inevitably have had characteristics peculiar to itself. But this is not so. The specific peculiarity of living organisms is only that in them there have been collected and integrated an extremely complicated combination of a large number of properties and characteristics which are present in isolation in various dead, inorganic bodies. Life is not characterized by any special properties but by a definite, specific combination of these properties.

In the course of the colossal length of time during which our planet, the Earth, has existed, the appropriate conditions must certainly have arisen in which there could have been the conjunction of properties which were formerly disjoined to form the combination which is characteristic of living organisms. To discover these conditions would be to explain the origin of life.

From Uncombined Elements to Organic Compounds

Astronomers tell us that very, very long ago, millions, perhaps even thousands of millions of years ago, the Earth existed in the form of an enormous cloud of incandescent gas. We cannot yet form any accurate idea of the extreme heat which prevailed in that cloud which represented the Earth of the future. In any case it was considerably higher than the highest which we can yet obtain artificially, temperatures at which metals such as iron boil, turning into vapour like water when it falls on a red-hot stove. Under these conditions there could be no question of the occurrence of any chemical compounds. Even at lower temperatures all the compounds we know breakdown into their simplest components, the elements. These elements exist as very small particles of matter (atoms) which were distributed freely and haphazardly in space and constituted the earliest cloud from which the Earth was later to arise. This was the primaeval chaos in which, it seems, everything was in disorderly, unrelated and irrational movement.

We can form some idea of such a state of matter from a study of the gases or vapours obtained by raising a great variety of materials to white heat. In the puffs or clouds of these vapours the individual particles of matter are also in constant motion, just as were the particles in the original cloud.

A study of matter in the vapour state has led scientists to the belief that even in the primaeval cloud there was not absolute chaos, but even there, affected by the eternally acting forces of physics, a certain order slowly but surely began to establish itself. In the first place the particles of the different elements of which the cloud was composed began to distribute themselves within it in some sort of order. Under the influence of that same force of gravity which attracts the falling stone towards the centre of the Earth, the heavier atoms in the cloud began to sink towards its centre while the lighter ones remained at its surface. Thus, the gases forming the cloud were more or less separated out into layers in it, the heavier ones being below, at the centre, while the lighter ones were on the surface.

As the cloud cooled, the material in it became denser and at a particular moment it went over from the vapour to the liquid state. In the centre of the cloud a red-hot liquid nucleus was formed, surrounded on all sides by an immense envelope of incandescent gas. It is quite reasonable that the nucleus should have been composed for the most part of the heaviest elements while the lighter ones remained in the gaseous atmosphere enclosing this nucleus.

According to the views of D.I. Mendeleev, the first nucleus of the Earth must have been composed of heavy metals, mainly iron, while further from the centre there were the alkali and the alkaline earth metals,* the metalloids and, finally, the outermost part of the atmosphere was composed of the lightest gases, mainly hydrogen. Carbon, the element which interests us most, should, by this scheme, be present in the primaeval nucleus of the Earth in very close association with iron.

The idea is not the result of some theoretical speculations, but is firmly based on facts. It is easy to convince ourselves of this by going back to a study of present-day conditions. In fact, if the heaviest elements were at some time in the centre of the Earth they should still be there. That is to say, if the idea put forward above were true the heaviest elements should be found in the depths of the Earth even today.

Unfortunately, only a thin skin on the surface of the Earth is accessible to study by Man. We can only penetrate a few thousand feet into the depths of the Earth and this means that we cannot see with our own eyes what exists in its interior. However, scientists have succeeded in obtaining a very clear picture of it in other ways. They have managed, though this may seem strange at first sight, to weigh the Earth as a whole. Of course its weight is extremely great. In round figures it is 4 quadrillion kg. By direct measurements of the surface they have also determined its volume. What they found was that the weight was nearly six times that of an equal volume of water. We know, of course, that the crust of the Earth does not consist of water alone, but even in its densest parts it does not have a mean specific gravity as great as five to six times that of water. The specific gravity of the crust does not exceed two and a half. Thus, the Earth as a whole has a far higher specific gravity than has the outer part of it which is accessible for us to study. It is so heavy that its weight can only be explained on the supposition that it has a nucleus of heavy metal inside it.

This view is also supported by study of the masses of lava which are extruded from the depths on to the surface of the Earth by volcanoes. The

---

*The commonest alkali metals are potassium and sodium. Calcium, magnesium, barium and strontium are alkaline earth metals. The vapour density of these metals is considerably less than that of the heavy metals iron, copper, lead, mercury, silver, etc.

older the mass and the deeper the region from which it poured on to the surface, the greater the amount of heavy metals it contains, especially iron.

Thus, the evidence which we can obtain by studying the state of affairs on the Earth now provides very definite confirmation of the ideas which we have put forward above. The results of studying the heavenly bodies are even more instructive.

Scientists now believe that each of the stars which we see originated, in the same way as we described for the Earth, from a gaseous cloud, by gradual cooling and increasing density of the vapours of which it was formed.

Depending on a number of factors (mainly on the size of the cloud) the process of solidification might occur quickly or slowly. The different heavenly bodies are now, therefore, at different stages of development. Some of these stars shine with a white or bluish light and are in the earliest stage of development, others, which have developed further, are yellowish and our Sun is one of these. Finally, the stars which have cooled most and are already going out shine with a red light. A further stage of cooling is represented by the planets which can no longer shine with their own light. Our Earth is one of these. Thus, a study of the different heavenly bodies gives us an idea of the different stages of cooling of our own planet.

This study has made great strides forward since Kirchhoff developed what is called the spectral method of analysis. The essence of the method is as follows. If a ray of white light is passed through a glass prism it is divided into its component parts and gives rise to a strip consisting of all the colours of the rainbow (spectrum). If we use the Sun (daylight passing through an opening in a shutter) or an electric light or any solid or liquid body heated to white heat as the source of light for our experiments, we shall obtain a continuous strip like a rainbow in which one colour gradually merges into the next. A different picture is obtained by passing light from incandescent gases through the prism. In this case the spectrum will not consist of a continuous strip but of individual lines, coloured by a particular colour and separated from one another by black spaces. In this connection it is especially interesting that each element has its own particular, completely characteristic distribution of bands in the spectrum. Thus, if we have an incandescent gas consisting of a mixture of elements we can, by studying the spectrum, find out just what elements are present in it. It is thus possible to analyse the mixture in this way.

This method of spectral analysis is so convenient and accurate that it has found wide application in the study and differentiation of many substances on the Earth, but its most important use has certainly been in astronomy as a method for studying the chemical composition of heavenly bodies.

From the furthest ends of the Universe innumerable heavenly bodies send their light to the Earth. By studying this light with a spectroscope we can determine with accuracy which elements are present in the incandescent gaseous envelope of the star in question.

Specially interesting information is obtained by spectral analysis of the gaseous envelope of the Sun. The Sun, as we have already said, is one of the yellow stars. In the centre of it there is a huge, red-hot liquid nucleus, the spectrum of which takes the form of a continuous, rainbow-coloured strip. This nucleus is surrounded on all sides by an envelope of incandescent gas, the atmosphere. Spectroscopic studies of the lowest layers of this atmosphere have shown that it is composed of the incandescent vapours of heavy metals. Here the spectroscope reveals the presence of iron, nickel, cobalt, calcium and manganese, and Roland has even succeeded in finding carbon here. A little higher, further from the centre of the Sun, there is a layer of the atmosphere in which it is easy to demonstrate the presence of the vapours of the lighter alkaline metals, potassium and sodium. Even higher, helium is predominant: this is an element which was first discovered on the Sun.*
Helium is a very light gas. Of all the materials known on the Earth hydrogen is the only one which is lighter.

Hydrogen, too, is found in the solar atmosphere. It lies just above the helium. Finally, above the hydrogen there is a layer of what must be an even lighter gas, coronia, which has not yet been found on the Earth.

Thus, the idea which we put forward about the arrangement of the elements in gaseous masses by layers and which was based on purely theoretical considerations has been completely vindicated by observations on the arrangement of the elements in the atmosphere of the Sun.

There was a time when the Earth, too, was passing through the same stage of development as the Sun, namely that of being a yellow star. Later, as it gradually radiated its heat outwards into the cold interplanetary space, it became cooler and cooler. It turned from a yellow star into a red one, its light became dimmer and dimmer and finally went out altogether. The Earth became a dark planet.

What was happening during these changes to the carbon and other elements which now enter into the composition of living organisms ?

We have seen that, at the time when the Earth was a yellow star the carbon was present partly in the form of incandescent vapours in the lowest layer of

---

*It was considerably later that the well-known British chemist Ramsay succeeded in isolating this element from an extremely rare mineral. Thus it was possible to confirm, by chemical methods, that helium had the properties which had for a long time been assigned to it on the basis of spectral analyses.

the atmosphere and partly in the molten state in the hot, liquid, central nucleus. In both places it was mixed with heavy metals, mainly iron. The temperature prevailing on the Earth at that time was still too high for any chemical compounds to be formed. The elements, though mixed with one another, remained free and did not combine with one another.

However, the Earth gradually cooled and the time must certainly have come when combination took place between the free elements which were mixed with one another. Spectroscopic studies of the red stars lead us to the conclusion that this must first have taken place when the Earth passed from the stage of being a yellow star to that of being a red one.

The first compounds to exist on the Earth must have been extremely stable to high temperatures because only compounds of this sort could have existed for long in the heat which then prevailed. The most thermostable compounds of carbon now known are its compounds with heavy metals, known as 'carbides'. The commonly known representative of this class of compounds is iron carbide.

At the period of existence of the Earth which we are considering carbon vapour was, as we have seen, mixed with the vapours of metals. There is, therefore, good reason to suppose that carbides themselves were the first compounds to arise on the Earth. The existence of other compounds at this time was unthinkable simply because of the temperature.

Only when the Earth had dissipated some of its heat and cooled still further did there arise the possibility of the formation of other compounds and they began to come into being, gradually clothing the central nucleus in a more or less thick envelope. This envelope, consisting of the substances which later gave rise to the rock formations, thus separated the carbides lying beneath them from the atmosphere of that time. However, the envelope was not very stable and in many places there must have been eruption of the internal material on to the surface of the Earth. At the same time, of course, the Earth was gradually cooling. The central nucleus shrank while its outer layers were forming a solid envelope. The latter could not follow the contraction of the underlying material and this gave rise to folds and cracks through which the red-hot carbides of metal poured out and erupted on to the surface of the Earth.

Such phenomena may be seen even now though, of course, on a much smaller scale. The eruption of volcanoes and the processes by which mountains are formed are explained by geologists in terms of just the same causes as we have given, namely the contraction of the Earth which is still continuing. It is true that the cracks which are formed now are, comparatively speaking, not very deep and the lava which erupts from volcanoes comes from a layer a long way above the central core, but it could not be otherwise, because the crust of the Earth has increased in thickness many times over since the time of the formation of the first envelope. Studies of volcanoes and masses of lava which have arisen at different periods of the existence of the Earth show that the most ancient volcanoes derived the products which they erupted from the deepest layers of the Earth.

Thus, at the period of existence of the Earth which we are considering, when it was a red star about to become extinguished, masses of carbides of iron and other metals which had formerly been concealed in its depths were being extruded on to its surface through cracks formed in its crust. Here, on the surface, they encountered the atmosphere of that time which differed in many respects from that of today. Water vapour was specially abundant in it. All the water in all the seas and oceans now on the Earth then existed in the form of superheated steam in the atmosphere. The carbides which flowed out on to the surface encountered this steam.

If we treat carbides of metals with superheated steam we obtain what are known as hydrocarbons, that is to say compounds consisting of carbon and hydrogen. These compounds must also have arisen when the carbides and steam met on the surface of the Earth. Of course some of these must immediately have been burnt, being oxidized by the oxygen of the air. However, under the conditions then prevailing this combustion must have been far from complete. Only a certain part (and a comparatively small one) of the hydrocarbons were fully oxidized, being converted to carbonic acid and water. A further part, owing to incomplete oxidation, gave rise to carbon monoxide and oxygen derivatives of hydrocarbons, while, finally, a certain proportion of the hydrocarbons completely escaped oxidation and was given off into the upper, cooler layers of the atmosphere without any alteration. The more the Earth cooled the lower became the temperature at which the interaction between the carbides and the water vapour took place, and less carbonic acid and more unoxidized hydrocarbons were formed.

Thus, the theoretical considerations put forward above lead us to the belief that at a particular time in the existence of the Earth compounds of carbon with hydrogen and oxygen were formed in its atmosphere. Let us see whether there are not facts in our natural surroundings supporting this idea.

Since the period under discussion is that during which the Earth passed through the stage of being a red star it would be quite appropriate to consider first what we know about these stars. Spectroscopic studies of the darkest red stars which are about to go out, carried out by the astronomer Vogel, led him to the conclusion that the atmospheres of these stars contain hydrocarbons. This fact was soon confirmed by several other workers.

Hydrocarbon lines have also been found in the spectra of comets, those heavenly bodies which from time to time pass through our solar system from interplanetary space. Furthermore, thanks to the studies of several scientists it has been found that cyan* (a compound of carbon and nitrogen) and carbon monoxide are present in the gases which form the tails of comets.

By origin comets are related to a further class of heavenly bodies, the meteorites. We have already discussed these in an earlier chapter. Meteorites are specially interesting because, in falling, some of them reach the surface of our Earth in a more or less undamaged state in the form of red-hot stones from the sky. Thus they are accessible to direct chemical examination. They are, so to speak, lumps of matter, samples reaching us from the boundless region of interstellar space. Analysis of meteorites and study of their composition gives us the opportunity of getting a direct knowledge of some of the materials of which the stars are made. Most meteorites consist of native iron, partly combined with carbon and sometimes containing carbon in such quantities that it has been possible to isolate it from certain falling stars in the form of diamond dust. This composition of the meteorites is an extra confirmation of the correctness of the view that carbon exists on heavenly bodies in the form of mixtures or chemical compounds with metals.

In meteorites, however, other carbon compounds have also been found. By causing samples from meteorites to incandesce by means of an electric spark, scientists have managed to show that the hydrocarbon lines are certainly present in their spectra. It has even proved possible to isolate from some meteorites a considerable amount of hydrocarbons and to establish their nature by chemical studies.

Thus, we can demonstrate beyond doubt the presence of hydrocarbons on a number of heavenly bodies. This fact gives full support to the conclusions we had already drawn. There came a time in the life of the Earth at which the carbon which had been set free from its combination with metal and had combined with hydrogen formed a number of hydrocarbons. These were the first 'organic' compounds on the Earth.

Although only two elements, carbon and hydrogen, enter into the composition of these compounds these elements can join together in the most varied combinations and give rise to the most varied hydrocarbons. Organic chemists can now list a very large number of such compounds.

As the properties of hydrocarbons have been studied in great detail, a study of the conditions prevailing on the Earth when these compounds came

---

* An obsolete term for nitrogen carbide, CN, now known to correspond to the gas C_2N_2 (J.D.B.).

into being makes it possible to put forward some suggestions as to which hydrocarbons were in fact formed. Without going into details we can only say that everything points to the view that it was the 'unsaturated' (free radical) hydrocarbons which were formed first, that is to say the most unstable members of the class we are discussing, having very large stores of chemical energy and great chemical potentialities, compounds which combine very easily both with one another and with other elements.

If these compounds could avoid oxidation at the time of their formation, then, during their stay in the hot, wet atmosphere of the Earth, they must certainly have combined with oxygen and given rise to the most varied substances composed of carbon, hydrogen and oxygen in various proportions (alcohols, aldehydes, ketones and organic acids).

Thus, all the considerations and facts which we have put forward above convince us that, even if not all the carbon, at least a great part of it, first appeared on the surface of the Earth, not in the form of the chemically inert carbon dioxide as had been thought, but in the form of unstable organic compounds capable of further transformation.

Let us leave these compounds for a while and take a look at what happened, during the period in the existence of the Earth which we are discussing, to the fourth element which enters into the composition of living things, namely nitrogen. At high temperatures nitrogen can form compounds with oxygen (the technical production of nitric acid depends on this). We are therefore justified in expecting the appearance of these compounds in the atmosphere of the Earth where the two elements involved were mixed. However, oxides of nitrogen are somewhat unstable. At temperatures of about 1,000°C these compounds break down and give off free nitrogen. Compounds of nitrogen with metals obtained industrially under conditions of white heat are far more stable. Such compounds must also have been formed in the atmosphere of the Earth by interaction between nitrogen and the incandescent vapour of the lighter metals. Later these compounds of metals with nitrogen, of a similar nature to carbides, were submitted to the action of superheated steam and formed ammonia,* which is a compound of nitrogen and hydrogen. Ammonia could also have been formed primarily at a far earlier stage in the existence of the Earth by the condensation of hydrogen and nitrogen in the upper layers of the atmosphere.

Furthermore, we cannot exclude the possibility of the formation of compounds of nitrogen and carbon. In this case the material obtained would be cyan, a substance with which we have already become acquainted when we were discussing the spectra of comets. Its presence in the gases surrounding

*As everyone knows, spirits of hartshorn is a solution of ammonia in water.

these heavenly bodies confirms the possibility that it might also have been formed on the Earth. Thus, the atmosphere of the Earth at a certain period of its existence must have contained compounds of nitrogen in the form of ammonia and cyan as well as oxygen derivatives of hydrocarbons.

Although, from our point of view, cyan can hardly have played any important part in the further transformations of organic substances, we mention it because it is interesting to us in another way. It forms the starting-point of the extremely far-reaching and well-thought-out theory of the origin of life put forward by the well-known German physiologist Pflüger. We shall try to summarize it here. Pflüger says that there is an essential difference between dead protein, such as we find in the whites of hen's eggs, and the living protein of which living material, protoplasm, is made. This consists in the presence of cyan groups in the particles of living protein. However, cyan is only formed at red heat, when nitrogen-containing compounds react with incandescent carbon. 'For this reason nothing can be more clear than the possibility of the formation of cyan compounds at the time when the Earth, as a whole or in part, was in a red-hot or white-hot state.' Only then was it possible for cyan to be formed that 'compound in which the beginning of life resides'. 'Therefore life arises from fire and its basis is derived from the time when the world was still a white-hot, incandescent globe.'

Pflüger also refers to the immeasurable length of the time during which the cooling of the Earth was taking place. 'Cyan and other organic compounds therefore had enough time and opportunities to indulge their great tendency to transformation and the formation of polymers.'* As a result of these transformations they gave rise to 'that self-transforming protein which constitutes living matter.'

The most recent studies do not confirm Pflüger's ideas as to the predominant part played by cyan. The occurrence of cyan groups in 'living proteins' has now come under grave doubt and even the concept of 'living protein' itself has become rather out of date. Protein does not form protoplasm, it only enters as a component part into this chemically and physically complicated formation. The 'self-transforming protein' as Pflüger described it, certainly does not exist. The ability of protoplasm to transform itself is inherent, not only in the chemical substances of which it is composed, but also in its physical structure or organization.

Nevertheless, Pflüger's theory has retained its importance until now. The fundamental proposition that 'life arose from fire' remains unshaken. Only

---

*Polymers is a name for substances having the same elementary composition but a different weight of their particles. Polymers with large particles are usually formed by the combination of two or more smaller particles.

in fire, only in incandescent heat could the substances which later gave rise to life have been formed. Whether it was cyan or whether it was hydrocarbons is not, in the last analysis, very important. What is important is that these substances had a colossal reserve of chemical energy which gave them the possibility of developing further and increasing their complexity. They contain, hidden within themselves, particles of that fire, that heat, that energy which the Earth so generously and prodigally scattered into the cold region of interstellar space. The hidden fire, this energy, served as the basis for the life that was to come.

From the Organic Substance to the Living Thing

In the last section we left off our discussion of the Earth at the time when it was gradually cooling and going over from being a red star to being a dark planet. Finally the time came when the temperature of the surface layers of the Earth fell to 100°C. It became possible for water to exist in the form of liquid drops. Continuous downpours of rain fell upon the surface of the Earth from the moist atmosphere. They inundated it and formed a cover of water in the form of the original boiling ocean.

The first organic substances which had hitherto remained in the atmosphere were now dissolved in the water and fell to the ground with it. What were these substances?

We have already remarked on their main property at the end of the last section. They were substances having a large store of chemical energy and possessing great chemical potentialities. While still in the terrestrial atmosphere they had begun to combine with one another to give rise to very complicated compounds. In addition, they combined with oxygen and ammonia to give hydroxy and amino-derivatives of hydrocarbons (i.e. compounds of hydrocarbons with oxygen and nitrogen respectively).

When these substances fell from the atmosphere into the primaeval ocean they did not stop interacting with one another. Individual components of organic substances floating in the water met and combined with one another. Thus ever larger and more complicated particles were formed.

We can easily create a fairly accurate picture for ourselves of this process of aggregation (polymerization) of organic substances on the Earth by studying it in our chemical laboratories. In fact, the conditions in which organic substances existed in the stage of development of the Earth which we are dealing with can be achieved comparatively easily in our present-day laboratories. If we submit such substances as hydrocarbon radicals to the conditions described above and leave them to themselves we shall find the

226

whole chain of reactions set out above taking place. The hydrocarbon radicals will be oxidized at the expense of the oxygen in the water and air to give the greatest variety of derivatives (alcohols, aldehydes, acids, etc.). This process takes place specially quickly at high temperatures and in the presence of iron and other metals.

Oxidized hydrocarbons readily combine with one another to form more complicated compounds. Many of these substances can also combine with ammonia and give rise to the development of the most varied nitrogen derivatives.

The process of aggregation of organic substances usually occurs rather slowly it is true. However, this is not very important. Whether it takes several months or several years, we still get, as a result of these processes, a mixture of various substances having a very complicated structure.

In these mixtures we may even find, among others, compounds of the nature of carbohydrates* and proteins. Both of these types of compounds play an important part in the structure of living material. We find them in all animals and plants without exception. In combination with other and yet more complicated substances they are, as it were, the foundation of life.

Of course, the substances which we produce artificially are not exactly the ones which can be isolated from living organisms. However, they are, if we may express it so, related to these compounds. The elementary composition, the structure of the particles and the chemical properties are almost the same in the one as in the other. The difference is only in detail.

The substances obtained by the method described above can serve as good nutrient material. They are specially nutritious for micro-organisms such as bacteria and moulds. This fact is specially important and we shall give a little more time to it.

One of the main objections brought against the possibility of the spontaneous generation of life in the distant past has been put in its general aspects as follows:

'If we assume', says W. Preyer, one of the opponents of the theory of spontaneous generation, 'that at some time during the development of the Earth living material arose by primary generation from non-living material then we must suppose that this is still possible. However, the failure of numerous attempts directed towards finding out how to do this has shown that it is unlikely to the highest degree. If, on the other hand, those studying

---

*Carbohydrates are organic substances composed of carbon, hydrogen and oxygen, the hydrogen and oxygen being present in the same proportions as in water. The various sugars such as glucose, sucrose and fructose as well as starch and cellulose are typical examples of carbohydrates.

the first emergence of life assume that it was only possible at some time in the distant past, but now cannot take place; this is also improbable since the conditions required for pursuing life exist now and in fact must also have existed at the time when it is presumed that living material originated from inorganic substances, otherwise the product of the first origin could not have remained alive for long. It is therefore hard to see exactly what is lacking at the present time when primary generation is impossible.'

We have already seen in the last section, that at present what are lacking above all are those substances containing much chemical energy which are the only things from which life could develop and which, themselves, could only be formed at extremely high temperatures. However, even if such substances were formed now in some place on the Earth, they could not proceed far in their development. At a certain stage of that development they would be eaten, one after the other. Destroyed by the ubiquitous bacteria which inhabit our soil, water and air.

Matters were different in that distant period of the existence of the Earth when organic substances first arose, when, as we believe, the Earth was barren and sterile. There were no bacteria nor any other micro-organisms on it, and the organic substances were perfectly free to indulge their tendency to undergo transformations for many, many thousands of years.

It is, of course, hard to say what these transformations were and what sort of substances resulted from them. The only thing that is certain is that these transformations were mainly directed towards an aggregation of material and the formation of more and more complicated and larger and larger particles.

However, we have seen in one of the preceding sections that substances with large and complicated particles have a great tendency to form colloidal solutions in water. Sooner or later such colloidal solutions of organic substances must have come into being in the watery covering of the Earth and once they had arisen they continued to exist, their molecules becoming more complicated and larger as time went on.

The state of colloidal solution is not, however, stable. For various, sometimes extremely slight causes, the dissolved substances come out of the colloidal solution in the form of precipitates, coagula or gels. It is impossible, incredible, to suppose that in the course of many hundreds or even thousands of years during which the terrestrial globe existed, the conditions did not arise 'by chance' somewhere which would lead to the formation of a gel in a colloidal solution. Such formation of aggregated pieces of organic material floating freely in the boundless watery spaces of the ocean which gave rise to them must certainly have occurred at some time in the existence of the Earth.

The moment when the gel was precipitated or the first coagulum formed, marked an extremely important stage in the process of the spontaneous generation of life. At this moment material which had formerly been structureless first acquired a structure and the transformation of organic compounds into an organic body took place. Not only this, but at the same time the body became an individual. Before this it had been inseparably fused with all the rest of the world, dissolved in it. Now, however, it separated itself out, though still very imperfectly, from that world and set itself apart from the environment surrounding it.

With certain reservations we can even consider that first piece of organic slime which came into being on the Earth as being the first organism. In fact it must have had many of those features which we now consider characteristic of life. It was composed of organic substances, it had a definite and complicated structure which was completely characteristic of it. It had a considerable store of chemical energy enabling it to undergo further transformations. Finally, even if it could not metabolize in the full sense of the word, it must certainly have had the ability to nourish itself, to absorb and assimilate substances from its environment, for this is present in every organic gel.

It is hard to say precisely how the further development of this first organism went on, but still it is quite possible to establish the general direction of that development. Let us assume that in one of the corners of the Earth, in the turbulent waves of the ocean, there were formed, either at the same time or one after the other, two bits of gel. Even if they separated out from the same solution they could not have been exactly alike. In one way or another they must have differed, for absolute identity does not exist on the Earth. Both bits were formed and floated in something that was not just water. They were immersed, so to speak, in a nutrient mixture, in a solution, though a very weak one, of different substances, among which there were various organic compounds. And each of these bits of slime absorbed these substances from the medium which surrounded it. Each grew at the expense of these substances, but as each bit had a different structure from the other they assimilated the material from the environment at different rates, one faster, the other slower. The one with the physico-chemical organization which made it possible to carry out the process of assimilation of hitherto foreign substances from the environment more quickly also grew faster than its weaker, less well-organized comrade. The more it grew and the larger its surface became the wider became this difference in the rate of growth.

As this went on the danger of the piece losing its wholeness by breaking or being broken up into larger or smaller parts also increased. This must have happened to different pieces in quite different ways for purely mechanical reasons, such as the breaking of waves or surf, or it may have been due to surface tension. All the same, in one way or another, sooner or later it must have happened. The bit of gel could not go on growing for ever as a continuous mass. It must have broken down and given rise to new pieces, new 'primitive organisms'. These latter were constructed or organized just like their parent though, of course, they only constituted parts of its body, and therefore their structure was inherited by them from the gel from which they were formed.

This structure, however, was not something immutable or constant. Naturally it depended to some extent on the chemical composition of the gel, but this was changing all the time. New substances were continually entering it from the external medium, new compounds were always being incorporated into its body and its physical and chemical structure was continually changing.

The bits which were formed by the breaking up of the original gel were, of course, similar to one another at first, but after division each followed its own path. Each began to grow independently and the structure of each began to undergo changes which were peculiar to itself. This meant that even after quite a short time the sister fragments must have differed from one another in their structure. The old story must have been repeated. The more efficiently constructed ones began to grow faster and the less efficient lagged behind in their growth.

This was repeated for many, many years. The structure of one gel with all the changes which had arisen in it was acquired and inherited by all the bits which owed their origin to the break up of that gel. The newly formed bits grew more, their structure again underwent changes in one way or another and the changes were once more transmitted to their offspring.

However, in the course of this process of change, selection of the better organized bits of gel was always going on. It is true that the less well organized could grow alongside the more efficient but they must have soon stopped growing. Even when there was enough of the dissolved nutrient substances for all, the leading part was always played by the qualitatively better organized entities. The growth in mass of the gels followed a geometrical progression and therefore bodies which had even a relatively slight superiority soon outstripped their less efficient comrades in regard to their growth and development. Thus, slowly but surely, from generation to generation, over many thousands of years, there took place an improvement of the physico-chemical structure of the gels, an improvement mainly directed towards increasing the efficiency of the apparatus for absorption and assimilation of nutrient compounds. On this basis a whole series of new properties must have arisen which had been absent from the original gel, among others the ability to metabolize.

Present-day organisms burn up in their bodies a part of the material which they absorb from their environment. This is inevitable as it is only by means of the energy obtained by this burning that the further growth of their protoplasm and further assimilation of nutrients can take place. In just the same way, too, the original organisms, when they had used up a considerable amount of the energy concealed in them, had to resort to a process of respiration or fermentation to acquire the energy they needed for their further growth and development. Only those among them which, during the preceding transformations, had developed within themselves an apparatus enabling them to burn or ferment, more or less quickly, a part of the nutrient substances absorbed by them, could grow and develop further. The rest must have halted in their development.

However, there arose among those fortunate ones which had developed this power of metabolism, a fierce struggle for existence, a fight to the death. The amount of nutrient organic material in the surrounding medium was getting less. Part of it had already been absorbed by the organisms, while part was broken down, burnt up in the process of respiration or fermentation. Only the most complicated and efficient could grow and develop, all the rest either ceased to develop or perished. The further life progressed the less nutrient substances were available to the organisms and the more strongly and bitterly the struggle for existence was waged and the stricter and stricter became 'natural selection', rejecting all that was weak or backward and allowing only the most efficient to live.

At last the time came when all, or almost all, of the organic substances which had hitherto served as the only food of the original living things had disappeared. Now only those organisms which could adapt themselves to the new conditions of life were able to maintain and prolong their existence. For this purpose there were only two paths open to them: either they could continue to use their old means of nutrition, acquiring the organic substances which they needed for their nutrition by eating their weaker comrades, or they could turn in a new direction and develop, create within themselves, an apparatus which would enable them to nourish themselves on very simple inorganic compounds.

Only those living things which followed one of these courses could preserve themselves for further life. Having developed and perfected themselves further they finally gave rise to all the forms of organisms which we can now observe.

If we turn to the study of these modern forms, investigating their internal structure and getting to know their means of nutrition, we shall see that the few facts which we have in this field are in complete accord with the hypothesis as to the origin of life. The internal structure of the cells of modern organisms is always changing, becoming more efficient and more complicated. It is only because of the imperfection of our methods of study that we cannot observe this directly and that this structure appears to us as something constant, cast in a definite and final form. This is not, in fact, true. If we compare the internal structure of the cells of higher and lower organisms we shall find a considerable difference between them. The cells of bacteria or blue-green algae have a considerably simpler internal organization than those of higher animals and plants. This is because these micro-organisms which stand on the lowest step of the systematic ladder, are the direct descendants of the most ancient classes of organisms. They have halted their development and retained unchanged all the features of the structure of their distant ancestors while all other living things, by continually altering and improving themselves, have attained a more complicated form of cell-structure.

Thus, the direct study of modern organisms convinces us that those forms which have a very complicated internal organization of their cells have arisen from simpler forms by successive changes and improvements. If this is so, then we have no reason to deny that these comparatively simple forms arose, in their turn, from beings which had an even simpler organization, one which even approached that of a colloidal gel. It is true that no trace of these primitive living things now remains on the Earth, but this is no proof that they never existed. It should not be forgotten that at a certain period of the existence of the Earth they must have been completely wiped out by their more highly organized comrades.

We obtain even more interesting evidence from the study of the means of nutrition of our modern organisms. A considerable proportion of organisms – bacteria, fungi and animals – can only feed on organic substances. It must be pointed out that this is the method of nutrition used by the least highly organized living things such as the rhizomastigina and protomastigina which are regarded by all present-day systematists as representatives of the kinds of organisms which were the ancestors of all the living things on the Earth. This fact fully supports the idea that the method of consuming organic substances is the most ancient means of nutrition. The power of independent, 'autotrophic' feeding could only develop later as a result of a number of internal transformations and changes in their physico-chemical structure. It could not, however, develop all at once. Our knowledge of the means of nutrition of modern lower and higher organisms leads us to the conclusion that living things underwent many changes and tried out many possibilities before they could achieve the best form of independent nourishment or inorganic substances. Among the lowest organisms, the bacteria, we find alongside forms which are nourished solely on organic materials, other forms which have set up within themselves an apparatus which enables them to feed in another way. Here we can observe an amazing variety of modes of nutrition, means by which organisms try to extract the energy they need for life from the inorganic medium surrounding them. One of them obtains this energy by converting hydrogen sulphide dissolved in the water into sulphuric acid. For the same purpose another converts ammonia into nitrous and nitric acids while a third transforms reduced iron salts into oxidized ones. Whether we like it or not, we get the impression that all these various forms of nutrition have been devised because the organisms were forced to find some way out, something which would enable them to exist in the absence of dissolved organic materials.

However, not one of these forms of independent nutrition became widely used among organisms. All these methods of obtaining the energy required for life from terrestrial sources were found to be inefficient. A far more efficient method was one based on the absorption and use of the energy which the Sun sends to us on the Earth in the form of rays of light. All present-day green plants, from the tiny single-celled algae of our ponds to the mighty giant trees of the tropical forests use just this means of nutrition. By means of a very complicated apparatus, in which the green pigment chlorophyll plays an essential part, these organisms trap the energy of the Sun's rays which fall on them and, with its help, break down the abundant carbon dioxide in the air. As a result of this breakdown the plants acquire the possibility of using the carbon in the carbon dioxide to build up new organic substances which also serve as nourishment for them. The form of nutrition described is very efficient but also very complicated. There can be no doubt that the extremely complicated physico-chemical apparatus needed for it could only have been created as a result of a long series of transformations and alterations of the living cell. We must therefore regard it as the latest and newest form of nutrition.

With this we end our discussion of the origin of life. In our minds we have followed a long path from the incandescent atoms of carbon of the earliest nebula to the living things of our times. We have seen how it is possible to explain the origin of life while basing our ideas all the time on scientifically established facts. Of course, the explanation given here is only one of those possible. We still have very few facts available to enable us to maintain with complete certainty that the process under discussion took place in just this way and not somehow else. We still know very, very little about the structure of colloidal gels and even less about the physico-chemical structure of protoplasm. But this ignorance of ours is certainly only temporary. What we do not know today we shall know tomorrow. A whole army of biologists is studying the structure and organization of living matter, while a no less number of physicists and chemists are daily revealing to us new properties of dead things. Like two parties of workers boring from the two opposite ends of a tunnel, they are working towards the same goal. The work has already gone a long way and very, very soon the last barriers between the living and the dead will crumble under the attack of patient work and powerful scientific thought.

Comments on Oparin's Paper on the Origin of Life

THIS paper by Oparin on the origin of life, which appeared in Russian in 1924, has been taken to represent the first and principal modern appreciation of the problem. Although it is one of the most often cited papers in the literature on the subject, this is the first time, as far as I can ascertain, that it has appeared in English. The English translation published in 1938 was based on Oparin's book published in 1936, which was virtually a second, and considerably revised, edition of the 1924 paper. On reading it now it is necessary to recall the state of knowledge at that time and to appreciate that it could not contain basic facts discovered after that date. Indeed, in 1924 modern biology, and particularly molecular biology, had hardly started. Even biochemistry itself was only in its first stages. In Haldane's book, *Enzymes* (1930), an enzyme is described as 'a soluble, colloidal, organic catalyst, produced by a living organism'.

On the other side, the theories on the origin of the solar system were still under the influence of untenable theories, old and new, such as that of its arising from a solar filament. It should be said that Oparin himself does not use this theory, but here assumes one of its most relevant consequences, that of the Earth first appearing in a high-temperature gas and dust form and then cooling down and solidifying.

Oparin's paper is really a monograph. It must not be considered as the fruit of long study by an expert, but rather as a young man's fresh approach to an old problem. It marked the beginning rather than the end of a new phase in the understanding of the processes involved in the origin of life; a beginning which has been followed up ever since then by Oparin himself and from which many researches of other people have stemmed. From these, one can except Haldane's approach, which, apparently, was quite independent.

The monograph is divided into five sections:

1. The theory of spontaneous generation;
2. The theory of panspermia;
3. The world of the living and the world of the dead;

4. From uncombined elements to organic compounds;
5. From the organic substance to the living thing.

The first two are concerned with the history of ideas on the origin of life. The very titles indicate their inspiration by the controversies of the nineteenth century, particularly the great debate between Pasteur and Pouchet on spontaneous generation. The apparent defeat of Pouchet made it very difficult to account for any natural origin of life, and the refutation of this view appears to have been very largely the inspiration of Oparin's work. He had to show that it was not really relevant to the problem. The spontaneous origin of life might be impossible to reproduce now, but under conditions in the dim and distant past it might well have occurred.

Another approach is discussed in the second section, the theory of panspermia. Oparin here shows that it also is essentially irrelevant. At any rate, it has nothing to do with the terrestrial origins of life because, even if it could be shown that life could come from outer space by a difficult and chancy process, it would still be necessary to explain how it arose in the first place. Panspermia only solves the problem of the origin of earthly life by multiplying it into an even more difficult one.

The third section begins to touch on Oparin's own contribution. It is one characteristic of a biochemist. It had been agreed ever since the work of Wöhler in 1828 that the elements of life were not specifically organic but were the same elements as were to be found in the Earth and the Sun. Here the differences observed were those of the extra complexity of the compounds involved in life and in the special mode of their transformation, where enzymes were involved, working at low temperatures in dilute solutions. Oparin raised the point that in this they resemble inorganic catalysts. At that time he did not go much further because very little was known about enzymes or about their mode of action, but this was to point the way to later analyses of proteins and the discovery of their genesis. It is in Section 2 that Oparin brings in the work of Graham and his recognition of the difference between crystalloids and colloids. Oparin saw it as pointing to life in the phenomena of colloids, particularly in the form of gels and coagulates. He saw in this the birth of the idea of coacervates, on which he was to do so much work in succeeding years. Here Oparin is following out the idea that in the coagulates we have the model of the first organisms. By dealing with them in a synthetic manner, Oparin attempts to bridge the main difference between the living and the dead, and, at the same time, abandons the old hypothesis of protoplasm, which he considers to be a colloidal substance of great complexity. In 1924, in the absence of a microscope of sufficient power, the degree of that complexity could not be dreamed of. It had to wait for two decades until the electron microscope was sufficiently developed. It is natural, therefore, that Oparin had to accept as the guiding idea of the genesis of organisms the ancient notion of matter and form:

All the same it is certain that protoplasm has a definite structure and is not a homogeneous lump of slime. This structure holds the secret of life. Destroy it and there will remain in your hands a lifeless mixture of organic compounds.

As the structure of protoplasm had

a whole network, a whole skein of fine threads which are interlaced, separating from one another and coming together again in a definite, complicated order. . . . There is no essential difference between the structure of coagula and that of protoplasm.

This knowledge Oparin then uses to explain in principle the general phenomena of metabolism: 'the ability of living organisms to metabolize to reproduce themselves and to respond to stimuli'.

His consideration of crystals, which also have the capacity of growth and replication of form, came very close to modern ideas of self-reproduction, which has been found to be the key to molecular biology, whose ideas were at that time far below the horizon of research.

Oparin continues by pointing to physical explanations of biological responses to stimuli, likening them to the discharge of unstable systems by some action-initiating nucleus, as in explosions. He concludes by saying:

The specific peculiarity of living organisms is only that in them there have been collected and integrated an extremely complicated combination of a large number of properties and characteristics which are present in isolation in various dead, inorganic bodies. Life is not characterized by any special properties but by a definite, specific combination of these properties.

The fourth section, which is Oparin's most original contribution to the question of the origin of life, is entitled 'From Uncombined Elements to Organic Compounds'. This is the forward-looking explanation of the thesis which inspires the whole work. At that time it was necessary to restate in modern terms the kind of historic process which might have led to life appearing on the Earth, in what I have called, in my own work, the myth.

Oparin had before him the task primarily of making the nature of the origin of life conceivable and defendable. He begins with cosmogony, the astronomical history of the Earth's formation, following Mendeleev, and bringing it up to date with his theory of the genesis of carbonaceous molecules through the interaction of water and metallic carbides. It is this part of the work which has suffered most from the changes in our knowledge of the

237

stars and planets and particularly of the inner structure of the Earth. The change over from a concept of an Earth primarily at high temperatures to one assembled from cosmic dust, with the surface at least always cool, has been the biggest change. Nevertheless, the differences in these theories on the origin of life turn out to be minimal. Nobody had worked out the nature of the crust on either hypothesis and therefore no one could discriminate between their results. The main difference lies in the presence or absence of carbonaceous and carbon and nitrogen compounds.

The idea that a complex organic compound can be formed from simple molecules was arrived at by logical deductions from the very existence of such compound structures in life. The experiments of Miller and his successors on the actual synthesis of such compounds from simple molecules, ultimately inspired by Oparin, were still more than a quarter of a century away.

The origin of the carbon compounds was traced by Oparin, following Mendeleev, to the interaction of the water in the primitive atmosphere, with the carbides formed in the iron core of the Earth. Oparin, at this stage, had not arrived at the idea of a primitive atmosphere without oxygen, for he says:

These compounds must also have arisen when the carbides and steam met on the surface of the Earth. Of course some of these must immediately have been burnt, being oxidized by the oxygen of the air. However, under the conditions then prevailing, this combustion must have been far from complete.

He supported his arguments further by considering the composition of the comets and meteorites:

This composition of the meteorites is an extra confirmation of the correctness of the view that carbon exists on heavenly bodies in the form of mixtures or chemical compounds with metals . . . Thus, all the considerations and facts which we have put forward above convince us that, even it not all the carbon, at least a great part of it, first appeared on the surface of the Earth, not in the form of the chemically inert carbon dioxide as had been thought, but in the form of unstable organic compounds capable of further transformation.

Oparin goes further to consider the formation of nitrogen compounds though he traces their origin to cyanogen, formed by the reaction of the metallic nitrides with carbon compounds. He quotes Pflüger,

Therefore life arises from fire and its basis is derived from the time when the world was still a white-hot, incandescent globe.

From this he jumps to molecular proteins:

238

As a result of these transformations they gave rise to 'that self-transforming protein which constitutes living matter'.

He subjects this hypothesis, at the same time, to a serious criticism.

The fifth and final section, 'From the Organic Substance to the Living Thing', traces the chemical evolution of complex carbon and nitrogen compounds in the primitive seas of the Earth. Here Oparin makes a very large assumption:

We can easily create a fairly accurate picture for ourselves of this process of aggregation (polymerization) of organic substances on the Earth by studying it in our chemical laboratories. In fact, the conditions in which organic substances existed in the stage of development of the Earth which we are dealing with can be achieved comparatively easily in our present-day laboratories.

Of course, the substances which we produce artificially are not exactly the ones which can be isolated from living organisms. However, they are, if we may express it so, related to these compounds. The elementary composition, the structure of the particles and the chemical properties are almost the same in the one as in the other. The difference is only in detail.

The modern biochemist has to abandon the idea that anything can be deduced from the experiments carried out now as to the impossibility of the independent origin of life.

However, even if such substances were formed now in some place on the Earth, they could not proceed far in their development. At a certain stage of that development they would be eaten, one after the other, destroyed by the ubiquitous bacteria which inhabit our soil, water and air.

The last few pages of the thesis are the most tantalizing. They are really the programme of work on studying chemical-physical and physical-chemical conditions of the complex organic substances involved in colloids in the primitive ocean. Oparin depends much on the idea that the source of free energy must be present. As to the further development of life, he sees this as a matter of chemical evolution envisaged as a competition and struggle for existence between different globules. These are not molecules but coacervate droplets, where natural selection favours the better organized fragments.

However, in the course of this process of change, selection of the better organized bits of gel was always going on. It is true that the less well organized could grow alongside the more efficient but they must have soon stopped growing. Even when there was enough of the dissolved nutrient substances for all, the leading part was always played by the qualitatively better organized entities.

The last few pages touch on other key problems in the maintenance of life and the renewed accumulation of energy in the primitive soup involved in taking in energy continuously from outside:

At last the time came when all or almost all of the organic substances which had hitherto served as the only food of the original living things had disappeared. Now only those organisms which could adapt themselves to the new conditions of life were able to maintain and prolong their existence. For this purpose there were only two paths open to them: either they could continue to use their old means of nutrition, acquiring the organic substances which they needed for their nutrition by eating their weaker comrades, or they could turn in a new direction and develop, create within themselves, an apparatus which would enable them to nourish themselves on very simple inorganic compounds.

Oparin realized that this was a problem of extreme complexity and required the most vigorous further research:

If we compare the internal structure of the cells of higher and lower organisms we shall find a considerable difference between them. The cells of bacteria or blue-green algae have a considerably simpler internal organization than those of higher animals and plants. This is because these micro-organisms, which stand on the lowest step of the systematic ladder, are the direct descendants of the most ancient classes of organisms.

And he sees the need to complete this mere verbal description by a new appreciation of microbiology, the discovery, so to speak, in detail of living forces:

Our knowledge of the means of nutrition of modern lower and higher organisms leads us to the conclusion that living things underwent many changes and tried out many possibilities before they could achieve the best form of independent nourishment or inorganic substances.

It can be seen that Oparin's essay contains in itself the germs of a new programme in chemical and biological research. It was a programme that he largely carried out himself in the ensuing years, but it also inspired the work of many other people. There is great value to be found in setting out a clear programme or declaration of intention. The programme may, afterwards, be remodelled or even, if necessary, changed, but it must serve as a starting-point. In many of the best achievements in the history of scientific thought, the young worker must start out by revealing the necessary condition of his ignorance but this is a fertile ignorance. Oparin's programme does not answer all the questions, in fact, he hardly answers any, but the questions he asks are very effective and pregnant ones and have given rise to an enormous amount of research in the four decades since it was written. The essential thing in the first place is not to solve the problems, but to see them. This is true of the greatest of all scientists, Newton, and also of Lavoisier, who consciously set about to make a revolution in chemistry and, finally, Pasteur from whose work all the key ideas on the biochemical nature of the origin of life have sprung. In particular, the distinction made between aerobic and anaerobic life was Pasteur's discovery and Oparin used it ultimately to lean towards the hypothesis of an early atmosphere without oxygen.

If we take the successive publications of Oparin on the subject of the origin of life [see main Bibliography], it can be seen that they have all been modified and in many cases even reversed; but in every case these reversals have been imposed by discoveries either in biochemistry or in cosmology. This paper is important because it is a starting-point for all the others and, though it is clearly defective and inaccurate, it can be, and has been, corrected in the sequel. This, in my opinion, fully justifies its republication in its original form.

The Origin of Life

J. B. S. Haldane

UNTIL about 150 years ago it was generally believed that living beings were constantly arising out of dead matter. Maggots were supposed to be generated spontaneously in decaying meat. In 1668 Redi showed that this did not happen provided insects were carefully excluded. And in 1860 Pasteur extended the proof to the bacteria which he had shown were the cause of putrefaction. It seemed fairly clear that all the living beings known to us originate from other living beings. At the same time Darwin gave a new emotional interest to the problem. It had appeared unimportant that a few worms should originate from mud. But if man was descended from worms such spontaneous generation acquired a new significance. The origin of life on the Earth would have been as casual an affair as the evolution of monkeys into man. Even if the latter stages of man's history were due to natural causes, pride clung to a supernatural, or at least surprising, mode of origin for his ultimate ancestors. So it was with a sigh of relief that a good many men, whom Darwin's arguments had convinced, accepted the conclusion of Pasteur that life can originate only from life. It was possible either to suppose that life had been supernaturally created on Earth some millions of years ago, or that it had been brought to Earth by a meteorite or by microorganisms floating through interstellar space. But a large number, perhaps the majority, of biologists, believed, in spite of Pasteur, that at some time in the remote past life had originated on Earth from dead matter as the result of natural processes.

The more ardent materialists tried to fill in the details of this process, but without complete success. Oddly enough, the few scientific men who professed idealism agreed with them. For if one can find evidences of mind (in religious terminology the finger of God) in the most ordinary events, even those which go on in the chemical laboratory, one can without much difficulty believe in the origin of life from such processes. Pasteur's work therefore appealed most strongly to those who desired to stress the contrast between mind and matter. For a variety of obscure historical reasons, the

Christian Churches have taken this latter point of view. But it should never be forgotten that the early Christians held many views which are now regarded as materialistic. They believed in the resurrection of the body, not the immortality of the soul. St Paul seems to have attributed consciousness and will to the body. He used a phrase translated in the revised version as 'the mind of the flesh', and credited the flesh with a capacity for hatred, wrath, and other mental functions. Many modern physiologists hold similar beliefs. But, perhaps unfortunately for Christianity, the Church was captured by a group of very inferior Greek philosophers in the third and fourth centuries AD. Since that date views as to the relation between mind and body which St Paul, at least, did not hold, have been regarded as part of Christianity, and have retarded the progress of science.

It is hard to believe that any lapse of time will dim the glory of Pasteur's positive achievements. He published singularly few experimental results. It has even been suggested by a cynic that his entire work would not gain a Doctorate of Philosophy today! But every experiment was final. I have never heard of any one who has repeated any experiment of Pasteur's with a result different from that of the master. Yet his deductions from these experiments were sometimes too sweeping. It is perhaps not quite irrelevant that he worked in his latter years with half a brain. His right cerebral hemisphere had been extensively wrecked by the bursting of an artery when he was only forty-five years old; and the united brain-power of the microbiologists who succeeded him has barely compensated for that accident. Even during his lifetime some of the conclusions which he had drawn from his experimental work were disproved. He had said that alcoholic fermentation was impossible without life. Buchner obtained it with a cell-free and dead extract of yeast. And since his death the gap between life and matter has been greatly narrowed.

When Darwin deduced the animal origin of man, a search began for a 'missing link' between ourselves and the apes. When Dubois found the bones of Pithecanthropus some comparative anatomists at once proclaimed that they were of animal origin, while others were equally convinced that they were parts of a human skeleton. It is now generally recognized that either party was right, according to the definition of humanity adopted. Pithecanthropus was a creature which might legitimately be described either as a man or an ape, and its existence showed that the distinction between the two was not absolute.

Now the recent study of ultramicroscopic beings has brought up at least one parallel case, that of the bacteriophage, discovered by d'Herelle, who had been to some extent anticipated by Twort. This is the case of a disease,

243

or, at any rate, abnormality of bacteria. Before the size of the atom was known there was no reason to doubt that

> Big fleas have little fleas
> Upon their backs to bite 'em;
> The little ones have lesser ones,
> And so ad infinitum.

But we now know that this is impossible. Roughly speaking, from the point of view of size, the bacillus is the flea's flea, the bacteriophage the bacillus' flea; but the bacteriophage's flea would be of the dimensions of an atom, and atoms do not behave like fleas. In other words, there are only about as many atoms in a cell as cells in a man. The link between living and dead matter is therefore somewhere between a cell and an atom.

D'Herelle found that certain cultures of bacteria began to swell up and burst until all had disappeared. If such cultures were passed through a filter fine enough to keep out all bacteria, the filtrate could infect fresh bacteria, and so on indefinitely. Though the infective agents cannot be seen with a microscope, they can be counted as follows. If an active filtrate containing bacteriophage be poured over a colony of bacteria on a jelly, the bacteria will all, or almost all, disappear. If it be diluted many thousand times, a few islands of living bacteria survive for some time. If it be diluted about ten million fold, the bacteria are destroyed round only a few isolated spots, each representing a single particle of bacteriophage.

Since the bacteriophage multiplies, d'Herelle believes it to be a living organism. Bordet and others have taken an opposite view. It will survive heating and other insults which kill the large majority of organisms, and will multiply only in presence of living bacteria, though it can break up dead ones. Except perhaps in presence of bacteria, it does not use oxygen or display any other signs of life. Bordet and his school therefore regard it as a ferment which breaks up bacteria as our own digestive ferments break up our food, at the same time inducing the disintegrating bacteria to produce more of the same ferment. This is not as fantastic as it sounds, for most cells while dying liberate or activate ferments which digest themselves. But these ferments are certainly feeble when compared with the bacteriophage.

Clearly we are in doubt as to the proper criterion of life. D'Herelle says that the bacteriophage is alive, because, like the flea or the tiger, it can multiply indefinitely at the cost of living beings. His opponents say that it can multiply only as long as its food is alive, whereas the tiger certainly, and the flea probably, can live on dead products of life. They suggest that the bacteriophage is like a book or a work of art, which is constantly being copied by living beings, and is therefore only metaphorically alive, its real life being in its copiers.

The American geneticist Muller has, however, suggested an intermediate view. He compares the bacteriophage to a gene – that is to say, one of the units concerned in heredity. A fully coloured and a spotted dog differ because the latter has in each of its cells one or two of a certain gene, which we know is too small for the microscope to see. Before a cell of a dog divides this gene divides also, so that each of the daughter-cells has one, two, or none according with the number in the parent cell. The ordinary spotted dog is healthy, but a gene common among German dogs causes a roan colour when one is present, while two make the dog nearly white, wall-eyed and generally deaf, blind or both. Most of such dogs die young, and the analogy to the bacteriophage is fairly close. The main difference between such a lethal gene, of which many are known, and the bacteriophage, is that the one is only known inside the cell, the other outside. In the present state of our ignorance we may regard the gene either as a tiny organism which can divide in the environment provided by the rest of the cell; or as a bit of machinery which the 'living' cell copies at each division. The truth is probably somewhere in between these two hypotheses.

Unless a living creature is a piece of dead matter plus a soul (a view which finds little support in modern biology) something of the following kind must be true. A simple organism must consist of parts A, B, C, D and so on, each of which can multiply only in presence of all, or almost all, of the others. Among these parts are genes, and the bacteriophage is such a part which has got loose. This hypothesis becomes more plausible if we believe in the work of Hauduroy, who finds that the ultramicroscopic particles into which the bacteria have been broken up, and which pass through filters that can stop the bacteria, occasionally grow up again into bacteria after a lapse of several months. He brings evidence to show that such fragments of bacteria may cause disease, and d'Herelle and Peyre claim to have found the ultramicroscopic form of a common staphylococcus, along with bacteriophage, in cancers, and suspects that this combination may be the cause of that disease.

On this view the bacteriophage is a cog, as it were, in the wheel of a life-cycle of many bacteria. The same bacteriophage can act on different species and is thus, so to say, a spare part which can be fitted into a number of different machines, just as a human diabetic can remain in health when provided with insulin manufactured by a pig. A great many kinds of molecule have been got from cells, and many of them are very efficient when removed from it. One can separate from yeast one of the many tools which it uses in alcoholic fermentation, an enzyme called invertase, and this will break up six times its weight of cane-sugar per second for an indefinite time without wearing out. As it does not form alcohol from the sugar, but only a sticky mixture of other sugars, its use is permitted in the United States in the manufacture of confectionery and cake-icing. But such fragments do not reproduce themselves, though they take part in the assimilation of food by the living cell. No one supposes that they are alive. The bacteriophage is a step beyond the enzyme on the road to life, but it is perhaps an exaggeration to call it fully alive. At about the same stage on the road are the viruses which cause such diseases as smallpox, herpes, and hydrophobia. They can multiply only in living tissue, and pass through filters which stop bacteria.

With these facts in mind we may, I think, legitimately speculate on the origin of life on this planet. Within a few thousand years from its origin it probably cooled down so far as to develop a fairly permanent solid crust. For a long time, however, this crust must have been above the boiling-point of water, which condensed only gradually. The primitive atmosphere probably contained little or no oxygen, for our present supply of that gas is only about enough to burn all the coal and other organic remains found below and on the Earth's surface. On the other hand, almost all the carbon of these organic substances, and much of the carbon now combined in chalk, limestone, and dolomite, were in the atmosphere as carbon dioxide. Probably a good deal of the nitrogen now in the air was combined with metals as nitride in the Earth's crust, so that ammonia was constantly being formed by the action of water. The Sun was perhaps slightly brighter than it is now, and as there was no oxygen in the atmosphere the chemically active ultra-violet rays from the Sun were not, as they now are, mainly stopped by ozone (a modified form of oxygen) in the upper atmosphere, and oxygen itself lower down. They penetrated to the surface of the land and sea, or at least to the clouds.

Now, when ultra-violet light acts on a mixture of water, carbon dioxide, and ammonia, a vast variety of organic substances are made, including sugars and apparently some of the materials from which proteins are built up. This fact has been demonstrated in the laboratory by Baly of Liverpool and his colleagues. In this present world, such substances, if left about, decay – that is to say, they are destroyed by micro-organisms. But before the origin of life they must have accumulated till the primitive oceans reached the consistency of hot dilute soup. Today an organism must trust to luck, skill, or strength to obtain its food. The first precursors of life found food available in considerable quantities, and had no competitors in the struggle for existence. As the primitive atmosphere contained little or no oxygen, they must have obtained the energy which they needed for growth by some other process than oxidation – in fact, by fermentation. For, as Pasteur put it, fermentation is life without oxygen. If this was so, we should expect that high organisms like ourselves would start life as anaerobic beings, just as we start as single cells. This is the case. Embryo chicks for the first two or three days after fertilization use very little oxygen, but obtain the energy which they need for growth by fermenting sugar into lactic acid, like the bacteria which turns milk sour. So do various embryo mammals, and in all probability you and I lived mainly by fermentation during the first week of our pre-natal life. The cancer cell behaves in the same way. Warburg has shown that with its embryonic habit of unrestricted growth there goes an embryonic habit of fermentation.

The first living or half-living things were probably large molecules synthesized under the influence of the Sun's radiation, and only capable of reproduction in the particularly favourable medium in which they originated. Each presumably required a variety of highly specialized molecules before it could reproduce itself, and it depended on chance for a supply of them. This is the case today with most viruses, including the bacteriophage, which can grow only in presence of the complicated assortment of molecules found in a living cell.

The unicellular organisms, including bacteria, which were the simplest living things known a generation ago, are far more complicated. They are organisms – that is to say, systems whose parts co-operate. Each part is specialized to a particular chemical function, and prepares chemical molecules suitable for the growth of the other parts. In consequence, the cell as a whole can usually subsist on a few types of molecule, which are transformed within it into the more complex substances needed for the growth of the parts.

The cell consists of numerous half-living chemical molecules suspended in water and enclosed in an oily film. When the whole sea was a vast chemical laboratory the conditions for the formation of such films must have been relatively favourable; but for all that life may have remained in the virus stage for many millions of years before a suitable assemblage of elementary units was brought together in the first cell. There must have been many failures, but the first successful cell had plenty of food, and an immense advantage over its competitors.

It is probable that all organisms now alive are descended from one ancestor, for the following reason. Most of our structural molecules are asymmetrical, as shown by the fact that they rotate the plane of polarized light, and often form asymmetrical crystals. But of the two possible types of any such molecule, related to one another like a right and left boot, only one

247

is found throughout living nature. The apparent exceptions to this rule are all small molecules which are not used in the building of the large structures which display the phenomena of life. There is nothing, so far as we can see, in the nature of things to prevent the existence of looking-glass organisms built from molecules which are, so to say, the mirror-images of those in our own bodies. Many of the requisite molecules have already been made in the laboratory. If life had originated independently on several occasions, such organisms would probably exist. As they do not, this event probably occurred only once, or, more probably, the descendants of the first living organism rapidly evolved far enough to overwhelm any later competitors when these arrived on the scene.

As the primitive organisms used up the foodstuffs available in the sea some of them began to perform in their own bodies the synthesis formerly performed haphazardly by the sunlight, thus ensuring a liberal supply of food. The first plants thus came into existence, living near the surface of the ocean, and making food with the aid of sunlight as do their descendants today. It is thought by many biologists that we animals are descended from them. Among the molecules in our own bodies are a number whose structure resembles that of chlorophyll, the green pigment with which the plants have harnessed the sunlight to their needs. We use them for other purposes than the plants – for example, for carrying oxygen – and we do not, of course, know whether they are, so to speak, descendants of chlorophyll or merely cousins. But since the oxygen liberated by the first plants must have killed off most of the other organisms, the former view is the more plausible.

The above conclusions are speculative. They will remain so until living creatures have been synthesized in the biochemical laboratory. We are a long way from that goal. It was only this year that Pictel for the first time made cane-sugar artificially. It is doubtful whether any enzyme has been obtained quite pure. Nevertheless I hope to live to see one made artificially. I do not think I shall behold the synthesis of anything so nearly alive as a bacteriophage or a virus, and I do not suppose that a self-contained organism will be made for centuries. Until that is done the origin of life will remain a subject for speculation. But such speculation is not idle, because it is susceptible of experimental proof or disproof.

Some people will consider it a sufficient refutation of the above theories to say that they are materialistic, and that materialism can be refuted on philosophical grounds. They are no doubt compatible with materialism, but also with other philosophical tenets. The facts are, after all, fairly plain. Just as we know of sight only in connection with a particular kind of material system called the eye, so we know only of life in connection with certain arrangements of matter, of which the biochemist can give a good, but far from complete, account. The question at issue is: 'How did the first such system on this planet originate?' This is a historical problem to which I have given a very tentative answer on the not unreasonable hypothesis that a thousand million years ago matter obeyed the same laws that it does today.

This answer is compatible, for example, with the view that pre-existent mind or spirit can associate itself with certain kinds of matter. If so, we are left with the mystery as to why mind has so marked a preference for a particular type of colloidal organic substances. Personally I regard all attempts to describe the relation of mind to matter as rather clumsy metaphors. The biochemist knows no more, and no less, about this question than anyone else. His ignorance disqualifies him no more than the historian or the geologist from attempting to solve a historical problem.

From The Rationalist Annual, 1929.

Comments on Haldane's Paper on the Origin of Life

IN this short but brilliant essay of eight pages, Haldane has compressed the leading ideas of the origin of life, which entitle him to be named, with Oparin, of whose work he knew nothing, as the joint originator of modern views on the origin of life. It contains, together for the first time, the two leading ideas which have run through the whole development of the subject: the existence of intermediate forms, in his case those of viruses, in particular bacteriophage d'Herelle; and the idea of an atmosphere that originally contained no oxygen. From the latter he draws the conclusion that at the time of the origin of life ultra-violet light reached the Earth from the Sun and was not cut off by the ozone layer, which would have been present had there been oxygen in the atmosphere. Hence the synthesis of the primitive soup.

As to the experimental basis, Haldane drew, not on Miller, who had not yet performed his experiments, but on Baly of Liverpool, who had shown the ultra-violet induced synthesis of sugars. Primitive organisms, he thought, must have obtained their energy from their food by fermentation, which follows from Pasteur's definition of fermentation as 'life without oxygen'.

Haldane realized that the first organisms could not have been as complicated as even the bacteria today, because the latter are organisms containing systems whose parts cooperate and, consequently, systems which require only a few types of molecules to live on.

He realized, further, that the unity of life is based on the asymmetric character of its molecule. At the end of his essay he speculated as to whether he would live to see artificial enzymes. This he certainly did, for the protein insulin, though strictly a hormone and not an enzyme, was synthesized in 1963.

The origin of life will remain a subject for speculation until a self-contained organism is made, but, as Haldane wrote, 'such speculation is not idle, because it is susceptible to experimental proof or disproof'. He neatly turns the argument about the incompetence of the scientific man on the subjects of the relations of mind and matter by saying that 'the biochemist knows no more and no less about this question than anyone else. His ignorance disqualifies him no more than the historian or the geologist from attempting to solve a historical problem'.

He speculated further as to whether the bacteriophage might not be a gene, about which very little if anything was known at that time apart from its deduction from Mendelian genetics. In a sense, he had followed out the mental processes needed to establish the gene as a material object, without expressly stipulating what kind of material object it was, certainly without any suspicion of the role of DNA.

On reading this essay, one is struck by the extreme justice of Haldane's views and by how far he anticipated things which occurred many years after he had written of them.

It is characteristic of science that the full explanations are often seized in their essence by the percipient scientist long in advance of any possible proof. X-ray analysis and the use of the electron microscope were to elucidate, many years later, the nature of the virus and its action, and this, in turn, was to provide an important clue in the essential coding of nucleic acids into proteins.

However, at the time, Haldane's ideas were dismissed as wild speculations. Only the clarity and beauty of his style and the attractiveness of his character ensured that they were read, albeit in small circles.

Appendix 2

Carbonaceous Meteorites and the Origin of Life

G. Mueller

CERTAIN meteorites contain carbon and are accordingly known as carbonaceous meteorites. Their significance, as far as the origin of life is concerned, is two-fold: (a) the possibility that the carbonaceous content is of biogenic origin; (b) the possible information that may be derived from them of the prebiological cosmological history of organic molecules.

1. History

The controversy regarding the interpretation of the carbonaceous content of meteorites started in the nineteenth century. J.J.Berzelius (1834) considered that it was not of biogenic origin. F.Wöhler (1860), however, claimed that the substances might be of ultimate biogenic origin. In this century, P.E.Spielman (1924) suggested that the organic molecules might have been formed through hydrolysis of carbides in the meteorites with terrestrial water. This interpretation, however, ignores the facts that meteorites collected soon after fall do not show any signs of such a reaction and that the isotopic composition of their water content is different from any terrestrial sample. These early theories were hardly more than speculations, since the classical methods of analysis were unable to provide data on the molecular composition of complex carbonaceous mixtures.

The first detailed study of the carbonaceous complex in the Cold Bokkeveldt meteorite by G.Mueller (1953) led to the conclusion that the assemblage of optically inactive molecules might have been produced through the abiogenic condensation of gases that were escaping from the condensing parent body of the meteorite. Mueller considered that the gas mixtures, which are detected in comets and in other cosmic settings, might have condensed to pre-biogenic carbonaceous complexes which might then have become preserved if the conditions on the parent body were not suitable for the emergence of organisms. From 1953 onwards, a series of experiments (Miller, Ponnamperuma etc., p. 52) showed that the whole range of conceivable cosmic gas mixtures produced complex mixtures of organic

255

molecules when exposed to any high energy agency (ionizing radiation, electrical discharge, etc.).

Then a paper by B. Mason (1960) aroused a new wave of interest in the problem. He proposed that the primary materials of all meteorites were hydrated silicates covered with a partially polymerized carbonaceous layer. These, on heating, would give rise to all the other types of meteorites – the chondrites and achondrites containing the dehydrated silicate, olivine and, on further heating and by the reduction of the iron in the silicates, the stony-iron and iron meteorites. This paper roused the interest of J. D. Bernal in the question of the carbonaceous meteorites, although he did not agree with Mason's theory of origin, and he contacted Mueller regarding the question.

In the meantime, Mason, wishing to get a more accurate analysis of the carbonaceous content of the Orgueil meteorite, sent some of the material to Nagy, Meinschein and Hennessy at the Esso Petroleum Laboratory. They subjected the material to routine tests for types of hydrocarbon and identified a number of paraffinoid hydrocarbon molecules in the C_{15}—C_{30} range, with peaks at C_{18} and C_{23}. They found that the pattern of distribution of these hydrocarbons was sufficiently similar to that observed in material of biological origin such as butter and recent marine sediments, to conclude that the material tested was of biogenic origin. Soon after this, Nagy (1962), in association with the botanist Claus, claimed that he had found 'organized elements' of biogenic origin in Type I (pp. 241f.) carbonaceous chondrites.

A controversy, which still proceeds, on the nature of the carbonaceous content of these meteorites, thus started in 1962.

Briggs and Kitto (1962) reached the conclusion that the microstructures in the Mokoia, Type II meteorite, were open to both biogenic and abiogenic interpretations. On the other hand, Fitch and his co-workers (1962) claimed that the microstructures in the Orgueil meteorite were mineral artifacts. On the more theoretical side of the argument, Urey (1962) favoured with certain reservations, the extra-terrestrial biogenic origin of most of the microstructures, and proposed that these originated ultimately from the surface of the Moon, which was contaminated by waters from the terrestrial oceans.

Since 1962 the discussion has become increasingly complex with the accumulation of often contradictory evidence (see Section 2).

2. The Properties and Classification of Carbonaceous Chondrites

The carbonaceous chondrites form a small but highly significant group, first classified as such in 1883, which is distinguished from the rest of meteorites by containing more than half of one per cent of carbonaceous matter and of hydrated silicates.

In recent literature, from 22 to 28 meteorites are enumerated or referred to, in which the presence of a carbonaceous complex has been experimentally proved, or inferred on grounds of similarity of petrographical structure and elemental composition with previously analysed members of the group.

The stones in question are dark, more or less friable, and they weather easily on exposure. For these reasons, all the material available at present, are 'falls', i.e. have been picked up a relatively short time after the observed impact.

From a petrographical point of view, the meteorites in question consist of a fine-grained 'ground mass' (grain size 1μ) of hydrated silicates and carbonaceous matter of evidently low temperature of formation. In this are embedded the globular crystalline aggregates, namely, the 'chondri' and fragments of minerals, which crystallize in the laboratory, exclusively or mainly, at elevated temperatures, from the molten state. These include olivine, pyroxens, felspars, magnetite, troilite and nickel iron. The latter mentioned minerals are also the main constituents of the other types of meteorites. It is evident that the mineral assemblage in the carbonaceous chondrites represents non-equilibrium conditions; the intermixing of the low-temperature ground-mass and the high-temperature mineral grains must have occurred subsequent to the cooling and solidification of the latter.

The 'carbonaceous chondrite' group was sub-divided by H.B.Wiik, (1956) into three types, according to percentage ranges of C, H_2O and S. Certain stones, for which these three main volatile constituents in question would indicate two distinct types, were included by Wiik in the type to which the general petrographical features of the stone in question bore the more close resemblance. It was found by G.Mueller, (in the press for *Meteoritika*, and partly unpublished) that the single parameter of 'Total volatiles', (TV), at 1,000° (5 minutes heating in N_2 atmosphere) distinguished the three main types without any ambiguity.

The C, H_2O, S and N percentages tend, by and large, to decrease together with the TV. The carbonaceous chondrites become gradually depleted from the rest of the relatively volatile elements, when compared with the mean chondrites, with the decrease of volatiles, and it appears that the more volatile elements become more drastically depleted than the less volatile ones. The elemental composition of the carbonaceous chondrites on a volatile-free basis closely resembles that of the mean for chondrites.

Type I. The stones are black and crumble to fine dust under the fingers. They consist of approximately 95 per cent ground mass, in which are

S

embedded numerous globular or rounded single crystals of olivine and magnetite, further globules of glass of olivinic composition, with diameters ranging between 1 and 50 μ. These structures were termed by Mueller (1962, 1963b) as 'microchondrules', some of which have exsolution cores (plates 1 and 2). Rarely, structures appear which consist of apparently partially cohered or sintered microchondrules, termed 'grape bunch chondrules' by Mueller.

Type II. The stones are firmer than the type I, and of greyish-black colour. The ground mass is approximately 60 per cent; microchondrules are subordinate, and the 'grape bunch' type chondrules dominate with mean diameters around 500 μ (plate 3). There are also chondrules which indicate a more intensive sintering, and eventual coalescence into single crystals, of the original microchondrules. Fragments appear.

Type III. The consistency is hard and colours varying between grey-black, greenish-black to grey. The ground mass is about 35 per cent, the chondrules are mainly of the highly sintered or single-crystal type (plates 4 and 5). In contrast, the chondrules of the non-carbonaceous chondrites are, as a statistical rule, of larger dimensions, more sintered and recrystallized. The stones also contain, as a rule, a high percentage of fragmented chondrules (plate 6).

3. The Properties of the Carbonaceous Complex

Up to the present only some 5 of the 28 carbonaceous chondrites so far known have been investigated in any detail with regard to the organic chemistry of their carbonaceous complex. The considerable structural and compositional similarity between these five and the others would support the drawing of general conclusions regarding the properties of the organic constituents in these meteorites. However, it should always be kept in mind, that stones with more or less anomalous carbonaceous complexes may be detected in the considerable volume of material not examined so far, or in future falls. It is possible that the application of more refined methods may reveal theoretically interesting differences even between the carbonaceous complexes of the hitherto studied stones. The present-day knowledge of properties which are of critical value from the point of problem of biogenic versus abiogenic origin of the carbonaceous substances, is briefly summarized below (see also Mueller 1963b).

(1) Isotopic Ratios of C, S, O, N and H
It has been well established in the literature that the ranges of isotopic composition of the above elements (those of C and S in particular) tend to differ

1 Large cored olivine microchondrule and several smaller magnetite microchondrules in the ground mass of the 'type I'. Orgueil. 250 ×, ordinary light.

2 The carbonaceous inclusion in Sharp's meteorite, illustrating the contrast between the statistical petrography of a type I stone (the inclusion at the bottom half of the microphotograph) and an ordinary chondrite; the host. 41 ×, ordinary light.

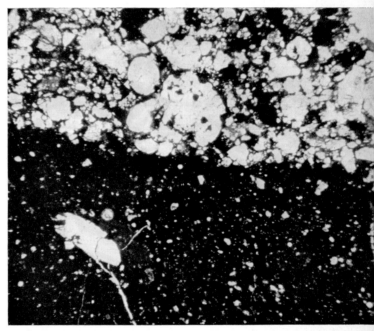

3 A 'grape bunch' type chondrule in the type II Murray, which shows statistical petrography typical for this class. Polarized light (slanted Nicolls), 41 ×.

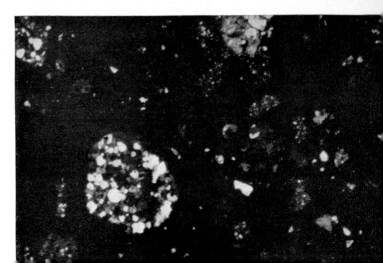

4 Chondrules of more sintered character in the 'type III'. Kainsaz. Polarized light, 120 × .

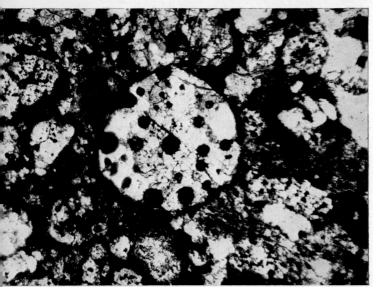

5 Sintered chondrules and fragments in the 'type III'. Lancé. Ordinary light, 125 × .

6 Statistical petrography characteristic of the non-carbonaceous chondrites (Gun Divinn). Note large coalesced (grating type) chondrule and high proportion of fragments. Ordinary light, 125 × .

(although they partially overlap) in biogenic and non-biogenic rocks. Regarding meteorites the data based on a few stones indicate that the C^{12}/C^{13} ratios remain well in the range of terrestrial juvenile carbon.

(2) Elemental composition

It was found by Mueller (1963c) through computation of data in the literature, that all the terrestrial fossil organic substances of ultimate biogenic origin (petroleums, asphalts, coals, etc.) are characterized by H/O ratios of above 4, whereas the few hitherto analysed carbonaceous substances for which a juvenile magmatic origin is indicated on grounds of geological evidence, show H/O values below 3. The H/O of extracts of Haripura, Cold Bokkeveldt and Mokoia are intermediate between the terrestrial biogenic and abiogenic range. Yet, according to some experience on terrestrial carbons, the meteorite as a whole would be richer in carbonized and more highly oxygenated substances than the extracts and this would tend to shift their H/O towards the abiogenic range.

(3) Trace Elements within the Carbonaceous Complex

Abiogenic terrestrial carbonaceous phases are markedly rich in minor elements such as V, U, Th, Ni, Cl, which enter through their 'carbophyl' chemical affinities into the carbonaceous complex. In contrast, in substances of biogenic origin, the 'biophyl' trace elements, required for the living processes, such as Mg, K, Na, Ca, predominate. Therefore, the composition in minor elements of a given carbonaceous substance may give us some information as to its likely origin. It was found by Mueller (1953), that the extracts of the Cold Bokkeveldt meteorite contain 48·1 per cent organic chlorine. Now chlorine is definitely not of 'biophyl' affinity and it is practically absent from all the terrestrial biogenic material of whatever geological age. Thus, the high percentage of organic Cl in this meteorite would indicate an abiogenic genesis, unless it were assumed that, either the organisms on the parent body were of a fundamentally different biochemistry, or that somehow the biogenic material became chlorinated subsequently. There is no known example of this here on Earth. The comparison of minor and trace element compositions of meteoritic and terrestrial carbonaceous complexes may yield theoretically significant data in the future, although the exact interpretation of these may be complicated due to the differences in elemental composition and physical conditions which prevailed on the surface of our planet and the parent body, respectively.

(4) The Molecular Composition of the Carbonaceous Complex

Although it has been demonstrated that a broad range of organic molecules may form through condensation of gases (Ponnamperuma (1964)), it was

259

claimed by Nagy and his co-workers (1961) that the relative abundances of paraffins and other organic molecules of varying chain lengths in peat and butter, closely resemble that found in the mass spectrograms of the Orgueil meteorite. The careful work of Meinschein (1963) compared the capillary column chromatograms of alkenes of biogenic and abiogenic origin with those from the Orgueil meteorite. There was a tendency for the odd-numbered carbon atom homologues of alkenes to predominate in the biogenic products and the Orgueil meteorite, but not in the abiogenic products. However, this tendency appears to be of a statistical nature; it was found actually to be reversed in one of the biogenic cases. In connection with the above results, Oró and his co-workers (1965) found that there is a slight tendency for odd-number carbon-chain to predominate between C_{23} and C_{30} in Orgueil, but the Murray (type II) and Mokoia (type III) carbonaceous chondrites do not show this tendency. Whereas the majority of biological samples showed some odd number C predominances, although to widely differing degrees, other biogenic samples revealed no predominance.

To summarize: the comparative studies of molecular composition are a potentially fruitful approach to the problem of recognition of biogenic material. Present data is not adequate to be of concrete diagnostic value. Certain similarities between biogenic material and the carbonaceous complex in meteorites tend to indicate a biological origin for the latter. Our knowledge of the ranges of abiogenic carbonaceous products, however, is too limited to exclude a chance similarity, and certain of the hitherto observed rather striking differences between the molecular composition of meteoritic carbons and the products of terrestrial organisms, seem to support an abiogenic genesis for the former.

(5) Optical Rotation

All the extracts from recent and fossil terrestrial biogenic substances rotate polarized light towards the left. The extracts of Cold Bokkeveldt (Mueller, 1953) and Mokoia (Briggs and Kitto, 1962), were shown to contain no active organic molecules, at least within the limit of sensitivity of the apparatus employed, which was about 1 ppm in both cases. According to Nagy and co-workers (1964b) there were optically active molecules of the order of 0·01 ppm in Orgueil. Hayatsu (1965) could not detect optical rotation in the same stone, by using methods of similar degree of sensitivity. Anders and co-workers (1964) claimed that if the amino acids, which they found in Orgueil were to be biogenic, then these alone should produce a rotation of 0·0046°, but the experimentally indicated rotation was equal to or below

0·001. However, in this connection, the gradual decrease in the rotating power of terrestrial biogenic substances, with their geological age should be also noted. It was stressed by Mueller (1964) that the eventual minute quantities of active molecules in question may have been introduced in the course of impact and subsequent museum storage of the meteorite, and until the degree of contamination were checked, through simulated impacts, etc., of synthetic replicas of carbonaceous meteorites, the search for optical rotation with the above extremely sensitive methods could not yield conclusive results. Nagy (1966) claimed a value for levorotation of −4·1 millidegree with an experimental error of ±0·3 millidegree and admitted that this slight levorotation might be caused by terrestrial contamination.

(6) Biogenic Molecules

Practically the entire range of organic molecules have been detected in the carbonaceous chondrites. These include paraffins, asphaltenes, naphthenes, aromatics, and their substitution products with N, S and Cl, further organic acids, heterocyclic bases, etc. (see Mueller, Calvin, Briggs and Nagy, quoted by Mason, 1962–3). Kaplan and co-workers (1962) found also amino acids and sugars. All the above types of molecules have been synthesized in experiments of gas condensations, and therefore their presence in the meteorites is of no diagnostic value. It seems, however, that such specific biological molecules as porphyrins and their fragments, would be generated in appreciable amounts only by living organisms. The careful work of Hodgson and Baker (1964), claims porphyrins from Orgueil, in an over-all concentration of the order of 0·01 ppm. It was noted, however, by Mueller (1964) that distillation products of terrestrial plants may enter the meteorites shortly after impact, and before the significance of the above work can be properly assessed, control experiments with simulated falls of porous meteorite-like material should be undertaken. It has been found (personal communication from J. Oró) that the hydrocarbon assemblages in Mokoia and Murray, which include the presumably biogenic phytane and pristane, can be replicated by cultures of microbes from the meteorites, which presumably invaded these in the course of museum storage, utilizing as nutrient the carbonaceous matter.

(7) Other properties

Certain physical and chemical properties of the stones or some of their constituents have been occasionally interpreted as indicative of biogenic origin. Thus it was claimed by Nagy and co-workers (1962) and (1963) that some of the constituents termed by them 'organized elements' in Orgueil can be stained by biological stains, but it appears from laboratory experience that these stains are not specific in normal laboratory usage, but they readily stain kimberlite, limonite and other porous terrestrial mineral matter as demonstrated by Anders and Fitch (1962). The same considerations apply for the fluorescent grains observed in Orgueil by the above workers and in Kaba by Mueller (1953). The presence of HF insoluble sheaths which cover some of the microstructures, may consist equally well of an abiogenical polymerized carbonaceous matter. It appears also that the mode of distribution of free radicals determined by Duchesne and co-workers (1964) cannot be safely interpreted as indicative of biogenic origin, as the features and properties in question have not been proved so far as specific for biogenic products.

It may be summarized that no clear indication for biogenic origin of any of the investigated carbonaceous complexes has been obtained so far through the above methods. On the other hand, evidences for their abiogenic origin seem to be of considerable weight, although also strictly inconclusive. The extension of detailed chemical studies to other meteorites may give us in the future additional relevant data.

(8) Interpretation of Microstructures

The carbonaceous substances appear to be uniformly dispersed throughout the ground-mass of the meteorites, which would tend to support an abiogenic origin, because in the case of the sedimentation of usually more or less colonial micro-organisms, 'sub-fossils', concretional structures usually occur, as revealed in numerous terrestrial Archaic sediments. The rather patchy distribution of the carbonaceous substances in Kaba according to Sztrokay and co-workers (1961) appears to be more a distillational feature, as well-defined patches of impregnation are seen in the ground-mass.

It was claimed by Nagy and co-workers (1962, 1963) that some of the microstructures in the Orgueil meteorite were of organic origin. However, brownish, translucent, isotropic, rather rounded hexagonal plates were interpreted by Mueller (1962) to be limonite pseudomorphs after troilite. It was further observed by Mueller (1963b) that only the small, 10–15 μ plates are totally oxidized; while, within the larger, 15–25 μ plates, islands of the opaque, magnetic troilite still remained, and the largest plates of up to 50 μ diameter, were, as a good statistical rule, only tarnished, but not oxidized through at any point. Anders (1962) also identified these same structures as troilite.

It is interesting to note that the presence of limonite in these hexagonal objects was proven through electron microprobes by Nagy and co-workers (1963a, b), and Urey (1965) considered that this indicated that the objects in question were 'fossilized' with limonite. Yet fossils of limonite are relatively rare on Earth. In other microprobe determinations, globular microstructures were also found 'fossilized' with Mg and occasionally Ni containing silicates. There are certainly no terrestrial remains 'fossilized' with anhydrous silicates (that is olivines or pyroxenes, etc.) of this composition, and even the corresponding hydrous silicates (serpentine, etc.) do not produce fossils under the usual terrestrial conditions. The microprobe results seem to support the conclusions of Mueller (1962, 1963b) that these are olivine grains, etc., as will be discussed below. The presence of HF insoluble residues, may be films of abiogenic carbonaceous matter, which condensed on the silicate grains, as already visualized by Mueller in 1953.

The second type of structures, which were interpreted as microfossils by Nagy and co-workers (1962, etc.) were from 2 to about 20 μ diameter, rather crinkled or pitted colourless or light brown globules. These objects were found to resist heating to 800°C, and they were interpreted by Mueller (1962) as solidified spray particles from incandescent clouds, that is, 'microchondrules' of an optically isotropic glass of approximately olivinic composition. The above conclusion is supported by the fact that in a rather low percentage of the similar glass or olivine microchondrules in Type II stones, opaque cores of magnetite, troilite and nickel-iron appear and the ratio of diameter of core to diameter of microchondrule remains reasonably constant for each meteorite. This would indicate the exsolution of a constant quantity of impurities from a spray particle that was heated above its melting-point in the course of the highest temperature phase of the incandescent cloud.

Beside the above described abundant structures, Nagy and co-workers (1962, 1963) observed rare structures, which would seem more likely to be contaminants, in view of their sporadical distribution. Indeed, some of them closely resembled terrestrial organisms. The most puzzlesome and strange looking of these structures were hexagonal brown plates with three darker brown protrusions on alternate faces. Some of these appear to resemble the limonite pseudomorphs of troilite plates with magnetite overgrowth on alternate faces noted by Mueller (1962). By a very considerable coincidence, however, the meteorite in question contains similar structures, although with better defined and more tubular protrusions which have been identified by Anders (personal communication) as ragweed pollen.

It may be summarized, that whereas the abundant structures in Orgueil and other carbonaceous chondrites appear to be mineral artifices, the rarer and sporadically distributed structures seem to be terrestrial contaminants.

(9) Indications for Carbonaceous Complexes in Cosmic Dust and Other Extra-terrestrial Settings

Cosmic dust from locations along the surface of our planet, is found to be a mixture of the primary finely dispersed matter, and abrasion products of meteorites or meteors, although the proportion between the two genetical types cannot be as yet estimated, in view of lack of relevant data as regards the differences in properties of the mean meteoritic matter and the cosmic dust. Samples of presumably mainly extra-terrestrial matter, which includes nickel-iron grains, were collected through melting the Antarctic ice from cliffs at Halley Bay, by Perkin (1964) and similar material was collected by Mueller from the Chilean bases of Antarctica. It appears that the red, greenish and brownish organic grains, which were repeatedly noted amongst the particles, are terrestrial contaminations, which originate from the similarly coloured micro-organisms, which live in the snow, although other sheath-like structures on certain grains may be more likely extra-terrestrial, carbonaceous matter.

Black spherules and other grains collected on Pacific islands, diverse sediments, etc. (for review of literature see Fredriksson and Martin (1963)) seem to be partly of extra-terrestrial origin, but contaminated with volcanic and industrial products of lower Ni percentage. The material has not been so far investigated for organic substances.

The cosmic dust collected in rockets is, of course, most likely free of terrestrial contaminations or meteorite abrasion product. In the course of collection of cosmic dust in N. Sweden, it was found by Wiit (personal communication) that the noctiluminescent clouds contain more particles than are obtained, at their height of 80 km, from a cloudless sky. The material closely resembles the constituents of Type I carbonaceous chondrites, at least from a purely petrographical point of view. Beside the flaky, 'ground mass'-like particles, there are present globular objects, and even some 'cored globules', which have been described as 'cored microchondri' by Mueller (1962, 1963b) from carbonaceous chondrites. It is likely that the properties of the carbonaceous complex of the cosmic dust may also prove to be closely comparable with that of the Type I carbonaceous chondrites.

It is anticipated that cosmic dust that was in relatively close proximity to the Sun or another fixed star at any stage of its history would contain a more carbonized organic complex. The eventual intermixing of cosmic dusts that were heated to different maximum temperatures in the course of their histories would cause a range of properties of the carbonaceous complexes collected.

The small quantities of cosmic dust available at present prevent detailed organic chemical studies, at least with the up-to-date standard methods; but it is hoped that an increase of the quantity of the material, on the one hand, and the devising of more sensitive procedures, on the other hand, will enable us in the near future to approach this fascinating organic cosmo-chemical problem.

The presence of simple carbon-containing molecules and groups was spectroscopically proved in the atmosphere of the planets, that of the satellite Titan, in the tails and heads of comets, in carbon stars, and interstellar matter (see Mueller 1963a and 1963c). The likely properties of carbonaceous complexes in these settings can be inferred through spectroscopical data, further extrapolations based on experiences in terrestrial organic geochemistry, and the organic cosmochemistry of meteorites. It was anticipated by Mueller (1963c) that the H/C and O/C of the mean pre-biogenic assemblage of carbonaceous complexes, termed the 'carbosphere', would decrease with decreasing gravitational mass of the given celestial body and the increase of temperature would have the same effect. Both the above factors would cause the escape of hydrogen, gradual polymerization, and the conversion of mainly saturated substances to aromatics, and heterocyclics. It was argued by Mueller (1963c) that the main effects of the living organism on a prebiogenic carbosphere would be to increase its overall percentage through the incorporation of CO_2, through photosynthesis, and to render it of higher H/C and lower O/C, through the elimination of the highly oxygenated low molecular products of metabolism.

The rocket photographs of the Moon by the USSR Zond 3 spacecraft, together with those made in 1959, indicate that there is no major sedimentary feature on the hemisphere of the Moon that is unseen from the Earth; the number of craters produced by impact and/or volcanism seems to be greater, and the continental areas predominate over the mares. It is further indicated by the photographs of the US Ranger spacecraft that water-deposited sediments are absent or very subordinate on Mars (at least on the scale of resolution of about 2 km of the photographs). The lunar photographs of Rangers 7, 8 and 9 (see Kuiper (1965)) indicate that sedimentary features are not detectable (at least within the portions of the Moon actually photographed), even on the optimum resolution photographs of 25 cm.

Recent high resolution photographs of the surface of the Moon, produced

265

after the soft landing of the Russian Luna 9 spacecraft, do not seem to reveal any stratified rocks. The 10 to 20 ft high pinnacles are new features, not seen in the photographs of adequate resolution by the Rangers. These may be structures characteristic of the landing area of Luna 9, and need careful study. They may be caused through some 'salt doming' and 'salt extrusion' effects from masses of fumarolic products condensed beneath the surface; or they may be ejected blocks or meteorites flanked by talus produced through solar erosion. To the writer, however, it appears unlikely, in view of terrestrial experience, that free water has played a role in their formation.

The above evidence from rocket photography indicates that celestial bodies up to the diameter of 6·620 km have not carried any appreciable amount of free water, at any stage of their cosmological histories, under the 'climatological' conditions which prevailed in the orbits of Mars or our planet. It appears, as will be discussed in the next section, that the lack of free water prevented the emergence of life on the parent bodies of the meteorites. This seems to indicate the possibility that we may find Mars inanimate and the Moon without any signs of fossil life. However, before risking a hasty prediction, it should be stressed that our conclusions are based on rocket photography, and future actual petrographical scrutiny could still reveal subordinate water-deposited sediments on these celestial bodies.

From the point of assessing the possibilities of a biogenic episode at a certain stage of the cosmological history of the Moon, the problem of the origin of the volume of carbonaceous meteorites is of greatest interest. In the event that all or some of these proved to be of lunar origin then our evidence of the apparent lack of biogenic material in the meteorites would point rather against the presence of life on the Moon at any epoch. On the other hand, if the meteorites had originated from smaller, asteroid-type parent bodies, it may be argued that conditions on the Moon would have been more favourable for the evolution of life than those on the parent bodies of the extra-terrestrial material at present to hand.

The absence of water-deposited sediments in the meteorites and the rocket-photographic indications of their absence or very subordinate distribution on the Moon would accord with the often proposed theory of the lunar origin of meteorites. However, it appears from the interpretation of Kuiper (1965) that the surface of the Moon contains a high proportion of lava, and a relatively low proportion of pyroclastics. On the other hand, well over 90 per cent of the total of meteorites (see Mason (1962b)) are chondrites, which are interpreted by the majority of workers as pyroclastics; and only less than 10 per cent achondrites, which are presumed to be solidified silicate melts, that is, lavas. If all, or even a considerable proportion, of the meteorites were to be of lunar origin, then a higher proportion of achondrites would be expected than is actually the case. Furthermore, the high-resolution photographs of the Moon fail to reveal any bright metallic objects that could account for the iron meteorites.

Although the interpretation of lunar photographs is at present still subject to controversy (see Heacock and co-workers (1965)), it seems from the above considerations that there is a substantial case against the lunar origin of at least the majority of the meteorites. Considerable similarity may possibly exist between certain lunar rocks and certain meteorites, and some meteorites in our hands might actually be of lunar origin, without their properties differing substantially from the rest. In this connection, the interpretation of Kuiper (1965) of the lightness of shade of certain lunar hills, presumably due to condensed fumarola products, is interesting. Mueller (1962) had already noted that the Type I carbonaceous chondrites closely resemble terrestrial fumarola rocks, in containing a high proportion of sulphates of Mg and Ca, which could produce such white efflorescence in a climate lacking running water.

(10) Cosmological Indicators

It was found by Mueller and co-workers (1965) that the carbonaceous chondrites start to lose an appreciable proportion of their volatiles, between $100°C$ and $300°C$, indicating that the ground-mass of the stones might have been within the temperature range of propagation of terrestrial organisms for rather prolonged periods of their cosmological histories. It was proposed by Nagy and co-workers (1962, 1963a, b) that the presence of hydrated silicates and sulphates of magnesium and calcium in Orgueil would indicate conditions close to those which would prevail within a terrestrial marsh-land. In this respect Mueller (1963b) noted that all the meteorites in question, including Orgueil, contain fresh, or only slightly altered, globular or rounded crystals of olivine and other silicates embedded in the porous ground-mass. Yet according to our experience here on Earth, no olivine is preserved in sedimentary rocks in contact for decades or, at most, for centuries, with free water.

The chemical nature of the carbonaceous complex, the lack of carbonate, save traces of braunerite in the Type I stones (see Nagy and Andersen (1964a)) and the chemistry of the inorganic mineral assemblage seem to indicate that the conditions were fairly oxidative at the locations of the carbonaceous chondrites, but that there was no appreciable free oxygen present. The previously mentioned partial oxidation of the troilite plates in Orgueil may have been caused by atmospheric oxygen during the fall and museum storage. The apparent lack of free oxygen on the parent bodies, would not have prevented, in itself, the development of certain types of terrestrial organisms.

In his review article on evidence for biogenic material in meteorites, Urey (1966) recognizes that there are no indications of water-deposited sediments in the meteorites to hand, and there are difficulties in visualizing the evolution of life without free water. Whereas the lack of sediments could be conceived when suggesting (somewhat on the lines of what was inferred by some workers for Mars), very small and shallow pools on the surface or beneath an ice cover or 'moistened areas', the above-mentioned presence of hydrolizable silicates seems to reduce the duration of such water-bearing structures to the time-scale of decades or centuries. It appears that no terrestrial organism, at any rate, can utilize the water bound in hydrated silicates.

In order to overcome the problem of the lack of free water, Urey (1962) suggested that the Moon, from which he considered the meteorites in question originate, became contaminated with terrestrial water in the course of escape from or capture by the Earth. The Type I carbonaceous chondrites, on which the claims for indications of life of Urey and his co-workers are mainly based, contain a total of about 6 to 10 per cent carbonaceous matter and 0·5 to 1 per cent of the minute globular objects, which are distributed with remarkable uniformity throughout the ground-mass of the stones. Yet, to the author, it would be impossible to conceive of a 'contamination' in the form of a 'splash' or a 'shower' resulting in the formation of the fine dispersions of 10 per cent or so of carbonaceous matter and the supposed microfossils, without any tide marks or other signs of penetration of the original material by the foreign matter. If the 'contamination' had been more than a mere 'splash', had been, say, the formation of a lake, however shortlived, then a smooth intermixing could better be visualized, but other contaminants (quartz sand or pebbles, etc.) and well-defined sedimentary features would then appear as well, which are absent from the stones in question.

Studier, Hayatsu and Anders (1966), claimed that hydrocarbon assemblages closely resembling those in the meteorites may readily form from hydrogen-rich mixtures approaching cosmic composition, through Fischer-Tropsch-type reactions at temperatures between 25° and 580°C. The actual molecular composition of the carbonaceous phases in chondrites may become even more closely matched by partial equilibration through the

268

sustained heating of the gas reaction products. In their comment on the above paper, Urey and Lewis (1966) stressed that, under the conditions envisaged by the former workers, graphite would be the stable phase, and that the aliphatic and aromatic molecules found in the carbonaceous chondrites would be unstable in the presence of graphite. But this is assuming that equilibrium is reached. However, Studier and co-workers (1966), in their reply to this criticism, stressed that even if graphite is the stable phase, the hydrocarbons would still remain present for several aeons within the gas mixture in question. Studier and co-workers believe that the carbonaceous complex of the meteorites formed within the original solar nebula, whereas Urey and Lewis suggest the possible later-stage formation of this within the condensing parent bodies. The second seems to be the only one in which a biogenic origin is possible although not necessary. My own view is that the temperature-pressure conditions which probably prevailed in the solar nebula may partially or fully overlap those likely to prevail at the surface of the de-gassing parent body, and for this reason we are not able to distinguish with our present knowledge between hydrocarbons formed (a) within the solar nebula; (b) within the parent body; (c) of hybrid origin, containing genetical types (a) and (b). The discussion outlined above casts light on certain aspects of the cosmological history of the carbonaceous complexes in meteorites, although, regarding the question whether these are of ultimate abiogenic or biogenic origin, the mere knowledge of their epoch of formation is of rather secondary importance.

To summarize: all the hitherto discussed cosmological indicators seem to point to the fact that the carbonaceous complex-bearing ground-mass of the stones was at low temperature throughout its cosmological history, but was not in contact with free water for any prolonged period.

Beside the above 'mean' conditions, certain processes in the cosmological history of carbonaceous chondrites have been visualized by Mueller (1963b, 1965, in the press for *Meteoritika*, and hitherto unpublished). The brief account below is restricted to those results which give us further insight into the problem of the circumstances under which, apparently, the living organism does not emerge from a given carbonaceous complex.

The interrelations between the total volatiles and the individual volatile constituents of the carbonaceous chondrites, seem to indicate, by and large, that the stones must have originated from different levels of a parent body, or closely comparable parent bodies, that had a thermal gradient. The volatiles were redistributed along this thermal gradient: the stones of higher total volatile content originating from the progressively cooler and closer-to-the-surface zones of the parent body. Thus it was found by

Mueller and co-workers (1965) that the volatilization curves of the carbon-aceous chondrites tend to shift towards lower temperatures with the increase of volatiles. It also seems to be highly significant that the three major volatile constituents, namely, C, H and S, and the minor constituent, N, tend to increase together, and the S/C ratio remains close to 1·5–2·0. If the carbon of the stones were to be essentially concentrated by a living organism of a S/C ratio of the order of 0·01 (i.e. that of a terrestrial organism) then a drastic reduction of the S/C ratio would be expected with increasing carbon percentage of the stones.

There is a tendency for the more common chalcophyl volatile elements to concentrate, with an increase in the total volatiles. The 'distribution pattern' of minor volatile elements is very closely comparable with that of the terrestrial hydrothermal deposits, which formed through the re-deposition of volatiles escaping from the interior of our planet. As a first approximation, the patterns of 'volatile minor elements' in the series of carbonaceous chondrites, Type I to III, closely resembles that in a terres-trial 'zoned type' hydrothermal deposit, if we proceed from the 'low-temperature' zone towards the 'high-temperature zone'.

It was also found that the lighter inert gases, A and Ne in particular, and further the lighter isotopes of C and H, tend to become depleted in Type I carbonaceous chondrites. This appears to indicate a proximity to the surface of the parent body, and the escape of these extremely volatile constituents through a system which is open towards the empty space. Further data given by Mason (1962a) and others, is in full accord with our above illustrative summary; it appears that the distribution pattern of other volatile elements in the carbonaceous chondrites closely resembles that in our terrestrial hydrothermal deposits, but it is totally dissimilar to any pattern that could be produced by an organism of terrestrial composition. To quote one more extreme example: published results show that Bi and Hg are the most highly concentrated elements in Orgueil, the value of *Bi (Orgueil)/Bi (mean chondrite)* being 43; and *Hg (Orgueil)/Hg (mean chondrite)* 86. The above two elements appear to be the most highly concentrated in the terrestrial hydrothermal veins of low temperature, but both are poisonous to terrestrial organisms.

The mechanism of the formation of chondrules and of the intermixing of these into the low-temperature ground mass is, as yet, another problem whose solution may yield some clues to the cosmological histories of the parent bodies. In this connection, Mueller (1963b, and hitherto unpub-lished) noted well-defined trends of a gradual increase of diameter and an increase of single-crystal grain size of chondrules with a decrease of volatiles.

This would seem to be best explained by supposing that the parent body had a spray-charged, incandescent cloud mantle, beneath unconsolidated cosmic dust or a dense cloud of it. Mild volcanic pulsation, that is, a gradual escape of the gases, produced two effects: (a) heating to differing degrees of the close-to-the-surface cosmic dust zones, which produced the previously described 'carbonaceous chondrite series' of decreasing volatiles, etc., towards the deeper zones of the cosmic dust; (b) limited intermixing of the spray particles from the incandescent mantle with the cosmic dust surface; the relatively higher zones of the cosmic dust surface received only a low proportion and gravitationally-sorted spray of small grains from the marginal zones of the incandescent cloud, whereas the deeper and hotter zones of the surface received already a higher percentage of spray particles of larger diameter, and from the deeper zones of the incandescent cloud mantle, as a statistical rule.

The above model envisaged by the author of the parent body of the carbonaceous meteorites is based mainly on observations of interrelations between the percentage and types of chondri and total volatiles of the stones. Most of the up-to-date alternative theories (for a summary see Anders (1964)) agree, as a rule, on the ultimate spray origin of the chondri, and that the intermixing of chondrules and cosmic dust probably occurred on an asteroid-sized parent body. Interesting exceptions are the theories of Mason (1960, 1962) and Levin (1965) which visualize chondrule formation through the metamorphism of cosmic dust. It appears to the author, however, that the petrography of the chondrules in the high volatile stones (particularly the 'cored microchondri', see 3(h)), clearly indicates an ultimate spray origin.

The above model is based on the hypothesis that the carbonaceous and non-carbonaceous chondrites would have a common parent body or, rather, a common set of rather closely comparable parent bodies. Evidence of a more direct nature which supports this hypothesis, are the inclusions, interbrecciations and inhomogeneities in carbonaceous chondrites. Thus, a grey fragment within the chemical and petrographical range of a pigeonite chondrite was described from the Type I (Orgueil) carbonaceous chondrite by the author (Mueller, 1963). More recently, Mueller (1966) observed a number of other examples as follows: (a) a small inclusion of a Type II carbonaceous chondrite in the Type I Orgueil; (b) a large angular inclusion of a Type III carbonaceous chondrite in the Type II Mighei; (c) a small, partially metamorphosed inclusion of a Type I carbonaceous chondrite in the Type III Renazzo; (d) smooth transitions between the main mass of the Type III Mokoia to portions with Type II properties; (e) ureilite type inclusions (carbonaceous chondrite) in the Type II Cold Bokkeveldt, which also contained some very small euhedral groups characteristic for the 'chondrite type' achondrites; (f) small achondrite-type inclusions in the Type III Kainsaz; and, finally, (g) the most striking example, recently discovered by Dr K. Fredriksson of an angular inclusion of some 15 mm diameter of a Type I carbonaceous chondrite in the Sharp's meteorite, which is a non-carbonaceous chondrite (plate 2). The above examples clearly demonstrate the close proximity of carbonaceous chondritic materials of diverse types to non-carbonaceous chondrites and achondrites.

All these examples show, particularly strikingly in the case of (g), that the different kinds of meteorites have at least some common parent bodies. The presence of a Type I carbonaceous chondrite embedded in a normal chondrite shows that carbonaceous chondrites are already fully formed on the parent body. The fact that it is also securely incorporated in this body and that it is a Type I carbonaceous chondrite fragment shows signs of a double contact metamorphism and indicates that the chondrules are at a higher temperature, but must have cooled from their temperature formation of an order of 1,500°C to a temperature of the order of a few hundred degrees. More detailed studies should show something of the mechanism of the formation of the different types of meteorites and of the parent bodies from which they originate.

4. Theoretical Conclusions

The scrutiny of the hitherto determined properties of carbonaceous complexes of meteorites leads us to the conclusion that these are more likely of abiogenic than of biogenic origin. It seems that the micro-structures present in Type I carbonaceous chondrites are not fossils, as interpreted by Nagy and co-workers (1962, 1963a), but fine spray particles of silicates, magnetite, etc., termed 'microchondrules' by Mueller (1962). In this connection it is interesting to note that the trend of decrease of chondrule diameter with increasing volatiles is unbroken, throughout the entire chondrite-carbonaceous chondrite series and therefore if no samples of Type I carbonaceous chondrites were available, the extrapolations of the interrelations in question would give us the same order of magnitude of chondrule diameter in the supposed 'high volatile' Type I stones as is actually found to exist. Finally, the abiogenic origin of the carbonaceous complexes is indirectly supported by the fact that the S and C increases in approximately constant ratio of $S/C = 1·5$ with the volatiles, whereas if C had been redistributed by a living organism of S/C in the order of $0·01$, a drastic reduction of the S/C with the increase of C should be anticipated.

It should be realized, particularly in relation to the last point, that the existence of primitive organisms for a brief epoch in the cosmological history of a given meteorite would be more difficult to detect than that of a prolonged period with higher organisms capable of redistributing the carbon and leaving behind recognizable fossils. Although stones from all petrographic and volatile percentage types have been studied in some organic-chemical detail, we are still not in possession of data regarding the entire range of variability of meteorites. In this connection the detailed investigation of certain partially 'anomalous' stones, such as Lance, which can be pinpointed through the comparative studies outlined above, may yield theoretically significant data.

Despite these uncertainties, it appears that, at least on the majority of parent bodies of meteorites, the conditions were adequate for the condensation of organic substances, that seem to be chemically complex enough to serve as nutrients for terrestrial micro-organisms, but inadequate for the evolution of life.. The conditions, which are indicated for these parent bodies can be briefly summarized as follows.

(1) It is generally agreed that all the carbonaceous chondrites and at least some of the enstatite chondrites are mixtures of grains of minerals of high temperature of formation (mainly chondri) and a ground-mass which was at no stage heated above 100°C to say 300°C throughout the cosmological history of the stones. The pattern of distribution of volatiles would indicate that the temperature may have been for considerable periods within the range of temperature of propagation of terrestrial organisms.

(2) The diameter of the parent bodies of meteorites has been estimated by various workers (see Mason, 1962) to be between that of the Moon and the comets, but the bulk of evidence based on the properties of high-temperature minerals point to intermediate asteroid dimensions of the order of 100 km diameter.

(3) The next problem (which is of some interest from the point of view of specifying conditions under which apparently life does not evolve) is the mechanism of the intermixing of the high- and low-temperature phases. Anders proposed that this happens in some fortuitous manner at a low temperature. Mueller, however, finds that the two phases are interdependent, except in obviously co-brecciated stones with the quantity of volatiles, both the quantity and the quality of the high-temperature constituents change, and vice versa. This would seem to indicate that the intermixing occurred at the stage of condensation of the asteroid-type parent body, through the formation of a thermal gradient along which the volatiles became redistributed.

T

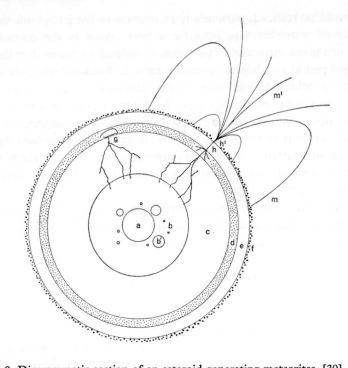

Figure 9. Diagrammatic section of an asteroid generating meteorites. [30].

(*a*) Hot liquid iron centre	*Generating* Iron meteorite
(*b*) Fused silicate with (*b'*) iron and sulphide inclusions	Chondritic and stony-iron meteorites
(*c*) Solidified silicate mantle	Achondrites
(*d*) Damp zone containing largely hydrated silicates and carbonaceous compounds (possibly site of origin of life)	Carbonaceous meteorite
(*e*) Frozen compact layer of same composition	Carbonaceous meteorite
(*f*) Cold dry outer layer consisting of volcanic ejecta mixture of rocks, chondritic particles, and dust	None

(*g*) Incipient
(*h*) Active } Volcanoes

(*h'*) Vent ejecting
(*m*) Recovered } Meteorites
(*m'*) Free flying

(4) Perhaps the most important question in specifying the minimal conditions for the evolution of life is the role of water in the cosmological history of the parent bodies. It appears from the lack of any typical sedimentary structures, and even more so from the presence of grains of olivine and other hydrolizable silicates in all the meteorites, that free water could not have been present for more prolonged periods than decades, or at the most centuries, throughout the cosmological histories of the parent bodies.

The above evidence points to the possibility that all the carbonaceous meteorites at present in our hands originate from asteroid-type parent bodies, without a permanent hydrosphere, which subsequently fragmented due to impact or, more likely, to a process of autofragmentation through explosive volcanism (figure 9). The difference between the age of the constituents of the meteorites and the fragmentation age spans, in most cases, several aeons (see Anders, 1964), indicating that the conditions for the development of life were not favourable on the parent bodies for prolonged periods of time. Our conclusion is, therefore, that the asteroid-type celestial bodies, or the other generally rather small-scale (100–1,000 km radius) condensations of matter from which meteorites may originate, would not permit the evolution of any life as we know it on Earth, or indeed any other type of existence, the presence of which would cause detectable deviations from the physico-chemical conditions that are reasonably expected to prevail on the inanimate bodies. One or another of the following reasons may help to explain our conclusion.

(1) Conditions on the parent bodies (or at least at the locations from which our meteorites originated) were constantly below the 'minimum' for the evolution of the organism.

(2) The emergence of a proto-organism needs a relatively narrow and specific set of conditions: life has a 'threshold' in its initial stages and, once this is surpassed, then the resulting 'established' organisms may adapt to a broader range of conditions. Such a 'vital threshold' has not been reached at any location of the parent body.

(3) The emergence of life depends on a 'probability factor', and the product of 'time by volume' of 'favourable conditions' was so small on the parent bodies, that the emergence of a proto-organism would be a very remote probability; as another alternative, a relative variability of conditions on the parent bodies would eliminate the probability of formation of life as a given assemblage or organic molecules would need a prolonged period of time to 'mature' (condensation and other pre-biological or life-threshold processes) before the evolution of a self-reproducing organism.

It is difficult to evaluate the relative roles of factors in connection of the apparent blocking of the evolution of life on the most likely asteroid-type parent bodies of the meteorites at the stage of the pre-biogenic carbonaceous complex. It is possible that all the above three factors may have played roles to a varying extent. It seems that the absence of free water for any prolonged period may prove to be the decisive obstacle in the path of evolution. At least one of the greatest tragedies of our Universe is thirst, which may prove to prevent the blossoming-out of life on innumerable celestial bodies, which are considerably smaller than our planet, but seem to have had otherwise suitable conditions for the propagation of organisms. It appears, through the evidence of the inability of life to use water of hydrated silicates in our deserts, that free water is the *conditio sine qua non* for the propagation of any organism of a terrestrial-type biochemistry, and indeed, of anything that is akin to life as we know it, to the degree of substantially altering the inanimate physico-chemical conditions of its habitat.

The photographs of Mars, published in 1965 from the Mariner spacecraft, indicate that even on this planet, with a diameter of 6,620 km, craters due to volcanic or meteoritic impact predominate, and water deposited sediments are absent or very subordinate. They also indicate that, if our interpretation of the origin of the carbonaceous complex in meteorites is the correct one, irrespective of the origin of the stones available to us, it would seem that the odds may point slightly against Martian life. Nevertheless, it should be stressed that the information about Mars and even the Moon is incomplete so far and it does not exclude the possibility of small quantities of water-deposited sediments on the latter, or even free water on the former.

We may put our arguments in another way. In the rather unlikely eventuality of the meteorites originating from the Moon or Mars, then it would appear that these celestial bodies are inanimate and that, in general, no life could be expected on condensations substantially smaller than our planet.

These are, of course, speculations based on a very small amount of factual evidence. It would seem probable that the ratio between the abiogenic and the biogenic carbospheres will prove to be very high within the cosmos.

References to Appendix 2

ANDERS, E. (1964) Origin, age and composition of meteorites. *Space Sci. Rev.* **3**: 583–714

ANDERS, E. & FITCH, F.W. (1962) Search for organized elements in carbonaceous chondrites. *Science* **138**: 1392–1399

ANDERS, E. *et al.* (1964) Contaminated meteorite. *Science* **146**: 1157–1161

BERNAL, J.D. (1962) Life-forms in meteorites: Comments. *Nature, Lond.* **193**: 1127–1129

BERZELIUS, J.J. (1834) Om meteorstenar *K. svenska Vetensk Akad. Handl.* 115–183

BRIGGS, M.H. & KITTO, G.B. (1962) Complex organic microstructures in the Mokoia meteorite. *Nature, Lond.* **193**: 1123–1125

CLAUS, G. & NAGY, B. (1961) A microbiological examination of some carbonaceous chondrites. *Nature, Lond.* **192**: 594–596

CLAUS, G. & SUBA-C, E.A. (1964) Organised element distribution in relation to size in the Orgueil meteorite. *Nature, Lond.* **204**: 118–120

DUCHESNE, J., DEPIREUX, J. & LITT, C. (1964) Free radicals in the Cold Bokkeveld meteorite. *C.r. hebd. Séanc. Acad.Sci., Paris* **259**: 1891–1893

FITCH, F., SCHWARCZ, H.P. & ANDERS, E. (1962) Organised elements in carbonaceous chondrites. *Nature, Lond.* **193**: 1123–1125

FREDRIKSSON, K., & MARTIN, L.R. (1963) Origin of black spherules found in Pacific Islands, deep-sea sediments, and Antarctic ice. *Geochim. Cosmochim. Acta* **27**: 245–248

HAYATSU, R. (1965) Optical activity in the Orgueil Meteorite. *Science* **149**: 443–447

HEACOCK, R.L. *et al.* (1965) *NASA Report*, 32–700

HODGSON, G.W. & BAKER, B.L. (1964) Evidence for porphyrins in the Orgueil meteorite. *Nature, Lond.* **202**: 125–131

KAPLAN, I.R., DEGENS, E.T. & REUTER, J.H. (1962) Organic compounds in stony meteorites. *Geochim. Cosmochim. Acta* **27**: 805–834

KUIPER, G.P. (1965) Lunar results from Rangers 7 to 9. *Sky Telesc.* **29**: 293–308

LEVIN, B.J. (1965) Origin of Meteorites. *Planet. Space Sci.* **13**: 243–260

MASON, B. (1960) Origin of chondrules and chondritic meteorites. *Nature, Lond.* **186**: 230–231

MASON, B. (1962) *Meteorites.* Wiley: New York

MASON, B. (1963) The carbonaceous chondrites. *Space Sci. Rev.* **1**: 621–646

MEINSCHEIN, W.G. (1963) Hydrocarbons in terrestrial samples and the Orgueil meteorite. *Space Sci. Rev.* **2**: 653–679

MUELLER, G. (1953) The properties and theories of genesis of the carbonaceous complex within the Cold Bokkeveld meteorite. *Geochim. Geophys. Acta* **4**: 1–10

MUELLER, G. (1962) Interpretation of micro-structures in carbonaceous meteorites. *Nature, Lond.* **196**: 929–932

MUELLER, G. (1963a) Organic cosmochemistry. In *Organic Geochemistry*. I.A. Breger, Editor, Pergamon Press: London & New York, pp. 1–35

MUELLER, G. (1963b) The interpretation of micro-structures in meteorites. In *Advances in Organic Geochemistry*, U. Colombo & G.D.Hobson, Editors, Pergamon Press: London & New York, pp. 119–140

MUELLER, G. (1963c) Properties of extraterrestrial hydrocarbons and theory of their genesis. *VI Wld. Petrol. Congr.* Sect.1, Frankfurt am Main, 382–396

MUELLER, G. (1964) Impact contamination of the Mokoia carbonaceous chondrite. *Nature, Lond.* **204**: 567

MUELLER, G. (1965) Interpretation of micro-structures in carbonaceous meteorites. *Nature, Lond.* **205**: 1200–1201

MUELLER, G., SHAW, R.A. & OGAWA T. (1965) Interrelations between volatilisation curves, elemental composition and total volatiles in carbonaceous chondrites. *Nature, Lond.* **206**: 23–25

MUELLER, G. (1966) Significance of inclusions in carbonaceous meteorites. *Nature, Lond.* **210**: 151–155

NAGY, B., MEINSCHEN, W.G. & HENNESSY, J.D. (1961) Mass spectroscopic analysis of the Orgueil meteorite evidence for biogenic hydrocarbons. *Ann. N.Y. Acad. Sci.* **93**: 25–35

NAGY, B., CLAUS, G. & HENNESSY, J.D. (1962) Organic particles embedded in minerals in the Orgueil and Ivuna carbonaceous chondrites. *Nature, Lond.* **193**: 1129–1133

NAGY, B. *et al.* (1963a) Electron probe micro-analysis of organized elements in the Orgueil meteorite. *Nature, Lond.* **198**: 121-125

NAGY, B. *et al.* (1963b) Ultra-violet spectra of organized elements. *Nature, Lond.* **200**: 565–566

NAGY, B. & CLAUS, G. (1963c) Mineralized micro-structures in carbonaceous meteorites. In *Advances in Organic Geochemistry*. U. Colombo and G.D.Hobson, Editors. Pergamon Press: London & New York, pp. 109–114

In *Advances in Organic Geochemistry*. U. Colombo and G.D.Hobson, Editors. Pergamon Press: London & New York, pp. 119–140

NAGY, B. & ANDERSON, C.A. (1964a) Electron probe micro-analysis of some carbonate, sulfate and phosphate minerals in the Orgueil meteorite. *Am. Miner.* **49**: 1730–1736

NAGY, B. *et al.* (1964b) Optical activity in sapinified organic matter isolated from the interior of the Orgueil meteorite. *Nature, Lond.* **202**: 228–233

NAGY, B. (1965) Optical activity in the Orgueil meteorite. *Science,* **150**: 1846

PERKIN, D.V. (1964) Cosmic dust in the Antarctic. *Bri. Antarct. Surv. Bull.* No. **3**: 23–27

PONNAMPERUMA, C. (1964) Synthesis of organic compounds in primitive planetary environments. Preprint, University of California Series, *Horizons in Space Biosciences: Exobiology*

SPIELMAN, P.E. (1924) Bitumen in meteorites. *Nature, Lond.* **114**: 276

STUDIER, M.H., HAYATSU, R. & ANDERS, E. (1965) Origin of organic matter in early solar system. I. Hydrocarbons. *Science* **149**: 1455–1459

STUDIER, M.H., HAYATSU, R. & ANDERS, E. (1966) Reply to Urey and Lewis 'Some comments on a recent hypothesis on carbon compounds in carbonaceous chondrites.' *Science* **152**: 106–107

SZTRÓKAY, K.I., TOLNAY, V. & FÖLDVÁRI-VOGL (1961) Mineralogical and chemical properties of the carbonaceous meteorite from Kara, Hungary. *Acta Geol. hung.* **7**: 57–103

UREY, H.C. (1962) Origin of life-like forms in carbonaceous chondrites. *Nature, Lond.* **193**: 1119–1123

UREY, H.C. (1966) Biological material in meteorites: A review. *Science* **151**: 157–166

UREY, H.C. & LEWIS, J.S. (1966) Organic matter in carbonaceous chondrites. *Science* **152**: 102–104

WIIK, H.B. (1956) The chemical composition of some stony meteorites. *Geochim. Cosmochim. Acta.* **9**: 279–289

WÖHLER, F. (1860) Neure Untersuchungen über die Bestandtheile des Meteorsteines vom Capland. *Sber. Akad. Wiss. Wien, Math-Naturw. Kl.* **41**: 565–567

Appendix 3

Generalized Crystallography

History

THE analogies between the growth of an organism and the growth of a crystal have been stressed for many years. Pasteur, himself, studied crystal growth from this point of view and showed, for instance, how readily a crystal repaired an injury done to it and restored its original state. One of the differences between the two modes, also noticed early and pointed out, was that in the first place crystals had regular forms whereas living things had very varied and irregular ones, though many exhibited close approaches to geometric symmetry.

However, all of these studies missed some of the essential features of the difference by restricting themselves to geometrical three-dimensional crystallography, that is, to the external morphology, which was the only form known before 1912 when von Laue discovered the lattice of the crystal by means of x-ray diffraction and the whole science and art of crystal structure analysis began.

For a long time after that, however, the predominance of the rules of regular crystallography remained. A crystal was conceived of as the regular piling together of absolutely identical atoms, ions or molecules; this implies that it is possible to deduce rigorously and geometrically a symmetrical structure with certain prescribed and certain forbidden types of symmetry. Every crystal must belong to one of the 32 crystal classes which involve symmetrical rotations of the orders of 2, 3, 4 and 6 and no more. No crystal, for instance, can be built with the rotation of 5 or 7, although such rotations are well known in the organic world, both in plants and in animals.

Now, x-ray crystal structure studies were able to show that most things hitherto not conceived of as crystalline, were in fact so, although built out of very small crystals invisible except in the microscope, even if it was admitted then, before the advent of the electron microscope, that some, like glass, had not any crystals in them. They were, in the strictest sense, amorphous, without shape, and this was found to apply particularly to most liquids.

Even among the crystalline bodies, organic substances were found to be somewhat irregularly crystalline: the crystals were either particularly small or they were distorted. This applied especially to organic fibres, such as cotton, wool and silk, and to stretched rubber. It was in the study of these intermediate, usually fibrous, substances, started by Mark and Meyer in the 1920's, that the first break occurred in this type of description. Substances like the keratin of wool, for instance, appeared to have some form of regular construction, but it was not in the strict sense of the word crystalline – it did not conform to the 32 permitted classes of symmetry.

In the long and somewhat slow progress of the study of the fibrous proteins, founded by Astbury in 1927, no satisfactory solution was found until Pauling [1], in 1951, on the basis of metrical studies of the peptide linked amino-acid residues which composed fibrous proteins, and with the idea of chains of these residues being linked together side by side by hydrogen bonds, proposed his celebrated α-helix structure with the hydrogen bonds linking, not different protein chains, as in stretched keratin or silk, but joining, at successive turns of the helix, amino-acid residues of the same chain.

This precluded any possibility of a symmetrical helix with turns of 2, 3, 4 and 6. It could only be satisfied by a helix with an irrational number of turns per unit, 3·7. The success of this model in interpreting at least the structures of the artificial polypeptide fibres or the polypeptides in wool with a more complex double twist or coiled coil, breaks the limitation artificially imposed on the associations of identical particles. Very soon it will be possible to express the x-ray patterns of such associations with approximately the same precision as those of crystals [2].

The same helical structure was later found in a number of different substances, among them that of the protein integument of the tobacco mosaic virus and that of the sugar phosphate polymer fibres of nucleic acids. When this was looked at geometrically, it appeared that what had been considered as the crystalline mode was only one way of arranging identical particles, one of which implied a regular lattice arrangement in three dimensions. The helical arrangement was, in fact, equally regular in itself, but regular only in one dimension, along the turn of the helix. The subsequent association of the helical molecules side by side obeyed the ordinary rules of crystallography. Some such arrangement might also occur – and probably does so – in certain of the fatty and liquid crystal substances. All these substances were characterized by their providing x-ray patterns with definite maxima, which were at one time taken to be sharp reflections from the different crystal planes, but are now known to correspond to extended maxima corresponding to those of Bessel functions. In other words, the x-ray diffraction gave an index to the type of order possessed by these partially crystalline bodies. The world of crystallography could then be extended to its full compass.

Definitions

The mathematical system of principles of systems consisting of units with metric and characteristic distances between points, and symmetric characteristic angles between lines to two different points, have yet to be established. Symmetry also includes the idea of identity or, rather, of indistinguishability. This, in its most complete form, is exemplified in the three-dimensional lattice.

These basic ideas, combined with geometry of a Euclidean character, will account for all forms of generalized crystallography. This depends on the topology or arrangement of the system, particularly those arrangements in which identical particles occur more than once and, in the ideal case, are repeated indefinitely. If this repetition occurs in three dimensions, we have the ideal crystal: in two dimensions, the ideal net: in one dimension, the ideal linear polymer.

At the other extreme, we have the statistical, amorphous aggregate or liquid. If indefinite repetition does not occur, finite systems must result. These give all the different types of molecule. For such molecules symmetry, not limited to 32 symmetry classes, may also occur. Five-fold and seven-fold, etc. axes may be found.

All these concepts are essentially metrical for any type of assembly – nucleonic, atomic, polymer or even larger ranges. The same kind of neutral, geometrical relations can be generalized irrespective of content. For instance, the symmetries shown in metazoa – bilateral, radial, etc. – and in the phyllotaxy of plants, belong to the same order of ideas. However striking in their appearance, they are simply logical consequences of a general notion of equality or quasi-equality.

This, in turn, gives rise to the idea of a scale. Each assembly type has its own scale, the nucleonic scale, the atomic scale, the polymer scale, the cellular scale, etc. It is in this way that the idea of measure arises and consequently, the possibility of science. This gives rise to the idea of the box within the box system, Charlier's Principle. The process, however, is one which runs both ways, small units being accumulated in larger units: similarly, larger units may be fragmented into small ones. Examples of this are the dislocations of crystals, the drops of liquids, the cracked rocks that break up into stones.

Both in the concept of accumulation and the concept of fragmentation there is the time element. There is a process of crystallization, for instance, and a mechanism involving dislocations and a process of fragmentation involving the primary and secondary and tertiary cracks, etc.

Many of the more striking and, at the same time, more useful parts of science have this common geometrical and therefore logical basis, which must be discounted in order to get real information about the system.

Equality

The property of equality or quasi-equality, indistinguishability or difficulty in distinguishing, is a basic concept of generalized crystallography. Both in the inorganic and organic worlds, we tend to take the properties of things for granted, without realizing what they imply. In the organic world, this applies in particular to the property of rigidity, a characteristic of solid crystalline bodies. This is, in effect, a by-product of the indistinguishability of atoms of the same element, that is, of atoms of the same atomic number or, at one further remove, atoms or ions of the same atomic size. It is only such atoms which can arrange themselves in rank and file order to form crystals, out of which most solid bodies are constituted, i.e. all metals and most minerals.

Many of the hard, organic substances, fibrous, like wood and cellulose (cotton and flax fibres); or simple crosslinked polymers without fillers, like wool, horn or leather; or with fillers, like bone, which owe their familiar properties or rigidity or hardness to a regular or crystalline order, in turn are necessary products of the equality of their parts, for only equal or quasi-equal particles can form the three-dimensional regularity that builds up a crystal.

It is true that rigidity can be obtained without regularity – and this is characteristic of the so-called amorphous bodies – but successive researches with x-rays, electron diffraction and electron microscopy, have shown that purely amorphous bodies are, in fact, very rare. Clays and muds are microcrystalline. The only really amorphous solids found in the mineral world are the glasses, particularly the volcanic glasses, and these have their rigidity on account of the multiplicity of possible arrangements of molecules or molecule ions like the tetrahedral silicon-oxygen group which have few points of attachment and, consequently, a multiplicity of arrangements of approximately the same energy. In a similar way, most of what appeared amorphous in the organic world is proved to be micro-crystalline or disordered-crystalline such, for instance, as the denatured proteins like the boiled white of egg and unstretched rubber.

286

In speaking of crystals, three-dimensional crystals have been implied with all the limitations as to the arrangements of symmetry that this involves. But two- and one-dimensional repeats are also consequences of quasi-identity of the constituting particles, and are free from these restrictions, being capable of taking up arrangements in which 5 and 7 and even irrational orders of symmetry occur.

The possibilities of crystallization, either in the three-dimensional form or the more free two- and one-dimensional forms, are direct consequences of the equality or quasi-equality of the parts, and have nothing to do with the constitution of the parts or of the nature of the links between them. These may be – and in most cases they are – fundamentally atoms or ions. They can also be larger entities such as molecules in ordinary organic crystals, and polymers, particularly in viruses and cell organelles. They can even be cells themselves, as shown in the regularities of phyllotaxy in botany, or the five-fold symmetry in echinoids in zoology (see D'Arcy Thompson's *On Growth and Form*) [3]. I have even seen a typical edge dislocation produced by an earthquake in a close-packed assembly of cannon-balls at Cape Coast Castle. Goldacre [4] has produced crystallization of whole bacteria and even of safety matches. Most of the arguments about the improbability of organisms being produced by chance totally ignore this effect of quasi-equality and the resultant crystalline processes.

Looked at energetically it is clear that only the three-dimensional indefinite lattices are thermodynamically stable, but the more complicated the parts, the less important is this limitation. Already, in simple inorganic crystals such as carborundum, there are a number of forms which range from true crystals to a statistical disorder of layers almost indefinite in number; but all the forms have approximately the same internal energy. Which one occurs depends on more or less fortuitous factors, mainly on the rate of growth. The kinetics are such that the lowest energy form will not be reached in a finite time and so the more energetic ones will appear. It is characteristic of micro-molecular organic systems, which lack three-dimensional order, that they are not strictly minimum energy systems.

Between precise equality or quantum theory indistinguishability of entities and completely disparate arrangements there is a necessarily indefinitely divisible zone in which it is possible to discern and describe some intermediate stages. One of these has already been mentioned, that of quasi-equality – equality sufficient to admit more or less completion of regular crystals. Lower down the scale comes a degree of things about the same size, not sufficiently alike to produce crystals but sufficiently alike to produce homogeneous, amorphous arrangements as, for instance, the sands on the sea shore. Marine sands and marine clays are, in principle, distinguishable. That does not prevent the existence of intermediate states of muddy sands or sandy clays, but in nature and in technique it is impossible to separate them. It is this category of what may be called mono-disperse aggregates that furnish the basic requirements for liquids or for amorphous solid bodies. These cannot admit regular packing, but their forms of packing are not completely vague: they are subject to rules of space, to filling and so to the properties of dilatancy, first studied by Osborne Reynolds [5].

A liquid or amorphous body is characterized by packing considerations. Each particle tends to be linked with as many others as can fit round it without any necessary order, if they are quasi-equal. This number is generally of the order of 9. The 12, characteristic of crystalline packing, cannot generally be reached in such arrangements: if it could be they would be crystalline and their particles would be quasi-equal [6].

The forces holding the particles together may be of a strong chemical nature, as with covalent bonds, or weaker chemical forces such as van der Waals forces or hydrogen bonds, or, weaker still, in the interparticle forces operating through a medium, the so-called long-range forces responsible for most colloidal phenomena, or even, in the world of large particles, surface tension or gravity. But whatever the nature of the forces they will have a finite or indefinite effective range of activity [7].

In the case of chemical forces, these will have the order of magnitude of the atoms themselves, but with the colloidal forces it will be a different order of magnitude measured in thousands of Ångströms. With gravity-arranged particles, the forces will be limited to contacts between relatively infinite, rigid bodies. But, whatever the range of the forces, a particle in such an amorphous aggregate can be distinguishable from one which is outside it and which consequently has no – or only one or two – neighbouring particles. Thus the particles make up a distinct aggregate, with a definite outer boundary, of which individual particles are either inside or outside. The boundary, of course, is not necessarily impenetrable or fixed. More particles may join or more may leave, so the larger aggregate can grow or shrink.

These are perfectly general considerations, but their operations give rise to many phenomena observable in biology, with purely geometrical consequences of particle size and particulate interactions, and so convey no additional information as to organizing relations or vital forces.

It is in this range of generalized crystallography, that is, outside the strict crystallography of three-dimensional regular arrangements, that many of the characteristic biological structures occur. Many of these are strictly two-dimensional crystals. Two-dimensional crystallography does not necessarily apply only to a plane, in fact it applies rather exceptionally to it. The surface of the two-dimensional crystal is a topological surface in which the simplest forms, apart from the plane, are the open-ended cylinder and the closed sphere; in both cases equivalent particles have only certain determinate and limited modes of arrangement on both the surfaces.

Their geometry has now been worked out, but before it was worked out it was actually first observed with x-rays and then in electron-microscope studies on the long, spherical or polyhedral viruses [8].

Structures built of equivalent particles may be called elementary structures because they are produced by particles all of the same kind. Far more variety can be found by compounding structures by using definite ratios of two or more for different kinds of particles such as those, for instance, that build up some of the more complex viruses, those of bacteriophage, for instance, particularly T2 bacteriophage which has been the most studied. Here, as this is a DNA virus, it is possible by genetic studies to distinguish between at least five kinds of distinct external coat protein molecules, which build themselves together into the complex stages of correct structures – head, inner tube, retractile spring, hexagonal base plate and antennae (plate 3). All of these seem to be examples of a general principle of construction which I have called 'synisomery' – the capacity of odd-shaped products of specialized association areas to build complex structures automatically. This represents a higher stage of generalized crystallography.

The kinds of units between which synisometric relations may hold are: (1) *simple atoms*, attractions are directed indiscriminately to appropriate other simple atoms, for instance, of different charges; (2) *more complex atoms*, those of the transitional elements, for instance, have definite sets of interactions in which their specialized bonding capacity is exerted, the ligand structures, whose importance in chemistry and particularly in biochemistry is being fully recognized; (3) *simple molecules*, the distribution of different kinds of bonds can be made in space through different directions: for example, one face of a molecule may be positive, another negative, one hydrophilic, another hydrophobic.

With the larger molecules such as those of globular proteins, which are essentially molecular polyhedra, a difference in the electronic state of each face governs how they shall fit together and at what distance and, consequently, make complex structures possible of realization spontaneously. They are, so to speak, *prescribed* by the nature of the identical molecules building them up. Perutz [9] has suggested that the method of linking of molecular oxygen with haemoglobin, which is a molecule built of two pairs of slightly different protein units similar to myoglobin, depends on the different modes of aggregation of those units.

This may be, as I have suggested, a basis for the formation of a number of intra-cellular organelles, in the most complicated of which we recognize the structure of the ciliary base or centriole which has nine-fold symmetry with evidence of greater inner complexity [6]. Much of the internal structure of living organisms may be determined by such considerations.

Helical Structures: the Appearance of the Double DNA Helix

The single-polymer polynucleotide helix spiral is, by itself, a system liable to be markedly unstable. A model, first put forward by Furberg, of such a helical polymer, is difficult to arrange in a low energy form, because of the lack of fit of the large plane purine and pyrimidine bases. It is also, as a linear polymer, liable to twist on account of the asymmetry at each phosphate-sugar link. Only if these operate in the same right- or left-hand sense will a simple helical coil result, otherwise we should have a high-energy irregular tangle.

Folding and Looping

It is a known property of long linear polymers that they shorten their effective length and so diminish their external surface by folding and looping. This is a form of self-crystallization which was first studied in the simplest of such polymers, polyethylene, by Keller [10]. The polyethylene molecule has no asymmetry and the looping is accomplished by a simple back and forth folding. The period of the folding is, for any given temperature, a constant by one fold in about every 100 monomers at a temperature of 75°C, and one in every 120 at a temperature of 90°C. As a consequence, a single long-polymer molecule may make up a crystal in the form of a monomolecular plate, which can be made to increase in thickness by the presence of a single screw dislocation.

Looping, in the case of a helical polymer, must proceed somewhat differently from the folding back and forth of helical threads as the individual loops may result in the twining of two sections of the same polymer round each other in the same sense. This may lead, in the same way as in polyethylene, to an extended two-dimensional crystal. Such crystals, however, have not been observed among helical polymers, at any rate not among polynucleotides. The shortening of the polynucleotide by this looping process, however, is likely to be one of very low energy because such an arrangement would lead naturally to the imbrication of the purine and pyrimidine bases, which would not only be attached to one another in a pseudo-crystalline form by the packing considerations at a repeat distance of 3·4 Å, but would also, by means of the conveniently arranged hydrogen bonds of purines and pyrimidines, lead to a close linking of side groups which would stabilize each loop at the turn. It has occurred to me that this mechanism would furnish a natural explanation of the origin of the double helical structure which is the central point of the Watson-Crick hypothesis.

From it, would be a natural step to postulate that breaks occur at the unstable open ends of the loops, and thus to suppose that a single polymer will break up into lengths of associated double-helix polymer. These double helical lengths would have a tendency to associate sideways and this would be made all the easier by the effective rigidity of their structure – a rigidity which depends on a double helix and would not be seen in a single one. Hence the easier crystallization of DNA than RNA.

We know, however, that RNA can also form double-helical arrangements [11], but it would appear that they are not so dense and hence are of higher energy. The absence of one oxygen on every ribose molecule promotes this tighter packing (figure 10). This hypothesis, or something like it, may serve to explain the apparently ultra-complex and highly improbable structure of DNA and its variants. They would then be examples of generalized crystallography in which the stability of a complex system is assured by more or less geometrical accidental fittings of atoms.

This may seem, *a priori*, improbable, but it has certainly been known to occur and in the abiological part of nature, for instance, in the crystals of apatite, the most stable form of mineral phosphate. Here the imbalance between the charge of ten of the five positive calcium ions and a charge of nine of the three phosphate negative ions is made up by a charge of one negative ion from a fluorine ion that fits itself snugly in the interstices of this particularly well-fitting ionic complex. This fluorine is replaced in most organic phosphates, particularly in bone, by a hydroxyl ion, but this is by no means the most stable calcium phosphate in the soil, where ground water replaces the hydroxyl by fluorine, usually a very rare ion there. The existence of a snug hole for fluorine, so to speak, appears to act as a kind of fluorine trap. It is even probable that true bone, hydroxy apatite, appeared only as a secondary product in the original fluorapatite that once made up the external skeleton of the ancestral bony fish, the ostrachoderms, and was retained in their descendants only in the form of the enamel of teeth.

This digression is simply to show other examples of how the close packing of structures of some complexity can be actually favoured in nature even when they require rare constituents. The idea I have expressed here,

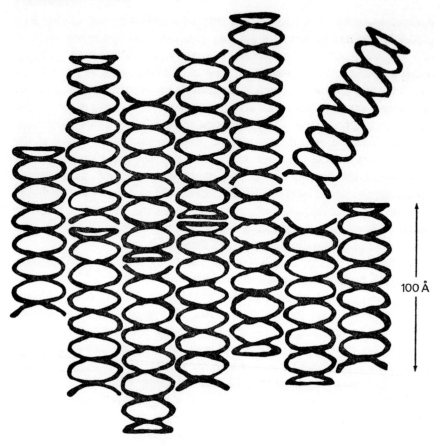

100 Å

Figure 10. Diagram of the arrangement of double-helical transfer RNA molecules in a crystal: the lines represent polynucleotide chains. A single molecule is shown at top right.

therefore, combines the two notions of generalized crystallography and of the segregation of particle atoms. Once a good fit has been achieved, it will tend to persist. For this reason, the single polymer of deoxyribophosphoric acid, only twines with a similar strand, but one not necessarily derived from the same original polymer. If the other strand comes from a different polymer, possibly from a different organism or proto-organism, we have the beginning of the phenomenon of sex.

The Effect of Shape

Despite the mono-dispersity in size that characterizes homogeneous amorphous bodies and their aggregates, it is necessary also to take into account the mono-dispersity in shape. So far, we have tacitly assumed that the particles are isodimensional or approximately so: that is that they can be represented ideally by spheres. But a large number of inorganic particles or molecules are not so. The contrast between clay and sand, for instance, depends even more on the difference of shape than on the difference of size. Clay particles, on account of intrinsic crystalline structure, occur in sheets and tend, if not too disturbed, to pack down in parallel and so to form plastic as against granular bodies. In the organic world anisodimensionality is less the rule than the exception, but here the frequency of polymerization opposes anisodimensionality of a fibrous rather than a platy form. Thus, such molecules tend to form, in solution or in suspension, liquid crystals which show flow birefringence, and in more concentrated anisotropic liquids divide into tactoids of spindle shape as, for instance, observable in tobacco mosaic virus suspensions. Platy particles can form tactoids also, as shown in inorganic alumina and other gels, studied by Zocher [12].

Coacervates and Tactoids

Large particles of the order of 1,000 Å in two dimensions or in one dimension, are in the colloidal solution subjected to mutual interactions. The nature of these has not been fully elucidated, though it seems to depend on naturally induced polarizations, rather as in the theory of the London van der Waals forces for atoms and small molecules, but on a correspondingly larger scale. These aggregates consequently show in different degrees of dilution all the phenomena of solids, liquids and gases, though in this case the units or atoms are themselves crystalline or amorphous.

If such forces exist and can be exerted through a medium, they show a lower state of energy in particular conditions, that is to say, at particular temperatures, because here the concentration of the particles in the solution and, even more, the intrinsic electrical properties of the solvent itself, are the most important factors. If the dilution of the particles themselves and the conditions of the solvent are such that they may be readily moved out of their spheres of mutual influence, a dilute sol is the result. If this is not the case, equilibrium can be reached best by dividing the solution into two parts – that of a concentrated sol and of a dilute sol. In other words, a precipitation of fluid drops occurs in a much more dilute solution. This is the origin of the *coacervates*, so much studied by Bungenberg de Jong and used by Oparin [13] to support a stage of the origin of life.

Normally, the coacervate drops precipitated in this way are in the form of isotropic droplets, but if constituent particles are anisodimensional, that is, flat plates or long rods, the spherical drops are replaced by the fusiform shapes of *tactoids* which are also necessarily anisotropic, as in the case of tobacco mosaic virus. The same effect can be reached in another form of spherical drop, that in which the long particles are arranged not in parallel but in a series of twisted helices, giving rise not to simple birefringence, but to rotary polarization, as in the drops of polybenzyl-glutamate studied by Conmar Robinson [14]

In the more extreme case of highly elongated particles, there may be a network of fibres running through the whole liquid. The tactoid becomes the continuous phase as well as the solvent, which interpenetrate as two topological lattices. The result is a gel, as in the collagen-stabilized gel of the vitreous humour of the mammalian eye.

Liquids

The most characteristic state of unequal particles is that of the liquid. The particular arrangements in any given region are also nearly equal in energy: the change of one of them to another is below the general level of thermal disturbance. This is also the case for crystalline bodies above their melting-point. Amorphous solids do not have melting-points, because their irregularity is the same at low and high temperatures, but the rate of change from one form of irregularity to another naturally increases as the temperature rises and, consequently, the viscosity diminishes. This is characteristic of the formation of glasses, where the viscosity changes over a range of temperature of 400°C-500°C for an ordinary soda glass, from 10^8 poises to 10^{16} poises to what is called the softening-point.

This is not strictly a physical phase change, for it depends on the rate at which it is arrived at: glass can be suddenly chilled practically unchanged by the irregularity of the viscous melt, or slowly annealed so that it gradually acquires the arrangement suitable for the lower temperature. The former retains much internal strain, which manifests itself by brittleness and cracking, and, in the more extreme case, by explosion, as in Rupert's drops; the latter acquires a homogeneity and toughness.

The differences of order between crystalline solid and liquid is by no means simple, because the order in the crystal can be of various dimensional types. Hermann [15] has distinguished nineteen intermediate states between liquid and the crystalline solid. Most of these have been realized in practice, particularly with molecular liquids which have molecules varying very much in dimensions – flat, long and thin, or ribbon-shaped.

These intermediate states are the so-called liquid crystals which play a large part in modern biology and are probably decisive in the earlier stages of the origin of life in combining the possibilities of reaction of the liquid with the strength of the solid.

References to Appendix 3

1   L. PAULING & R.B. COREY(1951) Atomic coordinates and structure factors for two helical configurations of polypeptide chains. *Proc. natn. Acad. Sci. USA* **37**: 235–240

2   W. COCHRAN, F.H.C. CRICK & V. VAND(1952) The structure of synthetic polypeptides, I. The transform of atoms on a helix. *Acta crystallogr.* **5**: 581–586

3   D'A.W. THOMPSON(1942) *On growth and form.* 2 vols. 2nd Edition. University Press: Cambridge

4   R.J. GOLDACRE(1954) Crystalline bacterial arrays and specific long-range forces. *Nature, Lond.* **174**: 732–734

5   O. REYNOLDS(1885) On the dilatancy of media composed on rigid particles in contact. *Phil. Mag.* **20**: 469–481

6   J.D. BERNAL(1964) The structure of liquids. *Proc. R. Soc. A.* **280**: 299–322

7   —— (1962) The structure of molecules. In *Comprehensive biochemistry. Vol. I. Atomic and molecular structure.* M. Florkin & E.H. Stotz, Editors. Elsevier: Amsterdam & New York

8   A. KLUG & D.L.D. CASPAR(1960) The structure of small viruses. *Adv. Virus Res.* **7**: 225–325

9   M.F. PERUTZ(1960) Structure of haemoglobin. *Nature, Lond.* **185**: 416–422

10 A. KELLER(1957) A note on single crystals in polymers: evidence for a folded chain configuration. *Phil. Mag.* **2**: 1171–1175

11 M. SPENCER *et al.*(1962) Determination of the helical configuration of ribonucleic acid molecules by x-ray diffraction study of crystalline amino-acid-transfer ribonucleic acid. *Nature, Lond.* **194**: 1014–1020

12 H. ZOCHER & K. JACOBSOHN(1929) Über Taktosole. *Kolloid-chem. Beih.* **28**: 167–206

13 A.I. OPARIN(1961) *Life: its nature, origin and development.* Translated by A. Synge. Oliver & Boyd: Edinburgh & London

14 C. ROBINSON & J.C. WARD(1957) Liquid-crystalline structures in polypeptides. *Nature, Lond.* **180**: 1183–1184

15 C. HERMANN(1931) Die Symmetriegruppen der amorphen und mesomorphen Phasen. *Z. Kristallogr. Kristallgeom.* **79**: 186–221

Appendix 4

Questions and Answers

Answers by J.D. Bernal to the questions posed by him in his paper on 'Molecular Matrices for Living Systems' presented to the Wakulla Springs Conference on *The Origins of Prebiological Systems*, Florida, October 1963.

(1) *Q.* Are the forms of life necessary or contingent?

A. The simpler are and the more complicated are not. Molecules such as adenine are apparently necessary. The form of any particular organism is not. It is contingent on the accidents of organic evolution.

(2) *Q.* Is there any evidence that the cosmically abundant elements of hydrogen, carbon, nitrogen, and oxygen are not the major basis of alternative forms of life?

A. None known to me, at least on Earth.

(3) *Q.* How can we separate from the possible ways in which life might have originated the actual path which its evolution on Earth followed?

A. By a careful study of the compounds involved and of the conditions in which they are formed in the laboratory.

(4) *Q.* Which of the various synthetic studies that have been made of the formation of elementary molecular compounds is relevant to the questions of the origin of life?

A. Those not involving starting with substances unlikely to be found on Earth, for instance, ethyl phosphate.

(5) *Q.* Are the carbonaceous compounds of the meteorites similar to those which on Earth have been considered as possible precursors of life?

A. Yes.

(6) *Q.* Were these compounds the product of pre-existing life on the parent bodies of the meteorites?

A. Very unlikely.

(7) *Q.* Are the pre-formed molecular species such as purines in the carbonaceous meteorites?

A. Apparently so.

(8) *Q.* Were the carbonaceous materials in the meteorites formed of meteoric dust by the action of radiation and subsequently condensed by loss of gases and water?

A. This remains a possible mechanism. The secondary formation of these mineral materials in vulcanism on asteroids is also possible, as put forward by Mueller.

(9) *Q.* Was the primary material from which life originated on Earth formed from pre-existing carbonaceous compounds derived from the meteoritic bodies from which the Earth was formed or was it produced on its surface or in its atmosphere subsequently by radiations (the Oparin-Haldane hypothesis)?

A. Many processes may have taken part in the formation of these compounds. They can be distinguished possibly by isotopic studies.

(10) *Q.* Was Stage II of biopoesis – the conversion of small molecular species such as purines and amino acids to the nucleic-acid-protein mechanism – carried out in the first place in the hydrosphere?

A. Yes.

(11) *Q.* How did the basic elements of molecular reproduction themselves originate?

A. The bases and amino acids were formed presumably abiotically and then selected. Some of the base and sugar phosphates have acted as protocoenzymes and were subsequently polymerized into nucleic acids. An intermediate stage in which short lengths of nuclear acids were attached to particular amino acids probably intervened, leading to the formation of transfer RNA, and hence to the whole process of replication.

(12) *Q.* Is there anything analogous to the nucleic-acid-protein mechanism which can operate in conditions of much simpler molecular structures?

A. Not so far known, but it can be sought for.

(13) *Q.* Did life, in the sense of exchanging metabolites and the using up of free energy, exist before there were definite organisms? In other words, were there indefinite and extensive sub-vital areas on which metabolic activities took place?

A. This is my opinion.

(14) *Q*. Did the first stages of life occur in a free aqueous medium or were they absorbed in certain deposits, possibly of clay or iron oxides?

    A. I still consider that adsorption was a probably necessary intermediate stage. But Calvin prefers the activity of special molecules such as the cyanamides.

(15) *Q*. At what stage did the colloid coacervates first appear?

    A. In the latter part of Stage II when the replication mechanism had already been evolved.

(16) *Q*. Were enzymatic actions first carried out by protoenzymes of essentially a transition-metal coordination type?

    A. Possibly, but not certainly.

(17) *Q*. What were the first protocoenzymes?

    A. Probably metaphosphates derived from minerals like apatite.

(18) *Q*. Did the polymerizations of nucleotide protocoenzymes lead to the formation of nucleic acids?

    A. Yes.

(19) *Q*. Was the nucleic-acid-protein cycle necessary to produce elements of organellar and cellular structure?

    A. Yes.

(20) *Q*. Are organelles formed by the association of specific proteins formed in the cell by a form of pseudocrystallization?

    A. In some cases, e.g. cilia, through specific protein formation; in others the formation of the organelles was dependant on that of membranes, as in mitochondria.

(21) *Q*. How, from a set of fairly simple chemical substances, can the whole of the complex reproductory metabolic mechanism be evolved without the benefit of any preformed structures?

    A. This is the major unsolved question of the origin of life.

(22) *Q*. Is the centriole a modified form of ciliary base and is it reduplicated by a virus-like mechanism in the cell?

    A. Yes.

(23) *Q*. Are the organelles found in cells made by an analogous mechanism; in other words, are they relics of earlier autonomous structures?

    A. Some are relics of earlier autonomous structures.

(24) *Q*. Are the molecular structures on which muscle action is based derived from previous molecules of the myosin-actin type which originally had no contractile function?

    A. Probably yes.

(25) *Q.* Are the complicated membrane foldings found in cells and mitochondria evidence that the size of the cell was once much smaller
and that it contained only spherical particles like mycoplasmas?

A. Yes.

(26) *Q.* Do cells contain volumes of high and low concentration of proteins
separated by partially permeable membranes?

A. Yes.

(27) *Q.* If biological structures and functions are determined by a prescription from a code carrier, how is the carrier affected by the
results of the prescription?

A. There are elaborate play-back mechanisms involving stopping,
starting and blocking mechanisms.

(28) *Q.* What are the general conditions necessary to produce any kind of
life?

A. The general geological conditions are those which persist in the
hydrosphere with sufficient radiation.

(29) *Q.* Is the unity of life on Earth primitive or the result of blending of
former partial lives?

A. The complete eukaryotic cell was apparently produced from
former prokaryotic cells appearing in it as organelles.

(30) *Q.* If life is the phenomenon of hydrospheres, are the life types in
different hydrospheres of different planets radically different?

A. Yes.

(31) *Q.* Is life on Earth a fair sample of life types on any hydrosphere?
A. Probably.

(32) *Q.* Can the life forms in different hydrospheres mingle or be mingled
to any extent?

A. This question is completely open and can only be determined by
trial

Bibliography

Bibliography

1   ABELSON, P.H.(1963) Paleobiochemistry. In *Evolutionary biochemistry*. A.I. Oparin *et al.*, Editors. Pergamon Press: Oxford

2   ABELSON, P.H.(1965) Abiogenic synthesis in the Martian environment. *Proc. natn. Acad. Sci. USA* **54**: 1490–1494

3   AKABORI, S.(1965) Asymmetric hydrogenation of carbonyl compounds. In *The origins of prebiological systems*. S.W. Fox, Editor. Academic Press: New York

4   ALVEN, H.(1954) *On the origin of the solar system*. Clarendon Press: Oxford

5   ANDERS, E.(1964) Origin, age and composition of meteorites. *Space Sci. Rev.* **3**: 583–714

6   ARISTOTLE (1927–52) *The works of Aristotle*. 12 vols. Translated under editorship of J.A. Smith and W.D. Ross. University Press: Oxford

7   BARGHOORN, E.S. & TYLER, S.A.(1965) Microorganisms from the Gunflint Chert. *Science* **147**: 563–577

7a BARGHOORN, E.S. & SCHOPF, J.W.(1966) Microorganisms three billion years old from the Precambrian of South Africa. *Science* **152**: 758–763

8   BASSETT, D.C. & KELLER, A.(1961) Some new habit features in crystals of long chain compounds. Part II Polymers. *Phil. Mag.* **6**: 345–358

9   BERKNER, L.V. & MARSHALL, L.C.(1965) History of major atmospheric components. *Proc. natn. Acad. Sci. USA* **53**: 1215–1226

10 —— (1965) On the origin and rise of oxygen concentration on the earth's atmosphere. *J. atmos. Sci.* **22**: 225–261

11 —— (1966) Limitation on oxygen concentration in a primitive planetary atmosphere. *J. atmos. Sci.* **23**: 133–143

12 BERNAL, J.D.(1951) *The physical basis of life*. Routledge and Kegan Paul: London

13 —— (1952) Keep off the grass: a review of a review. *New Biol.* **13**: 120–126

14 —— (1953) Evolution of life. *Sci. Cult.* **19**: 228–234

15 —— (1954) The origin of life. *New Biol.* **16**: 28–40

16 —— (1955) Molecular structure and the understanding of vital processes. *Trans. Bose Res. Inst.* **20**: 185–190

17 —— (1957) The origins of life. *Nature, Lond.* **180**: 1220

18 —— (1957) Origin of life on this earth. *Marxism Today* **1**: 50–57

19 —— (1958) Some reflections on structure and function in the evolution of life. *Trans. Bose Res. Inst.* **22**: 101–110

20 BERNAL, J.D.(1959) The problem of stages in biopoesis. In *The origin of life on earth*. A.I. Oparin *et al.*, Editors. Pergamon Press: London

21 —— (1959) The scale of structural units in biopoesis. In *The origin of life on earth*. A.I. Oparin *et al.*, Editors. Pergamon Press: London

22 —— (1960) Thermodynamics and kinetics of spontaneous generation. Note on D.E. Hull's communication. *Nature, Lond.* **186**: 694–695

23 —— (1961) The origin of life on the shores of the ocean: physical and chemical conditions determining first appearance of biological processes. In *Oceanography*. M. Sears, Editor. *Publs. Am. Ass. Advmt. Sci.* **67**: 95–118

24 —— (1961) The problem of carbonaceous meteorites. *The Times Science Review* **40**: 3–4

25 —— (1961) Significance of carbonaceous meteorites in theories on the origin of life. *Nature, Lond.* **190**: 129–131

26 —— (1962) Biochemical evolution. In *Horizons in biochemistry*. M. Kasha & B. Pullman, Editors. Academic Press (London)

27 —— (1962) Life-forms in meteorites: comments. *Nature, Lond.* **193**: 1127–1129

28 —— (1962) The structure of molecules. In *Comprehensive biochemistry*: Vol. I *Atomic and molecular structure*. M. Florkin & E.H. Stotz, Editors. Elsevier: Amsterdam & New York

29 —— (1963) Cosmic aspects of the origin of life. *5th Int. Congr. Biochem., Moscow* **3**: 3–11

30 —— (1964) Life beyond Tellus. In *Penguin Science Survey B*. S.A. Barnett & A. McLaren, Editors. Penguin: Harmondsworth

31 —— (1965) Molecular matrices for living systems. In *The origins of prebiological systems*. S.W. Fox, Editor. Academic Press: New York

32 —— (1965) Molecular structure, biochemical function, and evolution. In *Theoretical and mathematical biology*. T.H. Waterman & H.J. Morowitz Editors. Blaisdell: New York

33 —— (1965) The structure of water and its biological implications. In *The state and movement of water in living organisms. Symp. Soc. exp. Biol.* **19**: 17–32

34 —— & FANKUCHEN, I. (1941) X-ray and crystallographic studies of plant virus preparations. *J. gen. Physiol.* **25**: 111–146

34a BOSTRÖM, K. & FREDRIKSSON, K.(1966) Surface conditions of the Orgueil meteorite parent body as indicated by mineral associations. *Smithsonian Misc. Coll.* **151** No. 3

35 BROWN, H.(1964) Planetary systems associated with main sequence stars. *Science* **145**: 1177–1181

36 CALVIN, M.(1965) Chemical evolution. *Proc. R. Soc. A* **288**: 441–466

37 CASPAR, D.L.D.(1966) Design principles in organized biological structures. In CIBA Symposium on *Principles of biomolecular organization*. Churchill: London

38 CASPERSSON, T.(1947) The relations between nucleic acid and protein synthesis. I Nucleic Acid. *Symp. Soc. exp. Biol.* **1**: 127–151

39 CHARLIER, C.V.L.(1922) How an infinite world may be built up. *Ark. Mat. Astr. Fys.* **16**: No. 22: 1–34

40 DARWIN, C.(1887) *The life and letters of Charles Darwin*. F. Darwin, Editor. Murray: London

41 DAUVILLIER, A.(1965) *The photochemical origin of life*, translated by Scripta Technica Inc. Academic Press: London

42 DUCHESNE, J. & DEPIREUX, J.(1958) Ferromagnetism of meteorites. *Nature, Lond.* **182**: 931

43 FISCHER, A.G.(1965) Fossils, early life, and atmospheric history. *Proc. natn. Acad. Sci. USA* **53**: 1205–1215

44 FOSTER, SIR M., (1901) *Lectures on the history of physiology during the sixteenth, seventeenth and eighteenth centuries.* University Press: Cambridge

45 FOX, S.W. Editor(1965) *The origins of prebiological systems: and of their molecular structure.* Academic Press: New York

46 FOX, S.W. & HARADA, K.(1960) Thermal copolymerisation of amino acids common to proteins. *J. Am. Chem. Soc.* **82**: 3745–3751

47 GARSTANG, R.H.(1959) Peculiar stars. *Occ. Notes R. astr. Soc.* **3**: 234–252

48 GOLDSCHMIDT, V.M. *et al.*, (1923–37) Geochemische Verteilungsgesetze der Elemente, I–IX. *Skr. norske Vidensk-Akad.*

48a GRAVELLE, M. & LELUBRE, M.(1957) Découverte de Stromatolithes du groupe des Conophytons dans le Pharusien de l'Ahaggar Occidental. *Bull. Soc. Géol. France* **7**: 435–442

49 HAGGETT, M.L., JONES, P. & WYNNE-JONES, W.F.K.(1960) Peroxy-complexes as intermediates in the catalytic decomposition of hydrogen peroxide. *Discuss. Faraday Soc.* **29**: 153–162

50 HALDANE, J.B.S.(1929) The origin of life. *Rationalist Annual*

51 —— (1954) The origins of life. *New Biol.* **16**: 12–27

52 —— (1965) Data needed for a blueprint of the first organism. In *The origins of prebiological systems.* S.W. Fox, Editor. Academic Press: New York

53 HAMILTON, E.L.(1961) Stratigraphy of the deep-sea floor. In *Oceanography.* M. Sears, Editor. *Publs. Am. Ass. Advmt. Sci.* **67**: 51–84

54 HENDERSON, L.J.(1913) *The fitness of the environment.* Macmillan: New York. Republished (1959) by P. Smith: Gloucester, Mass.

54a HINTON, H.E.(1966) How insects adjust to changes in temperature. In *Penguin Science Survey B.* Penguin: Harmondsworth

55 HOLLEY, R.W.(1966) The nucleotide sequence of a nucleic acid. *Scient. Am.* **214**: No. 2: 30–39

56 HOROWITZ, N.H.(1945) On the evolution of biochemical syntheses. *Proc. natn. Acad. Sci. USA* **31**: 153–157

57 HULL, D.E.(1960) Thermodynamics and kinetics of spontaneous generation. *Nature, Lond.* **186**: 693–694

57a HURRY, S.W.(1965) *The microstructure of cells.* John Murray: London

58 HUXLEY, T.H.(1901) On the physical basis of life. In *Collected essays* Vol. 1. Macmillan: London

59 KELLER, A. & SAWADA, S.(1964) On the interior morphology of bulk polythene. *Makromolek. Chem.* **74**: 190–221

60 KENDREW, J.C.(1962) The structure of globular proteins. *Comp. Biochem. Physiol.* **4**: 249–252

61 KLUG, A. & BERGER, J.E.(1964) An optical method for the analysis of periodicities in electron micrographs, and some observations on the mechanism of negative staining. *J. molec. Biol.* **10**: 565–569

62 KUHN, T.S.(1962) *The structure of scientific revolutions.* University of Chicago Press

63 KUHN, W., *et al.*(1960) Contractile oxidation-reduction system consisting of pure poly (vinyl alcohol) and 2–methyl–1, 4–naphthaquinine. *Experientia* **16**: 106–107

63a KUNG, YUEH-TING *et al.*(1965) Total synthesis of crystalline bovine insulin. *Sci. Sinica* **14**: 1710–1716

64 LEVIN, B.Y.(1963) *The origin of the earth and planets.* 3rd Ed. Translated by A. Shkarovsky. Foreign Languages Publishing House: Moscow

64a LIQUORI, A.M.(1966) Minimum energy conformation of biological polymers. In CIBA Symposium on *Principles of biomolecular organization.* Churchill: London

65 LWOFF, A.(1965) The specific effectors of viral development. *Biochem. J.* **96**: 289–301

66 MACEWAN, D.M.C.(1962) Interlamellar reactions of clays and other substances. *Clays clay Miner.* **9**: 431–433

66a MATTHEWS, C.N. & MOSER, R.E.(1966) Prebiological protein synthesis. *Proc. natn. Acad. Sci. USA* **56**: 1087–1094

67 MILLER, S.L.(1953) A production of amino acids under possible primitive earth conditions. *Science* **117**: 528–529

68 MORA, P.T.(1963) Urge and molecular biology. *Nature, Lond.* **199**: 212–219

69 —— (1965) The folly of probability. In *The origins of prebiological systems.* S.W. Fox, Editor. Academic Press: New York

70 MOROWITZ, H.J.(1966) The minimum size of cells. In CIBA Symposium on *Principles of biomolecular organization.* Churchill: London

71 MUELLER, G.(1962) Interpretation of micro-structures in carbonaceous meteorites. *Nature, Lond.* **196**: 929–932

71a MUELLER, G.(1966) Significance of inclusions in carbonaceous meteorites. *Nature, Lond.* **210**: 151–55

72 NAGY, B., MEINSCHEIN, W.G., & HENNESY, D.J.(1961) Mass spectroscopic analysis of the Orgueil meteorite evidence for biogenic hydrocarbons. *Ann. N.Y. Sci.* **93**: 25–35

73 NEUGEBAUER, G., MARTZ, D.E., & LEIGHTON, R.B.(1965) Observations of extremely cool stars. *Astrophys. J.* **142**: 399–401

74 NEUGEBAUER, O.(1957) *The exact sciences in antiquity.* 2nd Ed. Brown University Press: Providence, R.I.

75 OPARIN, A.I.(1924) *Proiskhozhdenie zhizny.* Izd. Moskovski Rabochii: Moscow

76 —— (1936) *Vozniknovenie zhizny na zemle.* Izd. AN SSSR: Moscow

77 —— (1938) *The origin of life.* Translation of Russian Edition 1936. Macmillan: London. Republished 1953, Dover Publications: New York

78 —— (1957) *The origin of life on the earth.* 3rd Ed. Oliver & Boyd: Edinburgh & London

79 —— (1961) *Life: its nature, origin and development.* Translation by A. Synge of 1960 Russian edition. Oliver & Boyd: Edinburgh & London

80 —— (1964) *The chemical origin of life.* Translated by A. Synge. C.C. Thomas: Springfield, Illinois

81 OPARIN, A.I.(1965) The pathways of the primary development of metabolism and artificial modelling of this development in coacervate drops. In *The origins of prebiological systems*. S.W. Fox, Editor. Academic Press: New York

82 ——*et al.* Editors(1959) *Proceedings of the first international symposium on the origin of life on earth*. (English-French-German edition edited for the International Union of Biochemistry by F. Clark and R.L.M. Synge.) Pergamon Press: London

83 ORÓ, J.(1961) Comets and the formation of biochemical compounds on the primitive earth. *Nature, Lond.* **190**: 389–390

84 —— & KIMBALL, A.P.(1961) Synthesis of purines under possible primitive earth conditions: I. Adenine from hydrogen cyanide. *Archs Biochem. Biophys.* **94**: 217–227

85 —— —— (1962) Synthesis of purines under possible primitive earth conditions: II. Purine intermediates from hydrogen cyanide. *Archs Biochem. Biophys.* **96**: 293–313

86 ORÓ, J., *et al.*(1965) Hydrocarbons of biological origin in sediments about two billion years old. *Science* **148**: 77–79

87 PAULING, L. & ZUCKERKANDL, E.(1963) Chemical palaeogenetics. Molecular restoration studies of extinct forms of life. *Acta chem. scand.* **17**: suppl. 1, S9–S19

88 PAVLOVSKAYA, A.T. & PASYNSKII, A.G.(1959) The original formation of amino acids under the action of ultraviolet rays and electrical discharges. In *The origin of life on the earth*. A.I. Oparin *et al.*, Editors. Pergamon Press: London

89 PERRET, J.(1952) Biochemistry and bacteria. *New Biol.* **12**: 68–96

90 PERUTZ, M.F.(1960) Structure of haemoglobin *Brookhaven Symp. Biol.* **13**: 165–183

91 PIRIE, N.W.(1937) The meaninglessness of the terms life and living. In *Perspectives in biochemistry*. J. Needham & D.R. Green, Editors. University Press: Cambridge

92 —— (1952) Vital blarney. *New Biol.* **12**: 106–112

93 —— (1953) Ideas and assumptions about the origin of life. *Discovery, Lond.* **14**: 238–242

94 —— (1954) On making and recognizing life. *New Biol.* **16**: 41–53

95 —— (1965) Discussion, pp.278f. In *Origins of prebiological systems*. S.W. Fox, Editor. Academic Press: New York

96 PONNAMPERUMA, C.(1964) Chemical evolution and the origin of life. *Nature, Lond.* **201**: 337–340

97 —— (1965) Abiological synthesis of some nucleic acid constituents. In *The origins of prebiological systems*. S.W. Fox, Editor. Academic Press: New York

98 —— (1965) The chemical origin of Life. *Science Journal*, May, 39–45

99 PONNAMPERUMA, C., MARINER, R. & SAGAN, C.(1963) Formation of adenosine by ultra-violet irradiation of a solution of adenine and ribose. *Nature, Lond.* **198**: 1199–1200

100 —— SAGAN, C. & MARINER, R.(1963) Synthesis of adenosine triphosphate under possible primitive earth conditions. *Nature, Lond.* **199**: 222–226

101 RICH, A. & DAVIES, D.R.(1956) A new two-stranded helical structure: poly (adenylic acid) and poly (uridylic acid). *J. Am. chem. Soc.* **78**: 3548–3549

102 RUBEY, W.W.(1955) Development of the hydrosphere and atmosphere, with special reference to probable composition of the early atmosphere. *Geol. Soc. spec. Pap.* **62**: 631–650

103 RUTTEN, M.G.(1962) *The geological aspects of the origin of life on earth.* Elsevier: Amsterdam & New York

104 SAGAN, C.(1965) Primordial ultraviolet synthesis of nucleoside phosphates. In *The origins of prebiological systems.* S.W. Fox, Editor. Academic Press: New York

104a SAGAN, L. (1966) On the origin of mitosing cells. Personal communication

105 SCHMIDT, O.J.(1944) A meteoric theory of the origin of the earth and planets. *Dokl. Akad. Nauk* SSSR **45**: 229–233

106 SEARS, M. Editor(1961) *Oceanography: invited lectures presented at the international oceanographic congress held in New York, 31 August–12 September 1959. Publs Am. Ass. Advmt Sci.* **67**

106a SHKLOVSKII, L.S. & SAGAN, C. (1966) *Intelligent life in the Universe.* Holden-Day Inc.: San Francisco

106b STANIER, R.Y.,DOUDOROFF, M. & ADELBERG,E.A.(1963) *General microbiology.* 2nd Ed. Macmillan: London

107 STUBBS, P.(1965) The oldest rocks in the world. *New Scient.* **25**: 82

108 TEILHARD DE CHARDIN, P.(1955) *La phenoméne humain.* Editions du Seuil: Paris

109 THODE, H.G., MACNAMARA, J. & FLEMING, W.H.(1953) Sulphur isotope fractionation in nature and geological and biological time scales. *Geochim. cosmochim Acta* **3**: 235–243

110 THOMPSON, D'A. W.(1942) *On growth and form.* 2 vols. 2nd Ed. University Press: Cambridge

111 THORPE, W.H.(1965) *Science, man and morals.* Methuen: London

111a TULLOCH, G.S. & HERSHENOV, B.R. (1967) Fine structure of platyhelminth sperm tails. *Nature, Lond.* **213**: 299–300

112 TYNDALL, J.(1875) Presidential address, 1874. *Rep. Br. Ass. Advmt. Sci.*

113 UREY, H.C.(1951) The origin and development of the earth and other terrestrial planets. *Geochim. cosmochim. Acta* **1**: 209–277

114 —— (1962) Life-forms in meteorites. Origin of life-like forms in carbonaceous chondrites. *Nature, Lond.* **193**: 1119–1133

115 —— (1963) The origin of organic molecules. In *The nature of biological diversity.* J.M. Allen, Editor. McGraw-Hill: New York & London

116 VOLPIN, M.E. & SHUR, V.B.(1966) Nitrogen fixation by transition metal complexes. *Nature, Lond.* **209**:1236

117 VON WEIZSACKER, C.F.Z.(1944) Uber die Entstehung des Planetsystems. *Z. Astrophys.* **22**: 319–355

118 WALD, G.(1964) The origins of life. *Proc. natn. Acad. Sci. USA* **52**: 595–611

119 WHYTE, L.L.(1965) *Internal factors in evolution.* Tavistock Publications: London

120 WIENER, N.(1964) *God & Golem, Inc.* Chapman & Hall: London

121 WIGNER, E.P.(1961) The probability of the existence of a self-producing unit. In *The logic of personal knowledge. (Festschrift for Michael Polanyi).* Routledge & Kegan Paul: London

122 ZAHLAN, A.B.(1966) Levels of molecular organization and the origin of life problem. Personal communication

Glossary

abiogenesis: see *spontaneous generation.*

actin: a protein from muscle. It exists in two forms, a globular protein, G-actin, which can bind one ATP molecule, and a longer, fibrous, double-helix form, F-actin, which is produced by polymerization of G-actin, using energy liberated from the bound ATP. The basic contractile unit of the muscle cell, the myofibril, consists of bundles of F-actin filaments and myosin (*q.v.*) filaments, which alternate along the length of the fibril and give it a characteristic striated appearance. The filaments respond to a stimulus to contract by sliding over one another, thereby increasing the degree of overlap.

adenine: see *nitrogenous base.*

adenosine triphosphate (ATP): a nucleoside (*q.v.*) triphosphate, i.e. consisting of adenine (*q.v.*), ribose (*q.v.*) and three phosphate (*q.v.*) groups. It is a high-energy compound, i.e. when it transfers a phosphate to an acceptor a large amount of energy is released (7 kcal/mole). Loss of one phosphate converts ATP to a diphosphate, ADP; loss of two yields the monophosphate, AMP.

albumins: those globular proteins which are readily soluble in water. Typical of this large group are ovalbumin, the protein of egg-white, and serum albumin.

algae: a subdivision of the Thallophyta, the botanical group containing most of the primitive plants. The Thallophyta vary from single-celled to large multi-celled plants, but are distinguished from higher plants by having no differentiation into roots, stem and leaf. Algae are distinguished from the other main Thallophyte group, the Fungi, by containing chlorophyll (*q.v.*).

amino acid: a compound containing both an acidic carboxyl group (COOH) and a basic amino group (NH$_2$). In solution in water all amino acids have the ionized form:

$$H - \overset{\overset{\displaystyle H}{|}}{\underset{\underset{\displaystyle H}{|}}{N^+}} - \overset{\overset{\displaystyle H}{|}}{\underset{\underset{\displaystyle R}{|}}{C}} - C\overset{\diagup O}{\diagdown O^-}$$

where R represents the part of the molecule which varies from amino acid to amino acid (Fig. 11). They form the building blocks of proteins, in which they are joined by peptide bonds (*q.v.*). The sulphur-containing amino acid, cysteine (Fig. 25, p. 331) can contribute to the tertiary structure of proteins by formation of S–S

autoradiography: a technique for detecting the distribution of radio-active tracers (*q.v.*) by bringing the material

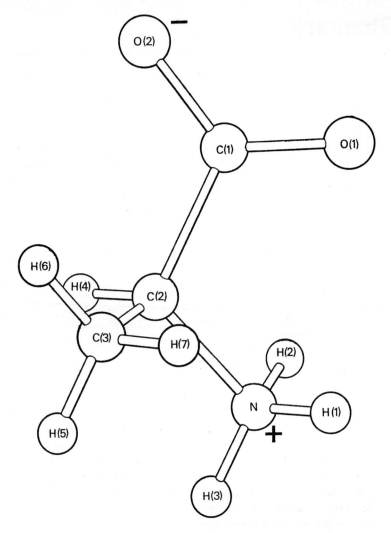

Figure 11. A three-dimensional drawing of the amino acid, L–alanine.

bridges between CySH molecules in different parts of the protein molecule.

ATP see *adenosine triphosphate.*

under study into contact with a photographic plate. The radio-active areas 'expose' the photographic emulsion so that, when the plate is developed, the exact locations of tracer-molecules are shown up as black dots (plate 26).

bacterial flagella: contractile threads serving the same purpose as the cilia (q.v.) of higher organisms but having a simpler structure. They consist of a spirally-wound protein thread (plates 7 and 8).

bacteriophage: a virus (q.v.) which attacks bacterial cells. Its nucleic acid component is DNA, which is contained in the polyhedral head (plate 3) with a certain amount of protein. The tail consists entirely of protein. When a T_4 bacteriophage attacks a bacterium, it attaches itself to its prey by the tip of its tail, which is hollow, pierces the bacterial wall and then 'injects' the contents of the head through the tail into the bacterium, where it first replicates and then produces a number of new bacteriophage particles.

Bode's Law: In 1772 Bode pointed out a simple numerical relationship connecting the distances of the various planets from the Sun. This may be obtained in the following manner. The series of numbers: 0, 1, 2, 4, 8, 16, 32, 64, 128, 256 are written down in which each number after the first two is double the preceding number. Then each term of this series is multiplied by 3: 0, 3, 6, 12, 24, 48, 96, 192, 384, 768. Next 4 is added to each term: 4, 7, 10, 16, 28, 52, 100, 196, 388, 772. Then, if the Earth's distance from the Sun is taken to be 10, these numbers are very approximately proportional to the mean distance of the planets from the Sun:

0	0	4	3·9 Mercury
1	3	7	7·2 Venus
2	6	10	10·0 Earth
4	12	16	15·2 Mars
8	24	28	27·7 Asteroid Ceres
16	48	52	52·0 Jupiter
32	96	100	95·3 Saturn
64	192	196	191·9 Uranus
128	384	388	300·7 Neptune
256	768	772	395·0 Pluto

Although the law held true for the planets known in 1772, and continued to do so for Uranus and the asteroid Ceres, Neptune and Pluto deviated from the predicted Bode distances and all attempts to find a theoretical basis for the law have failed.

catalyst: a substance which increases the rate at which a chemical reaction takes place, itself emerging unchanged at the end of the reaction. Since it is continually regenerated in its original form, a small amount of catalyst can effect a large increase in rate. Catalysts may be inorganic molecules e.g. Ziegler catalysts (q.v.) or complex organic molecules, e.g. enzymes (q.v.).

cellulose: a polymer (q.v.) of the sugar, glucose; forms the basis of cell walls in all green plants and some fungi. The glucose units are linked by 1·4-β-linkages to give unbranched chains (Fig. 12).

centriole: minute cylindrical body found just outside the nucleus in many resting cells. It is formed from nine fibres, each of which consists of three protein microtubules. Before mitosis (q.v.) it doubles by 'budding' another centriole at right angles to the first and the two centrioles move apart to form the poles of the mitotic spindle.

In some cells the centriole is connected to flagella or cilia (plate 10).

chlorocruorin: green respiratory pigment related to haemoglobin (*q.v.*), found in the blood of some polychaete worms. Unlike haemoglobin,

(d) are found in some algae (*q.v.*). All these compounds consist of a modified porphyrin (*q.v.*) containing a magnesium atom at the centre position and linked to the long-chain alcohol, phytol ($C_{20}H_{39}OH$) at position 7.

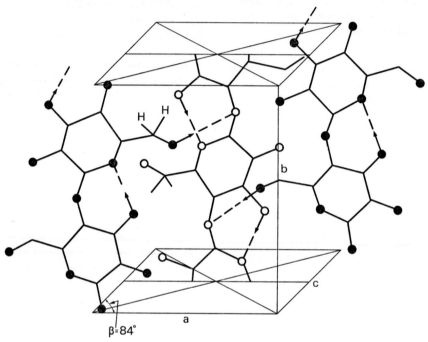

$\beta=84°$

Figure 12. Cellulose crystal structure. (View nearly normal to the rings, showing the internal hydrogen bonds (dotted lines).)

chlorocruorin does not occur in corpuscles, but circulates freely in the plasma in the form of regularly-arranged, high molecular weight aggregates of protein-porphyrin subunits (M.W. 3,000,000) (plate 15).

chlorophyll: green pigment, located in chloroplasts (*q.v.*), which has the property of absorbing light energy and passing it on to other pigment molecules (see *photosynthesis*). Two chlorophylls, (a) and (b), are found in higher plants and chlorophylls (c) and

chloroplast: a plastid (*q.v.*) found in all but the most primitive algae. Contains the green photosynthetic (*q.v.*) pigment, chlorophyll (*q.v.*). The interior of a chloroplast has an organized structure consisting of dense lamellae within a granular matrix material. The lamellae consist of phospholipid-protein membrane similar to that which surrounds the cell and all its organelles, but which is modified to accommodate many chlorophyll molecules in an orderly array. In the chloroplasts of higher plants regions are found where a number of adjacent lamellae have split into two layers and then packed closely together. This gives rise to disc-shaped structures of dense, highly regular material called grana, which are thought to act as 'light-traps' (plate 16).

chromosomes: thread-like bodies containing DNA (*q.v.*) and protein. They are found in all cells and are confined within the nucleus in eukaryote cells (*q.v.*). They constitute the hereditary organelles of the cell. In primitive organisms, e.g. bacteria, all the genes are located in a single chromosome. In higher organisms the full complement of genes in a cell is divided among several different chromosomes. In addition, each chromosome occurs twice (diploid), so that there are two pieces of genetic material controlling a given characteristic in any one cell. These two so-called 'alleles' are the two 'factors' postulated in Mendel's Laws (*q.v.*). When a eukaryote cell divides, the genetic information embodied in the DNA of the chromosomes is passed on to the two daughter cells by means of the mitotic mechanism (*q.v.*).

cilia: fine contractile cytoplasmic threads projecting in numbers from the surface of many cells, e.g. Ciliate Protozoan cells, and many internal surfaces in higher animals. They perform lashing or undulating movements which serve either to propel the cell or to move the medium past the cell. They have a uniform structure, throughout the animal and plant kingdoms, of nine peripheral fibres surrounding two central fibres, the whole being surrounded by a membrane sheath. Each fibre consists of two microtubules, i.e. cylindrical

protein structures. In certain cilia, modified so that they conduct impulses without moving, the central fibres are absent. Each cilium is associated with a basal granule which also has a fibrillar structure and appears to be homologous with the centriole (*q.v.*) (plate 7).

coacervate: a highly viscous phase, containing a mixture of colloid (*q.v.*) particles, which separates out from a mixture of colloidal solutions of opposite charge. It often divides into quasi-liquid drops.

coenzymes: small, non-protein molecules required by many enzymes before they can achieve catalytic activity. They may be loosely or firmly bound to the enzyme (in the latter case they are sometimes called prosthetic groups). Unlike enzymes, coenzymes may take part in a number of different reactions. Important coenzymes are ATP (*q.v.*) which mediates in phosphorylation (*q.v.*), Nicotinamide adenine dinucleotide (NAD or DPN) and flavine adenine dinucleotide (FAD) which take part in oxidations (*q.v.*) and reductions, and coenzyme A, which contains the vitamin pantothenic acid and mediates acyl group transfer (e.g. acetyl $CH_3CO—$) in fatty acid synthesis and oxidation.

collagen: an insoluble, fibrous protein. It has a high tensile strength and constitutes the main component of connective tissue, i.e. the membranes, tendons, ligaments and 'filling material' which give shape and support to the soft organs. Collagen is distinguished from all other proteins by the presence of hydroxyproline (plate 20). When heated in water it denatures into gelatine.

colloid: a substance consisting of particles which are separated to a greater or lesser degree by a continuous medium (solvent). The particles, which are usually defined as falling within the size range 10 Ångströms (0.000,000,1 cm.) to 1 micron (0.000,1 cm.) may be organized aggregates or crystals of atoms or molecules, or, in the case of many proteins, single molecules. Stable colloid particles are organized in such a way that the cohesive forces are directed inwards while at least part of the surface of the particle has an affinity for the continuous medium, which tends to keep the particles separate. Conditions which increase the cohesive forces between particles lead to the characteristic colloidal properties of gel formation (*q.v.*) and coagulation. The size of colloid particles is of the same order of magnitude as the wavelength of light. They therefore appear brown or red by transmitted light, and blue by scattered light, like the blue of dilute milk, smoke and of the sky.

conjugated protein: a protein which is linked to a non-amino-acid substance. The non-amino-acid moiety may be, for example, a metal, a porphyrin (*q.v.*) or a lipid (*q.v.*).

cristae: see *mitochondria.*

cysternae: see *endoplasmic reticulum.*

cytochromes: a group of pigments which act as electron acceptors in a number of electron transfer operations (*q.v.*). They consist of an iron-containing

porphyrin (*q.v.*) linked to a protein (*q.v.*).

DNA (deoxyribonucleic acid): see *nucleic acids.* DNA consists of nucleotides (*q.v.*) containing deoxyribose and one of the four nitrogenous bases (*q.v.*), adenine, thymine, guanine and cytosine (Fig. 19, p. 325). They are linked between the phosphate of one nucleotide and the sugar of the next (Fig. 13). The structure in which DNA usually occurs is that of a double-stranded helix, formed from two single polymers wound round one another. In this helix the nucleotides are twisted so that the sugar-phosphate backbones of the two polymers are on the outside; on the inside the flat ring-structures of the bases lie in planes nearly perpendicular to the axis of the helix, each base being hydrogen-bonded to a base in the opposite polymer (Figs. 14 and 15). The pairing of opposite bases is not arbitrary; a double-ringed base (purine) is always paired with a single-ringed (pyrimidine) base, and, further, adenine always pairs with thymine and guanine with cytosine, these purine-pyrimidine pairs being the most stable ones. This means that although the sequence of bases along a single polymer may vary greatly according to the source of the DNA, the two strands of a helix have strictly complementary sequences. This theory of the structure of DNA is known as the Watson-Crick hypothesis.

electron: an elementary particle having a very small mass and a negative charge. Each element possesses a characteristic number of electrons (the atomic number of the element)

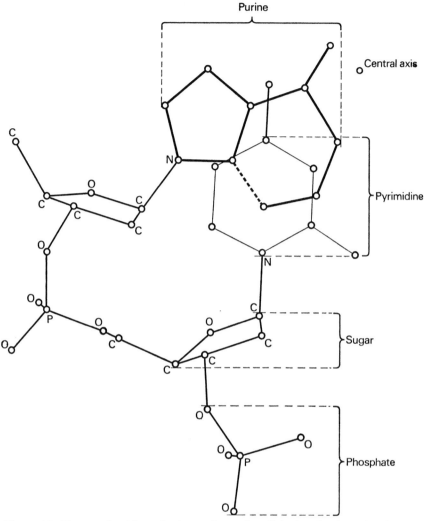

Figure 13. Two nucleotides, adenine and cytosine, linked and oriented as in part of the DNA chain. They are projected nearly perpendicular to the axis of the chain.

which 'orbit' the nucleus in a number of so-called shells, and are responsible for the chemical properties of the element.

electron transfer operation: an oxidation-reduction reaction (see *oxidation*), mediated by an enzyme, which results in one substance receiving an electron (*q.v.*) or electrons at the expense of another.

endoplasmic reticulum: a system of membrane-bound channels and vesicles, or cysternae, which interconnects throughout the cystoplasm of cells. The exterior of the system is con-

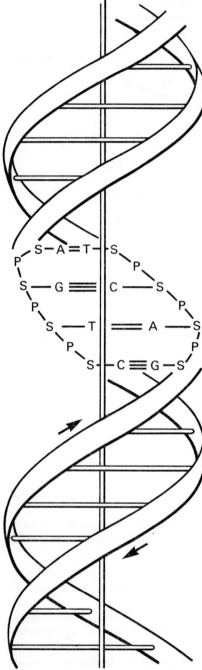

tinuous in places with the outside of the cell. The interior of the system, i.e. the surface in contact with the cytoplasm, sometimes carries large numbers of ribosomes (*q.v.*). This so-called 'rough' membrane has been termed the ergastoplasm and is found in cells which are actively synthesizing protein (Fig. 7, p. 134).

entropy: a measure of the degree of disorganization of a system. The entropy of a system can only be decreased, i.e. the system can only become more organized, if it is supplied with free energy, i.e. energy capable of doing work.

enzyme: protein which acts as a catalyst (*q.v.*) in organic reactions. Catalysis by enzymes differs from other forms of catalysis in its greater efficiency and in the extreme degree of specificity shown by the enzymes. Most enzymes catalyse one reaction, or closely related group of reactions, only.

ergastoplasmic systems: see *endoplasmic reticulum.*

eukaryote: see *nucleated cell.*

ferredoxin: an iron-containing protein with a great avidity for electrons. It acts as the immediate acceptor of energy from light-activated chlorophyll (*q.v.*) in photosynthesis (*q.v.*).

flavonoid: a compound containing flavin, e.g. the co-enzyme flavin adenine dinucleotide (FAD).

Figure 14. The DNA double helix.

Flavin

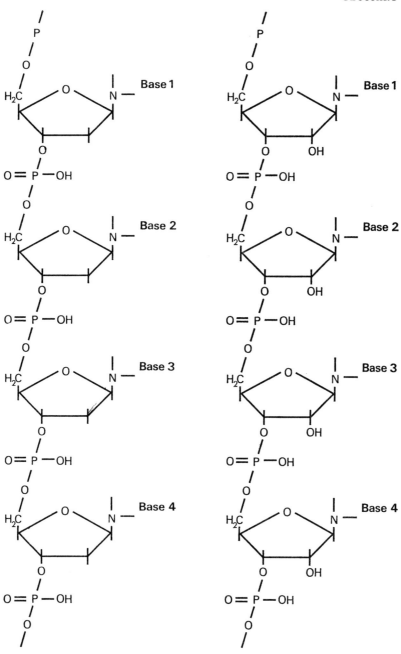

(a)   DNA polynucleotide   (b)   RNA polynucleotide

Figure 15. Notice the absence in the DNA polynucleotide of the hydroxyl, OH, in the sugar molecule.

319

gel: a colloidal solution (see *colloid*) in which the fibrous-colloid particles have interacted to form a network, within which much of the solvent is trapped, e.g. gelatin, a gel of collagen and water, and vitreous humour.

gene: a unit of heredity. A unit portion of the genetic material, providing the genetic code (*q.v.*) for one enzyme (*q.v.*) or sub-unit of an enzyme.

genetic code: the four nitrogenous bases (*q.v.*) (A, C, T and G in DNA and A, C, U and G in RNA) constitute an alphabet of four letters, and their sequence along a DNA or RNA molecule forms a code which contains the genetic information in accordance with which the cell synthesizes new protein. This code is known to consist of three-letter 'words', e.g. GAC, UUA, each of which is the code for

First position	Second position				Third position
	U	C	A	G	
U	phe	ser	tyr	cys	U
	phe	ser	tyr	cys	C
	leu	ser	(normal "full stop")	tryp	A
	leu	ser	(less common "full stop")	tryp	G
C	leu	pro	his	arg	U
	leu	pro	his	arg	C
	leu	pro	gln	arg	A
	leu	pro	gln	arg	G
A	ileu	thr	asn	ser	U
	ileu	thr	asn	ser	C
	ileu?	thr	lys	arg	A
	met ("capital letter")	thr	lys	arg	G
G	val	ala	asp	gly	U
	val	ala	asp	gly	C
	val	ala	glu	gly	A
	val	ala	glu	gly	G

Figure 16. The genetic code. In the left-hand column are the initials of the four RNA bases representing the first "letter" of the codon triplet; the second letter is represented by the initials across the top, while the third but less important letter appears in the final column. For example, tyrosine (tyr) is coded for by either UAU or UAC. Amino acids coded by each codon are abbreviated as in Fig. 25, p. 331.

an individual amino acid (Fig. 16). Thus the sequence of amino acids in each protein in the cell depends on the sequence of nucleotides (*q.v.*) in a portion of the DNA in the nucleus of that cell.

Transcription of the code is medi-

stacked together near the nucleus; present in most animal cells (and possibly in some plant cells). Its function is not certain; it is thought to play a role in the secretion of large molecules, and in the generation of membranes.

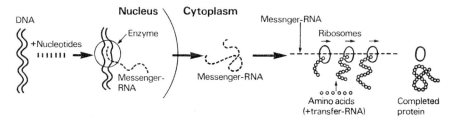

Figure 17. The principal steps in protein synthesis.

ated by RNA molecules. A diagrammatic representation of the steps involved is given in Fig. 17. mRNA is synthesized using the DNA base sequence as a template for the mRNA sequence. The messenger molecule is then bound to a ribosome (*q.v.*). An activating enzyme causes the linkage of individual amino-acids to specific tRNA molecules which are able to 'recognize' the three letter mRNA 'codon' for their particular amino acid. The amino-acid-tRNA complexes align themselves along the messenger molecule in the order dictated by the codons, peptide linkages (*q.v.*) are formed between adjacent amino acids and the protein chain is formed.

globulins: globular proteins which are sparingly soluble in water, but soluble in salt solutions, e.g. many enzymes (*q.v.*).

Golgi apparatus: a structure consisting of smooth membranous vesicles

grana: see *chloroplast.*

haemocyanin: blue respiratory pigment found in the blood of some molluscs and arthropods (plate 15). Unlike haemoglobin (*q.v.*), it does not contain an iron-porphyrin compound, but consists of a protein to which copper is linked. Like chlorocruorin (*q.v.*), haemocyanin circulates freely in the plasma in the form of organized protein 'corpuscles' of approx. M.W. 6,760,000.

haemoglobin: respiratory pigment found in the red blood cells of vertebrates. Each molecule consists of two pairs of protein sub-units (globins): an iron porphyrin (haem) is associated with each sub-unit. Normal adult haemoglobin contains two β and two α globins, foetal haemoglobin contains two β and two γ globins, α, β and γ being distinct but related protein chains. The four units are arranged tetrahedrally in a dissociable, nearly-spherical molecule. Haemoglobin acts as an oxygen-carrier by binding one molecule of oxygen to each iron atom. The first two molecules are bound more tightly than the other two, giving haemoglobin its characteristic sigmoid oxygen-dissociation curve (Fig. 18).

hydrogen ion: the ion H^+, the hydrogen nucleus or proton. It is the characteristic ion of all acids. The ease with which an acid can lose hydrogen ions is a measure of its strength. The small size of the hydrogen ion, due to the absence of electrons, makes it

Figure 18. Haemoglobin molecule, showing two pairs of sub-units and the position of the haem groups (shown as disks).

heliozoida: spherical, fresh water protozoa (*q.v.*) possessing a gelatinous or siliceous outer layer through which project cytoplasmic extensions supported by stiff axial filaments. These filaments are composed of bundles of microtubules similar to those found in cilia (*q.v.*) (plate 9).

heteropolymer: see *polymer*.

homopolymer: see *polymer*.

extremely mobile and highly penetrating of other molecules. It has a strong tendency to combine with hydroxyl ions OH^- (*q.v.*) to form H_2O. Chemically, it is the opposite of OH^-.

hydroxyl ion: the ion OH^-. It is a strong base, i.e. it has a strong tendency to combine with H^+ ions to form H_2O; by definition, therefore, a solution which contains excess OH^- over H^+ is alkaline (pH (*q.v.*) greater than 7).

insulin: a small protein hormone secreted by the Islets of Langerhaus in the pancreas. It controls the utilization of glucose in the body and thus affects the level of sugar in the blood.

isotopes: atoms of the same element which differ from one another in the number of neutrons in their nuclei and hence have different atomic weights. Most elements occur as a mixture of several isotopes, the relative proportions of which constitute their isotope ratios. Some elements have naturally-occurring radio-active isotopes; other radio-active isotopes can be made by bombardment of an element in an atomic pile. Since all the isotopes of a given element possess the same number of electrons (*q.v.*), and the same atomic number, they are difficult to distinguish chemically.

isotope ratios: see *isotopes.*

lipid: a collective term for molecules which are insoluble in water, but soluble in fat solvents. Prominent members of this group are the fatty acids (general formula $CH_3(CH_2)_n COOH$) and their glycerol esters, i.e. glycerides. Esters of glycerol phosphate are phospholipids. Most lipids are long straight molecules or bundles of them like the triglycerides, fats. Molecules of the same length exhibit a tendency to pack side by side in sheets, as in cell membrane.

lysosomes: organelles containing a number of digestive enzymes (*q.v.*) surrounded by a membrane which is sometimes many-layered and folded.

In dying or damaged cells the lysosomes break down and release their enzymes. It is thought that they may play a part in embryonic development, metamorphosis and wound-healing.

Mendel's Laws: two laws embodying the basic behaviour of the system of heredity in those organisms which reproduce by fertilization of an ovum by a sperm, i.e. by fusion of gametes.

I an individual possesses two 'factors' (or alleles) for any one of its characteristics: all the gametes produced by the individual will contain one or other of these factors, but never both of them. This leads to the segregation of the factors among the offspring of the individual.

II the factors governing different characteristics assort independently of one another. (We now know this to be true only for factors, i.e. genes (*q.v.*), which are carried on separate chromosomes (*q.v.*).)

metazoa: animals in which each individual is made up of many cells.

mitochondria: spherical, rod-shaped or filamentous organelles found in all cells except bacteria and blue-green algae. They are bounded by two membranes, the inner membrane forming folds, or cristae (*q.v.*). which project into the interior of the mitochondrion. All the enzymes for the oxidation of foods and for the 'fixing' of the energy so gained into the high-energy compound, ATP, are found in the mitochondria, either in the surface of the cristae or in the spaces between them (plates 5 and 6).

mitotic mechanism: the mechanism by which genetic information is transferred when a eukaryote (*q.v.*) cell

323

divides. It involves the duplication of each chromosome (*q.v.*) to give two identical sets of chromosomes. These are then separated by the formation of a 'spindle', probably organized by the centriole (*q.v.*), which draws them to opposite poles of the nucleus, by attaching to a specialized region of each chromosome, the centromere. Then the nucleus divides, followed by the whole cell, yielding two genetically identical daughter cells.

monomer: see *polymer.*

mycoplasmas: disease-carrying organisms smaller than bacteria and lacking the protective cell wall characteristic of bacteria. They contain DNA, RNA and a small amount of cytoplasm (plate 21).

myelin sheath: a sheath of fatty material which covers nerve fibres and facilitates rapid conduction of nerve impulses. It consists of a tightly-wound spiral cylinder of cell membrane material, i.e. the double-layered protein-lipid structure which surrounds all cells and their organelles (plates 18 and 19).

myoglobin: a respiratory pigment from muscle. It consists of one protein unit and one iron-containing porphyrin (*q.v.*) of the type found in haemoglobin (*q.v.*).

myosin: a fibrous protein from muscle which is responsible for its contractile properties (plates 12 and 24). It also has ATPase activity, i.e. it can catalyse the break-down of ATP to ADP. See *actin.*

nitrogenous base: an aromatic, nitrogen-containing compound with basic properties, i.e. tendency to acquire an H-atom. Important biological nitrogenous bases are the purines, which have a double carbon-nitrogen ring, and the pyrimidines, which have a single ring. The five bases commonly encountered are the purines adenine (abbreviated A) and guanine (G) and the pyrimidines thymine (T), cytosine (C) and uracil (U) (Fig. 19). Each of these occur in nucleic acids (*q.v.*) and in various coenzymes (*q.v.*).

nucleated cell (eukaryote): cell in which the chromosomes (*q.v.*) are contained in a membrane-bounded organelle, the nucleus. Cells with well-defined nuclei are termed eukaryote; those in which the chromosomes are free in cytoplasm, or merely localized in the cell with no surrounding membrane, are termed prokaryote, e.g. bacteria.

nucleic acids: polymers (*q.v.*) comprised of nucleotides (*q.v.*) and found in all living cells. Deoxyribonucleic acid (DNA) is found mainly in the nucleus and is the genetic material of most organisms. Ribonucleic acid (RNA) is found in both nucleus and cytoplasm and occurs in three forms, each of which plays a role in the synthesis of proteins. See *RNA, genetic code, chromosome.*

In some viruses (*q.v.*), RNA is the genetic material; no case is known in which a compound other than a nucleic acid forms the genetic material.

nucleoside: see *nucleotide.*

nucleotide: a molecule containing a nitrogenous base (*q.v.*), a pentose

DNA	RNA

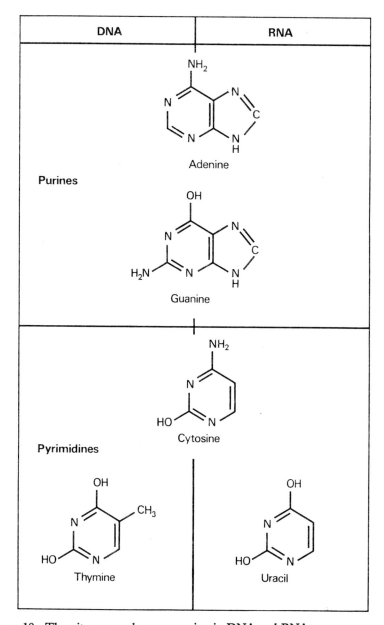

Figure 19. The nitrogenous bases occurring in DNA and RNA.

sugar (*q.v.*) and phosphate (*q.v.*) (Fig. 13, p. 317). The base and sugar alone constitute a nucleoside.

nucleus: the resting nucleus in eukaryotes (see *nucleated cell*) is the organelle containing the chromosomes *(q.v.)*. It is bounded by a double membrane through which it communicates with the rough side of the endoplasmic reticulum *(q.v.)*.

organelle: any discrete structure within a cell, e.g. a mitochondrion *(q.v.)*, a ribosome *(q.v.)*.

oxidation: originally defined as the addition of oxygen or removal of hydrogen. It is now understood that these reactions are only part of a wider concept, i.e. that oxidation involves loss of electrons *(q.v.)*, while the opposite process, reduction, involves gain of electrons.

pentose sugar: a carbohydrate (general formula $(CH_2O)_n$) containing five carbon atoms, e.g. ribose, which forms part of RNA, and deoxyribose, which forms part of DNA (Fig. 20).

peptide bond: the bond formed when the amino group (NH_2) of one amino acid *(q.v.)* reacts with the carboxyl group (COOH) of another to form an amide group (—CO—NH—) with the elimination of a molecule of water. The atoms of the amide group all lie in the same plane (Fig. 21).

Periodic Table: if the elements are arranged in order of increasing atomic number (see *electron*), it is found that elements having similar properties occur at regular intervals in the list. In the Periodic Table the elements are tabulated in such a way that these similar ones come together in groups or 'families'. The eighth family contains the inert gases, e.g. Neon, Argon which are characterized by having a full complement of eight electrons in their outer electron shell. The other families vary in properties according to the number of electrons they possess in this shell. Certain groups of ele-

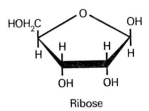

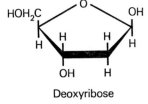

Ribose   Deoxyribose

Figure 20. The pentose sugars found in nucleic acids.

peptide: any compound formed from two or more amino acids *(q.v.)* linked by peptide bonds *(q.v.)*. Technically, therefore a protein *(q.v.)* is a peptide, but the term is usually reserved for molecules of low molecular weight (of the order of 1,000 or less). Peptides have little secondary structure (see *protein*). They are straight chain, or sometimes cyclic, molecules.

ments interrupt the pattern of families. The increase in atomic number from one of these transition elements to another occurs by addition of electrons to an inner shell rather than to the outer one. These elements have characteristic properties such as the ability to form a number of ions with different valencies, e.g. iron, manganese.

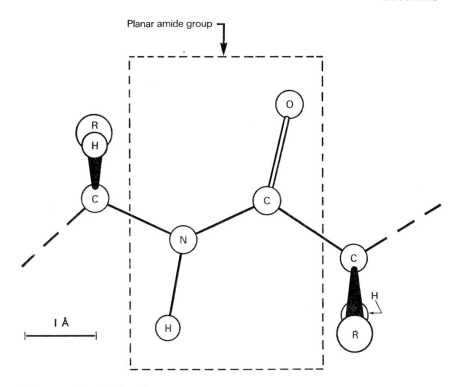

Figure 21. Peptide bond.

LONG PERIODIC TABLE

A GROUPS				TRANSITIONAL							B GROUPS							ZERO GROUP
I	II	III	IV	V	VI	VII	VIII				I	II	III	IV	V	VI	VII	0
H1																		He2
Li3	Be4	B5												C6	N7	O8	F9	Ne10
Na11	Mg12	Al13												Si14	P15	S16	Cl17	A18
K19	Ca20	Sc21	Ti22	V23	Cr24	Mn25	Fe26	Co27	Ni28		Cu29	Zn30	Ga31	Ge32	As33	Sc34	Br35	Kr36
Rb37	Sr38	Y39	Zr40	Nb41	Mo42	Tc43	Ru44	Rh45	Pd46		Ag47	Cd48	In49	Sn50	Sb51	Te52	I53	Xe54
Cs55	Ba56	Rare Earths 57-71	Hf72	Ta73	W74	Re75	Os76	Ir77	Pt78		Au79	Hg80	Tl81	Pb82	Bi83	Po84	At85	Rn86
Fr87	Ra88	Ae89	Th90	Pa91	U92													
		Trans- uranic 93–																

La57	Ce58	Pr59	Nd60	Pm61	Sm62	Eu63	Gd64	Tb65	Dy66	Ho67	Er68	Tm69	Yb70	Lu71

Np93	Pu94	Am95	Cm96	Bk97	Cf98

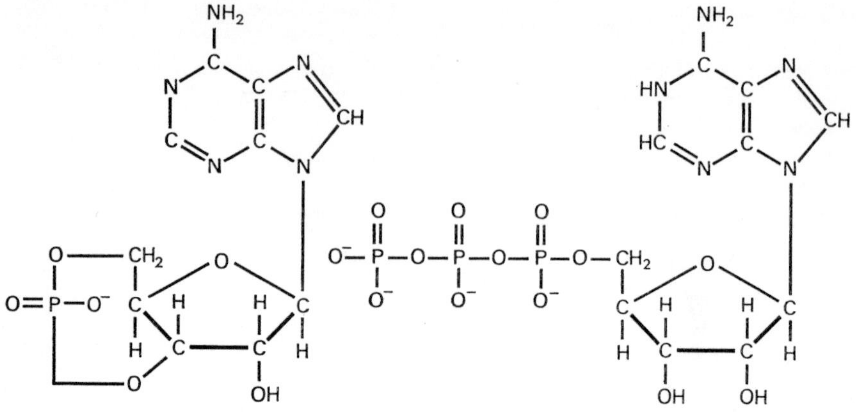

Cyclic AMP   ATP

Figure 22.

pH: a quantitative measure of the acidity or alkalinity of a solution. Theoretically, $pH = -\log[H^+]$, where $[H^+]$ is the concentration of hydrogen ions (q.v.) in the solution. This relationship gives rise to a scale running from 0 to 14, in which pH 0 corresponds to the most acid solution, pH 7 corresponds to neutrality and pH 14 corresponds to extreme alkalinity.

phosphates: the ions, salts and esters derived from the inorganic acids of phosphorus. The orthophosphate ion is PO_4^{3-}, the metaphosphate ion is PO_3^-, and the pyrophosphate ion $P_2O_7^{4-}$. The commonest inorganic phosphate is calcium phosphate ($Ca_3(PO_4)_2$) which forms a large part of bone and of tooth enamel, and occurs widely in the mineral, Apatite. In organic phosphates both chain phosphate structures and cyclic phosphate structures occur, e.g. ATP and cyclic AMP. (Fig. 22).

phosphorylation: the transfer of phosphate (q.v.) to an acceptor molecule.

photosynthesis: the process occurring in all green plants, by which light energy is used to 'fix' CO_2 from the atmosphere in the form of carbohydrates. This is achieved by a complex process involving many intermediates, but basically two reactions occur. In the 'light' reaction, light energy trapped by chlorophyll (q.v.) molecules is used to produce ATP and to split water into oxygen and hydrogen, the hydrogen being held as 'reducing potential' in the form of a reduced coenzyme (q.v.). In the 'dark' reaction the ATP provides energy for the reduction of CO_2 to carbohydrate. The overall reaction for this CO_2 fixation can be written:

$$n(CO_2 + H_2O) \rightarrow n(CH_2O) + nO_2.$$

plastids: small, self-propagating organelles (q.v.) found in plant cells. Some are colourless and act as starch depositories in deep-seated tissues. The others contain pigments such as chlorophyll (see chloroplast) and the red, orange and yellow pigments, the carotins and xanthophyll.

polyethylene: see *polymer.*

polyisoprenoid character: the structural relationship between many biological compounds and polyisoprene, the basis of natural rubber. These compounds can be regarded as multiples of a five-carbon isoprene-like unit.

$$CH_2=\overset{\overset{\displaystyle CH_3}{\displaystyle |}}{C}-CH=CH_2$$

isoprene (2-methyl butadiene)

polymer: a molecule formed by the linear linking of a number of fundamental units termed monomers (*q.v.*).

Polymerization may occur by addition, in which case the whole of the monomer molecule is incorporated into the polymer (e.g. polyethylene), or by condensation, in which the linkages are formed with the elimination of a small molecule, (e.g. H_2O in the case of the peptide linkage (*q.v.*) in protein (*q.v.*) formation).

polysomes: collections of ribosomes connected by a thin thread: thought to represent protein synthesis 'assembly lines' in which a molecule of messenger RNA is being decoded by one ribosome after another. Each ribosome binds to the molecule at one end

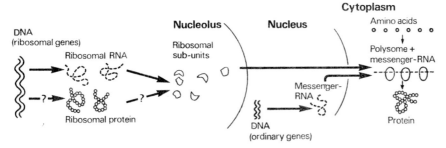

Figure 23. Genesis of polysomes. Composite picture of the assembly of the cell's protein-synthesizing mechanism as suggested by research on ribosomal sub-units and nucleolar genes.

If the monomers are all identical, a homopolymer is formed. If different monomers are combined in one polymer, it is termed a hetero-polymer (e.g. Ethylene, $CH_2=CH_2$ forms a homopolymer polyethylene (polythene) — CH_2 — CH_2 — CH_2 — CH_2 etc.) Whereas amino acids (*q.v.*) can combine to form heteropolymers, proteins (*q.v.*).

polymerization: the formation of a polymer (*q.v.*) by a succession of similar linkages between monomers (*q.v.*).

and moves along it as amino acids are incorporated into the protein chain. At the other end the ribosomes detach from the mRNA, and release the completed protein molecule (Fig. 23) (see *genetic code*).

porphyrins: compounds derived from the tetrapyrrole compound, porphin, (Fig. 24) by substitution of side-chains at the eight hydrogen atoms marked in the diagram. They have the property of binding a metal atom at the central position, X; the most

329

important metallo-porphyrins so formed are those containing iron or magnesium (see *chlorophyll, haemoglobin, cytochromes*).

prokaryote: a cell that is evolved without a nucleus (see under *nucleated cell*).

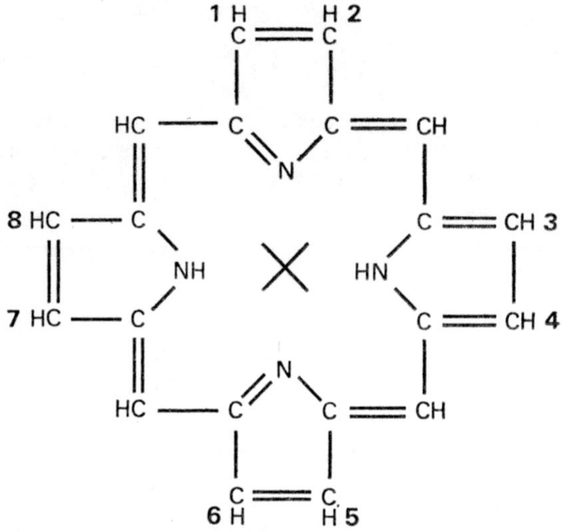

both an enzyme and a structural protein. Protein molecules show three degrees of structural organization within one molecule. The Primary structure is the sequence of the amino acids along the polymer, which is determined by a sequence of nucleotides

Porphin ($C_{20}H_{14}N_4$)

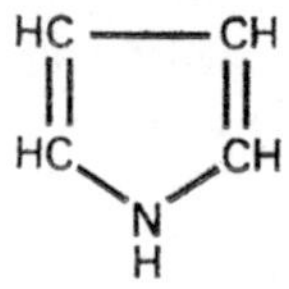

Pyrrole

Figure 24.

protein: a polymer of amino acids (*q.v.*) joined by peptide bonds (*q.v.*). Some twenty amino acids are commonly found in proteins and most proteins contain all twenty (Fig. 25). The variety of structures and properties which the R-groups of the amino acids contribute to proteins make them the most versatile of biological molecules. Their most important role is that of enzyme (*q.v.*) function; they also constitute structural materials, e.g. collagen (*q.v.*), some hormones, e.g. insulin (*q.v.*) and a number of other physiologically active substances. Some proteins have a dual function, e.g. myosin (*q.v.*), which is

in the DNA (see *genetic code*). The Secondary structure arises by a twisting of the peptide-bonded 'backbone' of the polymer to give shorter helical or 'pleated' molecules. This is the degree of compactness found in the structural proteins, e.g. collagen (*q.v.*). A definite molecular weight cannot always be given to this type of protein. The Tertiary structure is achieved by further folding, bending and sometimes cross-linking between sulphur-containing amino acids, giving a compact, relatively rigid globular molecule. Simple proteins of this type have molecular weights of up to 17,000. The term Quaternary structure

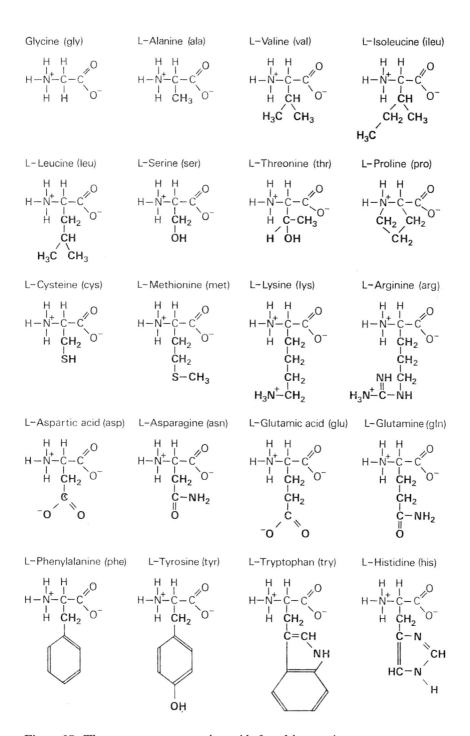

Figure 25. The twenty common amino acids found in proteins.

is sometimes used to describe complex proteins in which two or more sub-units are aggregated to give the complete, active protein, These proteins have molecular weights of up to and exceeding 100,000, e.g. haemoglobin (*q.v.*) M.W. 68,000.

proteinoid: high molecular weight polymers produced by Dr S. W. Fox by heating mixtures of amino acids containing high proportions of aspartic and glutamic acids. These synthetic molecules have many of the properties of proteins to some degree, e.g. catalytic activity, nutritional value.

protoplasm: an obsolete term for the semi-fluid, semi-transparent sub-stance of which all living things were supposed to consist, until increasingly powerful microscopes showed the diversity of structural organization within the cell.

protozoa: animals consisting of one cell only, but having one or more well-defined nuclei.

purines, pyrimidines: see *nitrogenous base*.

ribose see *pentose sugar*.

ribosomes: small granules consisting of RNA and protein, found either attached to the endoplasmic reticulum (*q.v.*) or free in the cytoplasm. They are the sites at which protein synthesis takes place (see *RNA, genetic code*). Ribosomes can be dissociated into two smaller particles distinguished by their sedimentation properties. 70s (bacterial) ribosomes dissociate into a 50s and a 30s particle. 80s (yeasts, animals) ribosomes dissociate less easily into a 60s and a 40s

particle. The biological properties of these ribosomal sub-units are not yet fully understood.

RNA: see *nucleic acids*. RNA consists of polynucleotide chains similar to those of DNA, but containing ribose instead of deoxyribose and uracil instead of thymine. Three forms of RNA are found in cells: messenger RNA (mRNA), transfer RNA(tRNA) and ribosomal RNA (rRNA). None of these has the regular helical structure of DNA although short regions of helix are thought to exist in tRNA and rRNA (see *genetic code*).

spontaneous generation: the origin of living organisms from non-living matter. Also known as abiogenesis, the opposite of which is biogenesis, i.e. the origin of living things from other living things only.

substrate: a substance which is activated by an enzyme (*q.v.*), thus being enabled to take part in a reaction.

sugar: a carbohydrate (general formula $(CH_2O)_n$). The most important simple sugars are those containing five and six carbon atoms in a ring structure (pentose, *q.v.*, and hexose). The simple sugars are the basis for sugar polymers, or polysaccharides, such as the straight chain cellulose (*q.v.*) and of the nutritional polymers, starch and glycogen.

symbiotic organism: an organism which lives in association with another, dissimilar organism. In some associations the gain to either symbiont may only be that of camouflage or mobility; in other cases this is extended to a sharing of foods and in the most extreme cases of symbiosis, metabolic interdependence is found.

tracers: compounds which have been 'labelled' by replacement of an atom by its radio-active or 'heavy' isotope (*q.v.*). When such a compound is fed into a complex biological system, its fate can be singled out by methods for detecting radio-activity, e.g. auto-radiography (*q.v.*), or differences in Molecular Weight, e.g. mass spectrometry.

transition elements: see *Periodic Table.*

viruses: disease-causing particles (plate 25), much smaller than bacteria, which are only able to multiply inside a host cell. They consist of a small piece of genetic material (either DNA or RNA) surrounded by a protein coat built up symmetrically from a number of protein sub-units. Three structural types have been found, those with cubic symmetry (usually icosahedra), those with helical symmetry, and complex structures which may contain both cubic and helical parts. When a virus infects a cell, the protein coat is discarded outside the cell. Inside the cell the viral genetic material multiplies many times and produces new protein coats, all the time utilizing the nucleotides, amino acids and ribosomes of the host cell. The genetic material and protein coats reassemble into mature viruses and are released by bursting of the cell.

vitamin B_{12}: a coenzyme (*q.v.*) in a number of diverse reactions. It consists of a ring system similar to a porphyrin (*q.v.*) and contains a cobalt ion.

Watson-Crick hypothesis: see *DNA.*

yeasts: single-celled fungi used widely in biochemistry as a source of enzymes.

Ziegler catalysts: inorganic catalysts (*q.v.*) composed of a mixture of tri-alkyl aluminium (R_3Al, where R represents a hydrocarbon group) and a metal halide, usually titanium chloride. They catalyse the polymerization of molecules of the type $RCH=CH_2$ (e.g. ethylene, $HCH=CH_2$), the products being highly stereo-regular.

z

Name Index

335

Subject Index

Page numbers in italic type refer to main references

Actin, 83, 97, 299, 311, pl. 13, pl. 14
actomyosin, 94
adenine, 62, 169, 299, 324f
   in ATP, 167, 311
   in nucleic acids, 75, 316f, 325
   synthesis of, 42, 45, 189
adenosine diphosphate, *see* ADP
adenosine monophosphate, *see* AMP
adenosine triphosphate, *see* ATP
ADP, 61f, 311
adsorption, on clay minerals, xi, 9, 57, *128f*,
   145, 301, pl. 1
agriculture, *12f*, 163, 176, 180
alanine, 170, 312, 331
albumen, 68, 126, 131, 172
alcohol, 63, 227, 246
algae, 46, 90, 94, 101, 105, 106, 111, 154,
   232f, 240, 311, 314, pl. 23
aluminium, 57, 333
amino acids, 311f, 331
   in formation of simple organism, 150f
   in primitive soup, 54, 57, 84, 171, 300
   in proteins, 6, 9, 31, 55, 66, 74, 167, 331
   synthesis of, 45, 125
ammonia
   action of bacteria on, 233
   excretion of, ix
   in primitive atmosphere, 21, 33, 122, 224
   in synthesis experiments, xi, 28, 46, 246
   low-temperature production of, 182
   on planets, 26, 40
amoebae, 91, 202, pl. 22
AMP, 61f, 311, 328
animals
   as emblems, 17
   classification of, 18
   domestication of, 12f
   evolution of, 88, 101, 108f, 130f, 161f,
   178f
antibiotics, 51, 93, 188, 194
apatite, 50, 60, 157, 291, 301, 328

Aristotelian thought, 16, 18, 25, 70, 140,
   160, 167, 174f, 199
aspartic acid, 125, 331
asteroids, 9, 33, 38ff, 44, 46, 51, 101, 115,
   122, 143, 266, 273ff, 300
astronomy, 4, 15, 36f, 100, 120, 159, 204
astrophysics, 5, 36–44 *passim*
asymmetry, in living material, 144f, 247f,
   250
ATP, xi, 61f, 63, 148, 151, 167, 192, 311,
   315, 328
autoradiography, 66, 133, 155, 157, 312,
   pl. 26

Bacteria
   action of, 26, 111, 200, 202, 213, 227f,
   232f, 242, 244ff
   adaptation of, 93
   evolution of, 101, 133, 136, 187f
   structure of, 79ff, 154, 240, 250
bacteriophage, 27f, 68, 95, *154f*, 251, 287,
   313
   d'Herelle, 154, 243ff, 250f
   T2, 95, 273, 289
   T4, 96, 313, pl. 3
barnacle geese, 17
bathybius, 27, 79
Berkner-Marshall hypothesis, 105ff, 113,
   130, 136, 187
bestiaries, 17f
Bible, 14ff, 140, 166, 177, 200
biochemistry, xi, xvi, 2, 5, 22f, 24, 29, 31,
   34, 45, 48f, 53f, 79f, 120, 148, 161,
   165, 172, 182, 241
biogenesis, 5f, 191ff
biology, xiff, xvf, 136, 159, 172f
birth, 16, 162, 175
blood cells, 51, 83, 92, 167, 175
Bode's Law, 114, 313
bone, 92, 286, 291, 328
Buddhism, 178

339